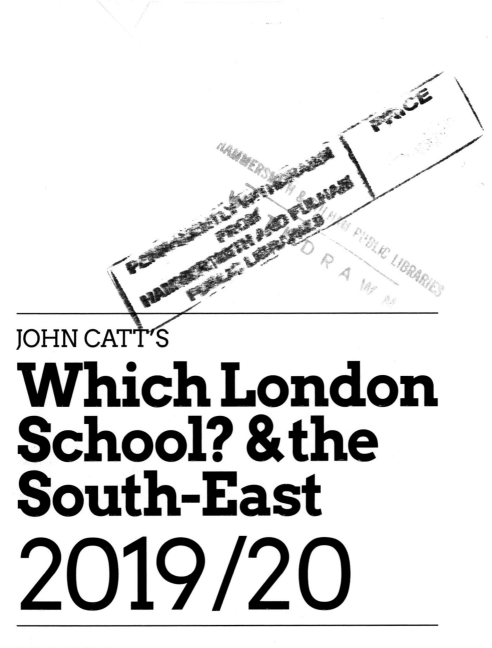

JOHN CATT'S

Which London School? & the South-East

2019/20

30th Edition
Editor: Jonathan Barnes

JOHN
CATT
EDUCATIONAL
LIMITED

Published in 2019 by
John Catt Educational Ltd,
15 Riduna Park,
Melton, Suffolk IP12 1QT UK
Tel: 01394 389850   Fax: 01394 386893
Email: enquiries@johncatt.com
Website: www.johncatt.com
© 2019 John Catt Educational Ltd

Designed and typeset by John Catt Educational Limited

**A CIP catalogue record for this book is available from the
British Library.**

ISBN: 978 1 912906 05 5

Contacts
Editor
Jonathan Barnes

Advertising & School Profiles
Tel: +44 (0) 1394 389850
Email: sales@johncatt.com

Distribution/Book Sales
Tel: +44 (0) 1394 389863
Email: booksales@johncatt.com

Contents

The best of both worlds

Andrew Johnson, Headmaster of St Benedict's School in Ealing, west London, explains why the advantages of going to school in and around London go well beyond excellent academic results

Speaking as someone who was Headmaster of a rural boarding school for 10 years, and now at the helm of a London day school, I think I am pretty well placed to appreciate the sharp contrast between the two educational settings. Gone are the green rolling acres, rural peace and glorious isolation. And in its place? "You find no man, at all intellectual, who is willing to leave London. No, Sir, when a man is tired of London, he is tired of life; for there is in London all that life can afford." No commendation of London life would be complete without a quote from Samuel Johnson.

An obvious advantage of studying in London is that museums, galleries, libraries, theatres, universities and many other wonderful resources are on our doorstep, bringing learning to life. These world-class institutions are so adjacent – just a few tube stops away, or even a moderate walk – that they really do feel like an extension of the classroom.

Pupils can explore Britain's Roman beginnings, by visiting the Roman Amphitheatre, or chart maritime history at Greenwich. They can see the influence of our entire procession of monarchs, from William the Conqueror's White Tower to the Palace of Westminster. Artists can research and be inspired at the Victoria and Albert Museum, Tate Modern or the National Gallery. Younger pupils can learn about plant biology at Kew Gardens, or visit the Victorian Ragged School in the east end. The Great Fire of London can be brought vividly to life at the Museum of London, and children can follow in Samuel Pepys' footsteps. If Ancient Egyptians are on the syllabus, the British Museum can transport them to the land of the pharaohs. Keen mathematicians can attend stimulating masterclasses at the Royal Institution, while Classicists can attend performances of Greek plays, often staged at universities such as UCL.

Inspirational visiting speakers – from politicians to poets – are easy to attract to London schools, since many live in or near the capital. (Six authors recently attended our Book Week.) Interesting events and opportunities abound: If there's an open lecture at the London School of Economics, or the British Library is running research workshops, we can easily attend. Our singers can perform alongside world-renowned professional choirs, such as VOCES8, and work in partnership with them to encourage singing in primary schools. Drama students can watch outstanding performances at Shakespeare's Globe, National Theatre, or in a host of smaller venues such as the Lyric, Hammersmith.

London pupils have the best of both worlds: the metropolitan and the local. Our capital city of 8 million people is a collection of boroughs and sometimes village-like districts, each with their own identity. Schools can enjoy strong connections with their local communities, through voluntary service, for example, in residential homes and primary schools, or by supporting local charities. This local engagement is vital if children are to understand that they can play a part in society; that education is for the greater good and not just for self-advancement.

London day schools reflect the hugely rich and diverse demographic of the city. St Benedict's currently has pupils who are of 33 different nationalities. London's cosmopolitan and multi-cultural environment is a positive feature of school-life, as children learn about cultures and

> Our capital city of 8 million people is a collection of boroughs and sometimes village-like districts, each with their own identity. Schools can enjoy strong connections with their local communities, through voluntary service, for example, in residential homes and primary schools, or by supporting local charities.

languages other than their own. This is also enormously beneficial to our Modern Languages department, as pupils can practise their German, French or Spanish-speaking with their peers.

Bright young graduates are often eager to start their teaching careers in the capital, which gives London schools a distinct recruitment advantage, especially if the school is able to offer accommodation to its young teachers. There are several creative collaborations throughout London, affiliated to several universities. The West London Teaching School Alliance, for example, which works closely with St Mary's University in Twickenham, enables St Benedict's to recruit and train excellent new teachers.

City day schools benefit from a high degree of connectivity, and nowhere more than in London. This offers many opportunities for the strongest careers provision possible: at St Benedict's, we welcome in the brightest talent to give pupils a head start and a global perspective on working in a world city. Professionals from many walks of life, such as lawyers, CEOs, engineers, tech specialists and medics offer their expertise at our Careers Fair, and give frequent workshops and talks.

Alumni networks are alive and well within the capital, too, since many establish their careers in London. Former pupils are a valuable source of advice, work experience, internships and mentoring, and are extremely generous with their time in guiding our pupils as they consider their future paths.

There are indeed many advantages to London education, rich in the potential to enhance personal development, extend knowledge and deepen understanding in all areas of the curriculum. To return to Dr Johnson, London is a place for the curious; the life-longer learner; for anyone, of whatever age, who is open to new experiences. And who could tire of that?

For more information about St Benedict's School, see page 78

How to use this guide

Are you looking for...

Help and advice?

If so, take a look at our editorial section (pages 5-45). Here you will find articles written by experts in their field covering issues you may well come across when choosing a school for your child.

A school or college in a certain geographical area?

Then you need to go to page D111 to find the directory page reference to a particular area. We suggest that you look first in the directory for basic information about all the schools in each region, complete with contact details, so that you will be better informed about the choices available to you. From this section you will be directed to more detailed information in the profile section, where this is available.

A certain type of school or college in a particular area?

Look in the directories for the area you want (again, you can find the directory page reference on D111). Underneath each school listed you will find icons that denote different types of schools or qualifications that they offer. You can find a key to these icons on the following page; this key is repeated at the front of each section of the directory.

Schools featured in this guidebook are also profiled on its accompanying website: www.whichlondonschool.co.uk and www.schoolsearch.co.uk

School profiles include embedded Twitter feed and YouTube/Vimeo video, direct links to email, website and social media. Users can search by region, county, or postcode; and by age, gender and day/boarding.

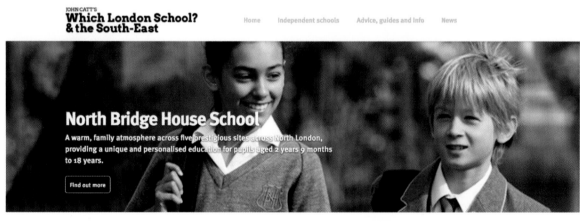

Independent schools in London and the South-East

Are you looking for an independent school in London? Search here to find and compare independent schools and colleges in London and the South-East, including day and boarding schools, boys' schools, girls' schools, prep schools, senior schools, and sixth forms.

You can search for day and boarding schools, prep schools, senior schools, sixth forms and international schools in London, Greater London and the South-East region, which includes Surrey, Kent, Essex, Berkshire, Buckinghamshire, and Hampshire.

You will find schools in London listed at the bottom of this page with some basic directory information; you can use the filters to narrow your search, and find schools near you with our postcode search.

A specific school or college?

If you know the name of the school or college but are unsure of its location, simply go to the index at the back of the guide where you will find all the schools listed alphabetically. You will find that some page numbers are prefixed with the letter D, this denotes that the school appears in the directory section. Schools with page numbers not prefixed by the letter D are those that have chosen to include a fuller school profile, which will provide you with much more extensive information.

Maps?

See pp 48, 85 and 98 for maps of London, Greater London, and the South-East. There are also maps within the directory sections on D112 (Central London), D133 (Greater London) and D141 (South-East).

More information on relevant educational organisations and examinations?

Look in the examinations and qualifications section and the useful organisations section, both located towards the back of the guide.

Key to directory

County ————————————— **Wherefordshire**

Name of school or college ————————————— **College Academy**
Indicates that this school has a profile ————————————— *For further details see p. 12*

Which Street, Whosville,
Wherefordshire AB12 3CD

Address and contact number ————————————— **Tel:** 01000 000000

Head's name ————————————— **Head Master:** Dr A Person
School type ————————————— **Type:** Coeducational day & boarding
Age range ————————————— **Age range:** 11–18
Number of pupils. B = boys G = girls ————————————— **No. of pupils:** 660 B330 G330
Fees per annum. ————————————— **Fees:** Day £11,000 WB £16,000 FB £20,000
Day = fees for day pupils.
WB = fees for weekly boarders.
FB = fees for full boarders.

ⓘⒶ🏛£✐⑯

Key to directory icons (abridged)

Key to symbols:
⚤ Boys' school
⚤ Coeducational school
⚤ Girls' school
🌐 International school

Schools offering:
Ⓐ A levels
🏛 Boarding accommodation
£ Bursaries
⑯ Entrance at 16+

ⓘⒷ International Baccalaureate
✐ Learning support
⑯ Tutorial/sixth form college
🎓 Vocational qualifications

Opening up opportunities to all

Guy Sanderson, Headmaster at Eltham College, explains the ethos behind a move to co-educational status

If you were to open any school prospectus you will undoubtedly see the same vision outlined: that the school in question aims to prepare children for adult life, both academically and socially. And yet, some people still seem to believe this can be achieved in the highly artificial environment of a single-sex school.

The number of single-sex private schools has halved in the last 20 years amid a long-term "shift towards co-education", according to research. Girls' schools make up just 13% of the ISC's membership, with boys' schools only representing 9%. Meanwhile, the number of schools with approximately equal proportions of boys and girls has more than doubled over a similar period.

One of the mixed blessings of working in education is that it is a topic on which everyone has an opinion. Combine this with discussions about gender identities, #metoo and the gender pay gap and opinions run riot.

The question is not whether we want to live in a society which values men and women differently – we are

generally agreed that we do not – but what we need to do to move towards realising that more equitable society. This means challenging assumptions and the status quo. Questions of opportunity, of power and of access need to be asked and answered if we are to make any progress. A widespread emphasis on equality means that it becomes harder and harder "to sustain the argument that children have to be separate to be equal."

The question of whether a single sex or co-educational model works best has been rehashed time and time again and any amount of research, in addition to mention emotional energy and anecdote, can be wheeled out to support the argument on both sides. Articles on this topic are often so keen to make the case for one model over the other that they lose all sense of perspective and nuance. It is surely possible to acknowledge that girls and boys are different and develop differently over adolescence without falling back on unhelpful and monolithic gender stereotypes

> The question is not whether we want to live in a society which values men and women differently – we are generally agreed that we do not – but what we need to do to move towards realising that more equitable society. This means challenging assumptions and the status quo.
> **Guy Sanderson**

which fail to treat each young person as an individual. As Tony Little, who before becoming the Head of perhaps the world's best known all boys' school was for many years Head at a thriving co-ed school, notes "What makes a good school is so much more than its organisation by gender."

Forty years ago, Eltham College, the school of which I am the Head, welcomed girls into its Sixth Form in what was then a radical move, so radical that one parent sued the school on the grounds that the introduction of girls would disrupt his son's schooling. Since then, from County and Regional Netball Champions, to Head Prefects, and also articulate and brilliant academic students, Eltham's Sixth Form girls have flourished, and, in turn, boys have benefitted from their presence whether in the classroom, on stage or in the concert hall.

What matters most for students is to find the school best suited to prepare each young person in and out of the classroom for life as an adult in an equitable society, where men and women work together easily, respectfully and collaboratively. There are single sex schools which do this very well for their students and co-educational ones which do not. What struck us here at Eltham College was that we were operating an increasingly outmoded half-way house which welcomed girls and their contributions in only one part of the school.

In many ways, this is an odd time to consider a change. Eltham College had its best ever GCSE results last year, is currently oversubscribed by six applicants

to every place and enjoys a reputation for not only academic excellence but wonderful co-curricular and pastoral care. "If it ain't broke, don't fix it!" is a persuasive cry. However, our governors and senior teachers saw that continued excellence requires a willingness to ask big questions and to act on the answers. Knowing the power of an excellent education to shape futures, we asked ourselves why were we limiting access for girls to the wonderful opportunities at Eltham and limiting access for boys to the invaluable opportunities to work with girls as equals? We asked ourselves why were we limiting opportunities for our students of both sexes to learn with and from each other until the final two years of school? And, in 2019, there was not a good answer to those questions. And so we made the decision to prepare our students better for the world in which they are growing up by welcoming both girls and boys not just in Year 12 but at all our key entry points with a view to being fully co-educational within six years.

My vision for our school in ten years' time is probably not far off many people's vision for our society as a whole. It is a place in which young women and men at all stages of primary and secondary education learn together, laugh together and learn from each other with equal access and opportunities to develop their potential and contribute to their communities. Getting there will no doubt have its challenges but any goal worth pursuing usually does.

For more information about Eltham College, see page 58

Children who lack resilience have never learned the value of failure

Bryan Padrick, Vice Principal and Director of Studies at independent all-ability LVS Ascot, discusses why his school views resilience as a fundamental requirement for human progress and success

A new educational buzzword has appeared – 'resilience' – and I fear it will suffer the common, expected fate of all buzzwords: here today, gone tomorrow, replaced with the latest educational focus or fad. However, resilience is not a mere fad, a box to tick on the way to earning an 'excellent' or 'outstanding' or whatever the next superior grading mark from ISI or Ofsted might be. Resilience is not equivalent to raising self-esteem, identifying trigger warnings or arranging beanbags kinaesthetically during quiet reading time. No. Resilience is far more: resilience is a fundamental requirement for human progress and success. If that claim appears a bit grand, I challenge anyone to dispute the fact that without the ability to bounce back from adversity, to learn from mistakes –

without the sense of robustness these lessons instil – at the very least human history would look a lot different.

In many ways, it is a shame resilience has had to become an educational buzzword for its necessity to be recognised. As recently as a decade or so ago it was just a part of life. Fell off your bike? You shed a few tears, but climbed back on. Argued with your friends? You sorted the issue or got new ones. Failed a maths exam? Hopefully you learned from your mistakes and improved next time. Didn't improve? Well, maybe maths wasn't for you. However, for a number of (mostly well-intentioned) reasons, this capacity has been gradually educated out of students and their parents. A fear of upsetting someone's self-esteem or appearing to be too critical,

coupled with the desire to wrap children in metaphorical cotton wool to prevent them from needing to bounce back in the first place, has produced a generation of students who lack resilience. They have never learned the value of failure because they have never been allowed to fail.

Resilience is intimately connected to failure and for the former to be present, the latter must be allowed and even encouraged. This is where resilience encounters one of its greatest challenges: schools, and parents, who refuse to allow children to fail. Ones that do not allow young people to slip and fall, to make mistakes – to, in short, experience the very conditions which enable resilience to flourish. No longer learned through experience, resilience must be taught. To do that, one must be allowed – encouraged, even – to take risks.

Now, as I explained in a recent assembly, this encouragement to take risks is not permission to do stupid things: there is nothing positive about drink driving, taking dangerous drugs or attempting to shoot an apple off your best friend's head with an air rifle. But it doesn't take long to find examples of risk takers without whom our world would be a far less colourful and exciting place – a world without whom comfortable satisfaction with the status quo is preferable to challenging ourselves to progress, improve and change.

At LVS Ascot, we have convened a working party composed of subject teachers, department heads, pastoral staff and students to address these issues and identify ways to educate resilience back into children. The whole school, cross-curricular nature of the party is integral to its success: the teaching staff cannot insist on positive failure if the pastoral staff are not supportive,

and the students need to understand the advantages of being pushed outside their comfort zones. The initial challenge has been identifying the need to address our own difficult relationships with this topic. As educators and parents we have been lulled into discouraging risk-taking and failure and by doing so have diminished resilience, in both our students and ourselves, sometimes without even knowing it. Disagree? I'm sure most of us have been a part of a conversation where someone has confessed that, though they had been allowed to do X, Y or Z as a child, because of the state of the world today they would never let their children to do the same.

Whether changes in the state of the world are real or perceived is a topic for another time, but the point I am making is simple: addressing the issues preventing resilience requires a cultural shift amongst staff, students and parents. It is a challenge and a risk, certainly, but one we must be willing to take and one we must be willing to model. There should be no illusion that it is going to be easy, but if there is one lesson we can already learn from resilience, it is that worthy outcomes rarely are.

LVS Ascot is a co-educational, independent, all-ability school for children aged 4 to 18. The school's mission is to inspire independence. Character education is a key aspect to LVS Ascot life, starting with the Infant & Junior School where pupils from Reception to Year 6 study towards a diploma based on five sets of learning values and skills. These are risk taking and resilience, collaboration and self-confidence, initiative and independence, curiosity and creativity, and empathy and reflection. www.lvs.ascot.sch.uk

For more information about LVS Ascot see page 104

League tables or inspection reports – which is best when choosing a school?

James Barton, Director of Admissions at MPW, considers the important factors behind your decision

Choosing a school for your son or daughter is one of the most important decisions that you will make in your life. Naturally, there are lots of factors to consider, but league tables and inspection reports can be useful tools to help inform your decision.

However, there are some important factors to consider before you begin to review the evidence in front of you. Let's explore the advantages and disadvantages of using league tables, and what differentiates them from Ofsted and ISI reports.

How useful are league tables when choosing a school?

School league tables are based on GCSE and A level examination results. They are a quick and easy measure of success and can certainly provide a snapshot of performance or useful starting point in deciding which institutions to consider. However, they lack depth. Unlike university league tables, school rankings do not consider information such as teaching quality, student satisfaction, academic progression or pastoral support. 'Value-added' is not considered in a league table nor do they specify whether a school is academically selective. Whilst league tables are produced in good faith and are an accurate comparator of schools' results, they do not tell you the full story.

How to get the most from a league table

There are a range of tables available, all of which aim to present information about school results. The tables do differ so before drawing any conclusions consider the following questions:

- Have all of the schools in the country been included?

- Where has the data used to rank the schools come from?

- Is the comparison between schools accurate (e.g. are any schools in the table academically selective)?

Having a complete understanding of the information that is being presented will enable you to be make a more objective analysis, ultimately making it more useful. If any schools do stand out as a result of the information in a league table it is advisable to perform some additional research to gain a more in-depth understanding of that institution before drawing any firm conclusions.

Many schools and colleges are not included in league tables. This is not unusual and there are a number of reasons why that may be the case depending on each situation so do not be alarmed if an institution you are researching is not entered. Information about results will usually be available on any particular school's website or can be obtained from the Registrar or Head of Admissions if you would like to find out more.

What are Ofsted or ISI reports?

During an Ofsted or Independent Schools Inspectorate (ISI) inspection, a team of assessors visit a school or college at very short notice and spend a period of three consecutive days conducting research about that institution. They obtain evidence thoroughly via lesson observations, speaking to staff, students and parents, and surveying school paperwork, which enables the team to reach balanced conclusions about key areas of a school's performance. The chief inspector then releases a report summarising the findings of the team which is publicly available (and should be displayed on a school or college's website).

The care taken in the holistic gathering of evidence and the comprehensive impartial description of findings makes inspection reports the most useful resource for parents and students who want to learn more about a school. For those who do not want to spend a lot of a time ploughing through a long paper, the report begins with headline judgments summarising areas such as teaching, student welfare and governance. These judgments range on a scale of four from Outstanding to Inadequate (Ofsted) and Excellent to Unsatisfactory (ISI).

So which is best, league tables or reports?

Quite simply, both have a valuable role to play in helping you to choose the most suitable school. However, whilst league tables can provide a useful at-a-glance indication of the performance and quality of an institution, they should be treated as a useful starting point for your research, rather than providing you with a definitive judgement.

Which is where inspection reports shine. The methods of assessment and depth of reporting provide an extremely thorough, independent analysis for you to judge the overall quality of a school.

For more information about the inspection processes, visit the Ofsted and ISI websites.

MPW is delighted to be the only education group in England to have received the best in class rating from Ofsted/the ISI in every single category across all three of its colleges.

For more information about MPW – London page 68

Curiosity, Collaboration and the Arts

Claire Murdoch, Head of Faraday School, promotes a curriculum that inspires creativity and a love of learning

"But still try, for who knows what is possible?"
Michael Faraday

For parents and teachers everywhere, hearts sink at the defeatist cry of 'I can't do this' or 'I'm stuck'.

At Faraday school we turn that fear on its head. We believe that terrifying moment – when a solution seems impossible and you just want to give up – shouldn't be feared, but celebrated. The frontiers of your knowledge have met the march of your curiosity. And we are helping children to realise that THIS is the very moment where the challenge has been set, now it's time to knuckle down and give it your best shot.

By encouraging curiosity, our pupils reach a tipping point, and that is when the real learning begins…

It was in our quest to develop resilience and a growth mindset amongst the pupils that we have recognised

how important our investment in the arts and our close relationship with the wonderful local community has been. At Faraday, we find ourselves settled in a uniquely creative and inspirational environment at Trinity Buoy Wharf, East London surrounded by small businesses, entrepreneurs and artists, who have come together to form a burgeoning environment for the arts. The school has used its location as a springboard for its own development, knowing that risk-taking and being willing to fail is something that resonates particularly strongly in all creative endeavours.

The renowned physicist, Michael Faraday worked in an experimental lighthouse next door to our school for many years and some of his most exciting ideas were conjured up in his workshop overlooking the river Lea. As the figurehead of Faraday, we have absorbed some of his key characteristics of perseverance, persistence and

Science and the arts are for us the umbrella within which we can explore curiosity, enquiry and a curriculum that inspires children to keep on learning. When many schools around us are being forced to reduce the opportunities they can offer in these subjects, due to funding or curriculum restraints, we feel it is ever more important to offer an all-round education that really develops the creative side of learning.

Claire Murdoch

determination into the heart of our school. We know that much of Faraday's early success was based upon his making the most of every opportunity, secretly reading the books that he was binding as an apprentice and developing a love of science that saw him sneak into the back of lecture theatres to increase his understanding. He had an intense appetite for experimenting, spending hours trying out new methods and techniques before settling upon his theory, and it is this inquisitiveness and ingenuity that continues to inspire our students as they hope to live up to his legacy.

Science and the arts are for us the umbrella within which we can explore curiosity, enquiry and a curriculum that inspires children to keep on learning. When many schools around us are being forced to reduce the opportunities they can offer in these subjects, due to funding or curriculum restraints, we feel it is ever more important to offer an all-round education that really develops the creative side of learning. There is an abundance of evidence that shows the value of nurturing curiosity, creativity and collaboration and these three Cs are a key part of our mantra at Faraday. These key skills are not tied to specific subjects but can be seen across the curriculum wherever children are given opportunities to create, compose and use their imagination to problem-solve or explore alternative solutions where they thought there were none. One of the clear benefits from this approach has been how pupil well-being has been positively impacted and an individual's ability to traverse more difficult paths has increased through carefully designed artistic endeavours. From our initial projects, we have already begun to see how important these occasions can be for young people.

One of the achievements of which we are most proud has been the introduction of a new school newspaper the Trinity Times, due to print its first run in April 2019, with school reporters seen out about on the Wharf interviewing local residents and selling their new rag in the local café. Their articles have documented our achievements, featuring the collaborative artwork that the children exhibited locally and all the artists, scientists and sculptors that have been rallied to collaborate on installations and workshops in school, helping the pupils develop their ideas and show their work. Ultimately, our engagement with the local community has shown us that we are valued and opened our eyes to all the many organisations and volunteers who want to be involved in the education of our children.

Just as we are asking our children to do, it is vital that we are open and innovative in approach taking risks and trying new things. We have found evidence of all sorts of progress with our approach and this has allowed us to hone our curriculum by remaining flexible and reactive to the pupils' interests. Faraday, as part of the New Model Schools Company, has a not-for-profit ethos and a sustainable philosophy that hopes to enable as many children as possible to be able to access a broad, rigorous and exciting education at the lowest sustainable cost. By maintaining links with the community, inspiring our teachers and utilising the huge talent and experience within our staff, we can ensure that those at Faraday receive an invigorating and enriching education, rooted in knowledge but with no limits as to how it is developed or responded to by the pupils.

You have to be brave to open your doors to others but the opportunities you may find there will always make this step worthwhile. We look forward to what we can achieve at Faraday in the coming years, knowing that we have the full support of those around us.

For more information about Faraday School, see page 60

Dispelling misconceptions about the IB

Margaret Frazier, Headmistress of Marymount London, a girls' day and boarding school in Kingston upon Thames, explains the School's guiding principles

Marymount London is a school that celebrates student voice and choice. Marymount girls are prepared for the future by being front and center in their own learning. A proudly IB school and the first girls' school in the UK to adopt the International Baccalaureate curriculum in 1979, we have nearly four decades experience in doing something different – something guided by exploration, innovation, interdisciplinary connection, reflection, and risk taking. This makes Marymount unique.

Throughout my discussions with hundreds of prospective families over the past two years, I have seen first-hand that there are a growing number of London-based families interested in considering an alternative to the 11 and 13+ entrance exams as well as the GCSE and A-level curricula. Despite their enthusiasm for an interdisciplinary curriculum focused on critical thinking, exploration and intercultural understanding,

misconceptions and misperceptions surrounding the IB exist:

"The IB is only for children of diplomatic families. It only works for those who need a portable curriculum."
The IB is now 50 years old with nearly 5,000 schools worldwide. It is considered by the Harvard Graduate School of Education to be a "best practices" curriculum – one that engages a student in her learning and teaches skills along with content – that allows for the creative and critical thinking skills that are needed in the 21st century global world. It is not a "spoon feeding" experience, but rather one that is recognized as the gold standard for creating independent, collaborative, and engaged learners.

"Top universities in the UK and around the world don't know the IB and/or don't value it."

As an IB School, we don't require the 11+, and we are not an exam factory. We create a positive, joyful attitude around learning.
Margaret Frazier

At Marymount, we are proud of our outstanding results: a five-year average of 36 points (vs. 29 world average and 34 UK average) and a 100% pass rate in 2018. Our graduates earn offers at Russell Group/Top 20 universities in the UK, including Imperial, St. Andrews, UCL, Bristol, and Edinburgh. Outside the UK, we have graduates at Stanford, NYU, Barnard and University of Virginia in the United States, McGill in Canada and other top universities in Europe and Asia.

There is no question that UK universities place a high value on what an IB education delivers. Here is just one example: Our students have earned offers of 38 points to study law at Oxford, whereas it would have required AAA at A level or 38 points (two points above our average) to study Biological Sciences at Imperial instead of three As at A level.

"The IB is only for gifted students."
Everyone at Marymount participates in the IB program: Middle Years Programme (MYP) for Grades 6 through 10 and the Diploma Programme (DP) for the final two years in Grades 11 and 12. This is what our whole school is about. It is neither an add-on program nor a program for a small group of chosen participants, but rather a way of teaching and learning for our entire school.

"The IB is too much work, or it's too easy."
The IB places significant value on both breadth and depth – and not narrowing focus or limiting options too early. There are research projects that are challenging as well as opportunities in the Diploma Programme for higher level and standard level study. Our highly skilled and dedicated faculty are there every step of the way as subject teachers, advisors, year heads, and club moderators.

"What else makes a Marymount education unique?"
We believe in something bigger than ourselves. Our school is part of 18 other Religious of the Sacred Heart of Mary (RSHM) schools in New York, Los Angeles, Rome, Paris, Mexico, Portugal, Brazil and Mexico; we are members of a global network that offers service programs, student exchanges, leadership conferences, and travel for festivals in sport, drama, and Model UN.

As an IB School, we don't require the 11+, and we are not an exam factory. We create a positive, joyful attitude around learning. At Marymount, a student does not have to choose between physics and dance, geography and French, a love of literature or math. She can pursue her desire to conduct research in biology and be equally passionate about her extraordinary work in the art and design studios. Just this week, one of our Grade 7 students, inspired by Rebel Girls Stories, took the initiative to contact the quantum ballerina Dr. Merritt Moore and invite her to campus to share her story with our community.

"It has been said that Marymount girls love to learn and learn to love. How so?"
We are a school deliberately focused on cultivating positivity, respect, collaboration, and problem solving. Together, adults and students are inspired to be more open, discerning, humble, compassionate, connected, and kind. And we do all of this while remaining committed to the mission and principles of the IB and the RSHM.

For more information about Marymount London see page 94

Stories and storytelling are not just for Book Week

Jo Townsend, Deputy Head (Pastoral) at Broomwood Hall, extols the virtues of a good book

Every year, in March, schools across the country celebrate World Book Day. Whilst it generally involves some dressing-up and a lot of fun, the more serious message is to encourage children to share their favourite books and give them the message that "reading is power".

The importance of reading – or rather being read to – is underlined by some recent reports which show that a decline in "story time" affects pupil wellbeing.

The first, from Egmont, a leading children's publisher, highlights that only 32% of British children are read to daily by an adult for pleasure. The research shows that the number of children who receive story time sessions has fallen by 4 percentage points since 2012. It warns that the "steep decline signals a significant threat to children's wellbeing, with potential longer-term social impact," and has called for parents and government to take action by making 'storytime' sessions in primary schools an intrinsic part of the day. Whilst reading to children is a very effective way to encourage them to read independently, many parents simply don't know what a great impact they could have on their children's lives if they read to them daily.

Egmont's research shows that reading for pleasure has a four-times greater impact on academic success than a parent having a degree. However in another survey (Understanding the Children's Book Consumer), Renaissance UK revealed that only a quarter of school aged children get recommended reading for pleasure time and that only 19% of 8 to 10-year-old pupils have books read to them by an adult daily, down 3 percentage points since last year across all socioeconomic groups, irrespective of parents' education, household income or social grade class. The figure is even lower for boys at just 14% (contrasted with 24% of girls).

I urge you to remember that there's no age limit when it comes to the enjoyment of hearing someone reading aloud
Jo Townsend

War Horse author and former children's laureate, Michael Morpurgo has supported this call to action with a poem (https://youtu.be/9MtguIsBQJE) written especially for this cause, saying, "It is vital that children, young people and all of us have access to stories which give us the knowledge, empathy and understanding we need to negotiate life. But, just as importantly, we need to give children and their teachers and parents time to read."

At Broomwood Hall, reading is high on the agenda from Reception to Year 8. The children have many opportunities to read for pleasure and have stories and passages read to them for their enjoyment as well as their understanding and analysis. Libraries on each site allow the children freedom to choose books with guidance and knowledge from staff who are dedicated and passionate about their subject.

To further support reading and to help bring books to life, we encourage children to read, write and perform poetry from the moment they join our school by organising competitions and giving them the opportunity to act out some of their favourites. As well as these annual poetry competitions, there are also plenty of other opportunities for children to learn and appreciate the value of story-telling with reading aloud competitions,

visits from authors, workshops and regular theatre trips and visits to senior schools to take part in drama activity days or watch productions.

Children also write stories for magazines – two girls were published in last year's King's Canterbury's 'Mind's Eye' magazine and regularly win storywriting competitions. We also encourage children to write and perform their own stories, whether that's our 5- and 6-year olds bringing their stories to life through animation or our 12 and 13-year-old leavers writing and performing their own Revue.

During Book Week, we encourage older children to read aloud to younger pupils so that they can recognise the value and mutual pleasure gained on both sides.

At a time when there is so much concern about our children's mental health and wellbeing, it's worth remembering the value of a good book and the shared pleasure of a good story, well told.

I urge you to remember that there's no age limit when it comes to the enjoyment of hearing someone reading aloud – and that the pleasure of taking time out to read together is something that is always worth making time for.

For more information about Broomwood Hall (Part of Northwood Schools), see page 52

Berkshire's change for the better

An initiative to champion sustainability has been embraced by students

Leighton Park School in Reading, Berkshire, has achieved a landmark in the school's sustainability journey with the launch of the Change Champions initiative to students in Years 7 and 8 the start of term. It is vital that young people understand the critical importance of their role within a global community committed to nurturing the world in which we live for their own future and that of subsequent generations.

Change Champions was the brain child of the school's IT Support company, Commercial Group, and has been a key strategy for all their staff within that business. Leighton Park's Director of IT, David Pacey and Karen Gracie-Langrick, Deputy Head (Academic) tailored Commercial's Change Champions programme to work around the School's younger ages groups and designed sample projects for each team to attempt. Delivering this message from Commercial on launch day were Richard Blundell, Managed IT Divisional Director, and Grace Segrave, Sustainability Assistant. Commercial Group are made up of various divisions and Change Champions was originally started in the

Office Supplies Division, quickly spreading across the entire business. An IT consultancy may seem an unusual source of sustainability wisdom but Commercial have whole-heartedly embraced sustainability and their Co-Founder, Simone Hindmarch-Bye, is so determined to make a difference that she has employed two full time members of staff dedicated to the creation and implementation of a Change Champions programme within her business. Aiming to inspire similar behaviours in the School community and specifically within the Year 7 and 8's Community Action Service (CAS) programme, Commercial shared the success of their sustainability formula with Leighton Park's students.

As Grace Segrave, explained to the students, "Every little thing you do can make a difference, every choice you make, every item you pick, has a ripple effect. You are tomorrow's leaders and you will be responsible for changing the planet from what it is today and making it better."

"The Change Champions initiative, which we will deliver through our weekly CAS sessions, is about empowering our students to be real drivers of change as they look at their role as stewards of the planet and to action their pioneering ideas to make a difference and to reduce our carbon footprint," added Karen Gracie-Langrick, Deputy Head (Academic).

Through Commercial's presentation, students discovered that the three pillars of sustainability; environmental, social and economic, or colloquially, planet, people and profit; support the Quaker values at the heart of Leighton Park's ethos. Considering your environmental impact, remembering to reuse, reduce and recycle, taking decisions that reduce your carbon footprint, all speak to the testimonies of simplicity and sustainability. The need to select suppliers and buy products from organisations who treat their workers with respect, integrity, equality and peace, pay a fair wage for work, offer benefits that improve the life/work balance and don't take advantage of people is vital for a sustainable workforce. A business must be profitable to be sustainable but profit at any cost is not economically sustainable. The truth is also that it is not necessary to be greedy or deceitful in the pursuit of profit and organisations must consider their corporate social responsibility, risk management and governance strategies to ensure that their desire for profit does not overwhelm the other two pillars of sustainability. The option which seems financially the cheapest often has a much higher cost to the planet or its people. Sustainability is about recognising that and

achieving an acceptable balance between the three pillars.

It was fascinating to hear some of the initiatives that Commercial's own employees have undertaken. There were activities ranging from planting a living wall over recycled plastic benches creating mindfulness areas at their headquarters to refusing to supply their clients laptops with precious metal components mined in countries where workers are exploited; from using delivery vans that run on hydrogen and emit only water to supporting a female farming project on a Kenyan palm oil plantation to reduce their carbon footprint. Recognition of their laudable efforts came last year in the form of the Queen's Award for Enterprise in the sustainability category, and Commercial are delighted to be pioneers as the only member of the Ethical Trading Institute (ETI) in the office supplies industry, leading the way for others to follow.

As the presentation came to a close, the students were buzzing with ideas "It was good," commented Maurice (Year 7). "I was really inspired by the tiers of sustainability," added Jack (Year 8) "I don't know what I'm going to do next but I want to do something for good." Co-ordinator of the CAS programme, Pablo Gorostidi, was pleased the launch had been well received, reflecting, "Not only is our CAS Change Champions initiative about sustainability but it is in itself sustainable. The Year 7s will begin their project this year in a group mixed with Year

8s and next year they will continue their activity in Year 8 with some new Year 7s on their team and so on. It is a rolling responsibility and commitment."

Already underway with the school's commitment to sustainability is Grounds and Facilities Manager, Tom Sheldon. "We are trying to achieve as much sustainability across the Park as we can." Tom explained. "It's important that we work with the right companies and find suppliers who are local to us to help reduce our carbon footprint."

The rolling programme for the replacement of furniture has enabled Tom to order modular sofa units with timber frames certified by the Forest Stewardship Council and with high quality production values so that they can be re-upholstered in the future rather than replaced. Although the upfront costs are higher, this approach will extend the sofa's lifespan from 10 to 30 years. In addition, the soft and durable fabric covering the new sofas is incredibly made from recycled plastic bottles! Over the next three years all the boarding house couches will be replaced with sustainable sofas and this term the Individual Learning Centre is also being kitted out.

Tree Preservation Orders are active across the 65 acre park and although the estates team do occasionally have to fell mature or over-mature trees, they are careful to plan two new trees in a nearby location. "I'd love to see every child joining the School planting their own tree on the Park," mused Tom, recognising the value of saplings which use up more carbon dioxide as they grow than older trees.

One of the biggest differences Tom has made to the School's carbon footprint recently is through the compacting of waste. The school previously generated eleven bins of cardboard waste per week necessitating frequent waste collections. By compacting the cardboard and arranging for it to be collected weekly by a recycling company we have avoided unnecessary CO2 emissions and converted the waste into recycling. The waste that cannot be recycled is collected by Select Environmental who ensure 0% landfill by incinerating the waste. They employ special filters on the emissions resulting in an output which is actually cleaner than the air we are already breathing!

Fuel for the school's five minibuses is now delivered to site for onsite refuelling, rather than all five buses being driven to a service station each week for diesel. The fleet of golf buggies and the catering van have all been changed to electric vehicles and the move

towards electric, rather than petrol powered, tools such as mowers, hedge cutters and strimmers etc, is 80% complete.

Keith Eldridge, Bursar, is proud of the School's commitment to solar power. "We have had solar panels on the swimming pool, Reckitt House and Oakview restaurant, and will have completed School House before the end of the summer." Alan Rumney, Estates Manager, explained "Since its installation in 2015 the 35kW array on the swimming pool has generated over 101 megawatt hours of free electricity for the School, a saving that equates to over 40 tons of carbon dioxide emissions from a power station." The 20kW array on Oakview and the 13kW array on Reckitt are as efficient although smaller. "We believe that 75% of all the electricity being produced is being used by the School, reducing our carbon footprint even further," concluded Alan.

It is clear that the Leighton Park community is already an educational environment that values sustainability. The School community is excited to see how much more they can do to make a difference.

For more information about Leighton Park School, see page 102

Be yourself, not somebody else!

Tutor Lucienne Sharpe offers some advice to bring out the best in your child's learning

When I am tutoring I am always struck by how students want to copy the teacher.

My message is always "Be yourself, not somebody else!"

Yes, as a student you need to listen and learn key skills and enhance your understanding, but not your own personality. This is your key and it's yours alone. So be bold and keep it safe!

When guiding students I am always influenced by their own interests and how they approach learning. If they just can't get excited about poetry show them that it isn't just words. It's about feelings and emotions and can be very relevant to today and the key influences on the world stage. Talk about this as though it's a film. Watch relevant films and discuss. Think about imagery.

- How do people feel when they become lost in another country?

- What kind of experiences was Shakespeare wanting to show us?

Forgetting the language and the difficulties that arise from that, can we see the music and the beat in that expression? Can we see the pictures as a moving film?

Talking to students is the best thing we can do. Not about the work and not about the targets but about what is the message in the writing and the message and the themes. I strongly believe we should not pay so much attention on terminology. I had a student who couldn't understand the meaning of grammatical functions but could understand grammatical devices!

Talking to students is the best thing we can do. Not about the work and not about the targets but about what is the message in the writing and the message and the themes. I strongly believe we should not pay so much attention on terminology. I had a student who couldn't understand the meaning of grammatical functions but could understand grammatical devices!

Are we so hung up on accuracy that we forget the essence? I know we need to understand them but let us start the other way round.

Creative response is a luxury that as a tutor you can ask for. How does creative learning impact on our writing?

Its not about the word 'imagery', it's about the words you can choose that convey your ideas. Creative writing is based on all kinds of language – even just two words can convey joy or sadness!

I encourage all my students to research the world stage before they even begin to analyse. How can you possibly understand the writer if you do not know the world as it was when the writer took pen to paper?

Then there is latent talent that is often ignored or lost just because of the demands of teaching and targets.

Let us think creatively. Creative thinking is about inspiration. It's like a little angel or goblin that taps you on the shoulder and says 'Hey you! Are you listening?' If you ignore it will go somewhere else. We need to take that angel seriously. It may be that you will become the next William Shakespeare!

Confidence is another key skill. How do we achieve that? So often I see my students become stressed because exams are fast approaching. Just help them to know they have the answers. After all they have been working hard. Now just go and enjoy the exam experience. It will embrace you!

If a student says to me 'Oh I hate this poetry', I always say, 'just learn to love it!'

Help the student when going for school interviews; tell them to take a good book that interests them and a hobby to speak about as well as a well prepared folder of all their successes. Certificates. Maybe a video. The school will be inspired by this, especially if the book is very topical. Look the interviewer in the eye and be confident!

The author Ken Robinson delivered a famous TED talk about the power of creativity.

Who would have guessed that this industry of the creative spirit, when you consider fashion and music, would change the world economy.

Preparing for the exams

Be clear and use a template for a strategy.

It is worth the time. I always ask my students to put large A3 paper in a place at home and keep adding notes up on it as it occurs. To keep looking at this paper and adding. Keep reminding the brain!

The strategy should be just pointers:

- What is the message?

- Who is the audience?

- Why was this written, what is the purpose and where is the evidence?

- Who can argue against proven evidence in the answers.

Most of all, each and everyone of us can achieve beyond our imagination. We just need to be really encouraged. It is about two-way learning. Tutor and student. It is not one-way learning.

For more information, see www.amazing-tutor.co.uk

Learning without walls

Maria Blake, Headteacher of Dallington School, champions the benefits of outdoor learning

Dallington is a school that holds a unique place in the constellation of outstanding London schools – a vibrant oasis of creativity; proudly and fiercely independent. Established and led for over 40 years by Mogg Hercules MBE, it has been the school of choice for parents seeking an exceptional education for their children. Taking over the headship presents a formidable challenge – how to celebrate and develop Mogg's legacy, whilst bringing to bear my own style and experience?

As I begin this fascinating journey, I hope to champion Outdoor Learning and to ultimately see our children fly the flag that will inspire other schools to recognise this learning as a fundamental part of the holistic education we all aim to offer.

We are living in a time when, as parents, we are more protective of our children than ever. The world can appear an unpredictable and dangerous place, so our parental instincts are completely understandable. For those of us raising children in cities, the potential for disaster can seem to lurk around every corner. These fears are naturally absorbed by our children and are reflected back at them through television, film and social media. Coupled with the increasing pressure on even the youngest of our children to outperform themselves academically, it should shock nobody that we are facing a national wellbeing crisis.

As schools are being increasingly expected to address this crisis, whilst simultaneously delivering

> We believe that our Outdoor Learning Programme is essential if our children are to develop the skills and qualities they will need to flourish and succeed in life, whatever their age and whatever life might throw at them.
> **Maria Blake**

outstanding academic results, it is clear that wellbeing cannot be improved by timetabling 'Wellbeing' for a Wednesday afternoon.

Here at Dallington, our Year 3 children are counting the sleeps until next Thursday, when they will be setting off for their first school camping experience. This camp is an integral part of the mosaic that makes up our enhanced Outdoor Learning Programme, which runs from Nursery through to Year 6. Whilst Outdoor Learning may be having something of a moment in wider education circles and the benefits of an inclusive, exciting, challenging programme well established, many schools have allowed such learning to be overshadowed by results-driven, academic priorities.

Having planned and led residential school trips for over 30 years, implementing full outdoor learning programmes in several schools around the world, I am in no doubt about the extraordinary impact these experiences have on children.

The Year 3 children who return from their camp next week will be subtly yet noticeably different from the children who set off. For many, simply saying goodbye to their parents will be a new experience and a considerable achievement. For every child, taking shared responsibility for their backpacks, tents and dinners will be fresh and exciting. Working together to keep every member of the team buoyant and busy, whilst immersed in activities and overcoming challenges, will be unprecedented. The collective sense of satisfaction in a job well done and – as they say – being their best selves together will be unlimited.

We believe that our Outdoor Learning Programme is essential if our children are to develop the skills and qualities they will need to flourish and succeed in life, whatever their age and whatever life might throw at them. Far more than just a fun time in a forest with their friends, the programme builds from Nursery onwards, incorporating experiences and challenges and, yes, a lot of fun in a variety of wild settings – from Highgate Wood to the Arctic wilderness of Northern Finland. We know that this learning will lead to improved performance, improved mental and physical wellbeing and improved behaviours and communication skills, both in school and at home. We hope too, that in a time when so many working parents are time-poor, the children themselves will discover new interests that they can share with their families, impacting quality family times.

Over the past 40 years, Dallington children have earned a well-deserved reputation for being independent, curious, critical thinkers and learners. They learn to recognise their own energies and to understand how this interacts with and impacts a group dynamic; how to use their communication skills to explore ideas and resolve conflicts; the importance of engaging with perspectives, experiences and opinions that are different to their own, at every age.

In developing our Outdoor Learning Programme, we are absolutely building on this legacy, promoting and celebrating the wellbeing of all our children in an inclusive environment, as they themselves prepare to forge a successful path in a rapidly changing world.

Meanwhile, in Year 3, there are 6 sleeps to go ....

• Please visit www.dallingtonschool.co.uk to learn more about our outdoor programme and our cross-curricular approach to learning. Join one of our daily tours and come and see us in action!

For more information about Dallington School see page 53

The intrinsic link between co-curricular activity and wellbeing

Tom Hadcroft, Vice Principal (Pastoral) at DLD College London, explains the additional benefits that schools and colleges can champion

In 2018 DLD College London chose to rethink completely how it approached student wellbeing in the College. The College already recognised that our students' emotional and mental health underpins their academic achievement here and their future successes. This year DLD committed to ensuring that every student at the College knows what wellbeing support is available to them and how they can access it.

The focus on mental health, championed by members of the British Royal family, has never had as much exposure as it currently commands. The need for greater awareness comes amid worrying statistics highlighting a rise in mental health illnesses. The proportion of young

people reporting symptoms of anxiety or depression increased from 18% in the period 2009 to 2010 to 21% in 2013 to 2014.[1] Wellbeing and mental health guidance from the Government in February 2018 highlighted that half of all mental health problems have been established by the age of 14, rising to 75% by age 24. It is incredibly important that the warning signs are acted upon and not allowed to fester.

With these trends on a rise DLD College London are focused on extending our provision through phase two of our wellbeing initiatives, focusing on empowerment and co-curricular initiatives. Firstly, we have now focused on our proactive measures to recognize and support those in need. We have now trained over 30 of our members of staff in Mental Health First Aid, with the intention of reaching out to all members of staff within the next 12 months. Additionally, we now have a number of parents and over 50 students and staff who have qualified in the Mental Health First Aid Lite course. This three hour programme raises awareness of the signs and symptoms of mental health concerns. We are focused on empowering our students to be readied with life skills which will benefit them beyond school and university and allowing parents to also feel empowered.

The sense of the word 'education' is far too often limited to a sense of success related to exam results. At DLD we focus on preparedness, seeing the emphasis on skills-based learning developing the individual beyond an exam result, focusing on holistic education inside and outside the classroom.

We are now close to developing our own DLD Health Charter, in conjunction with the students, to develop a proactive approach to wellbeing. The charter is focussed on the sense of belonging, their own wellbeing performance, diet, mindfulness and biorhythms for each student. We hope to demonstrate that proactiveness will assist in emotional health. The measures we have put in place aim to allow students a better sense of connectedness with themselves and a toolkit to allow them to develop as leaders in a diverse world.

Central to the focus of the Health Charter is the emphasis in importance of those activities we term, 'co-curricular activities' or CCAs. These activities take place outside of the normal curricular timetabled points of the day and allows the student to try something different or extend their understanding of their own area of interest. Irfan Latif, the Principal of DLD, is keen to focus that London is our classroom and it is through these co-curricular activities that we are utilising our central London location.

We are now focussed on developing the broad range of activities within the scope of the Health Charter emphasising the benefit that these activities, in addition to a range of mindful practices will strengthen resilience and wellbeing. Through organisations such as Action for Happiness, it is clear that there is a recognition that through promotion of a positive variety of different activities that positive mental health can follow.

Additional benefits of co-curricular participation include self-efficacy, satisfaction, feelings of support and institutional challenge, retention, academic achievement and intellectual engagement, enhanced understanding of others, deepened sense of spirituality, and practical skill acquisition such as interview skills and networking abilities.[2] Additionally, co-curricular experiences reportedly enrich student learning by complementing students' curricular education and enhancing holistic student development.[3]

Physical activity

The links between physical activity and mental wellbeing are well documented and long standing. Physical exercise does not need to be a chore, but instead can be something that we do to enhance wellbeing. The lessons learnt from being part of a team or setting a challenge and meeting milestones can be equally applied to the pitch or running track as the classroom.

While there is a relationship between students' participation in extra and co-curricular activities and student learning outcomes, the specifics can be unclear. Overall, extra and co-curricular activities are likely to be associated with a range of positive outcomes for students, such as higher grades, decreased absence, and increased educational achievement. [4]

Evidence has shown that positive development and growth of young adults is linked to the opportunities provided by schools and communities to learn physical, intellectual, psychological, emotional, and social skills in the presence of warm and nurturing relationships that enable social integration and a sense of belonging, and offer adult guidance and limit-setting alongside physical and psychological safety. High quality extra-curricular activities have been shown to include many of these development promoting features.[5]

It is important for educational settings to embrace and recognise these additional benefits and use them as conduits for those young people who are suffering poor mental health. Greater awareness and promotion of their benefits allows structured paths and avenues to build resilience and positive coping mechanisms. At DLD, we will ensure that this philosophy is embedded at the heart of the charter and the support of the students to develop their toolbox to deal with their future lives.

Endnotes

1. Office for National Statistics
2. Daniyal, Nawaz, Hassan, & Mubeen, 2012; Kilpatrick & Wilburn, 2010; Lourens, 2014; Pasque & Murphy, 2005; Turrentine, Esposito, Young, & Ostroth, 2012
3. Beltman & Schaeben, 2012; Elias & Drea, 2013; Foubert & Grainger, 2006; Kuh, 2001
4. Farb, A. F., & Matjasko, J. L. 2012; O'Donnell & Kirkener, 2014
5. Mahoney, Larson, Eccles, & Lord, 2005 cited in Metsäpelto & Pulkkinen, 2014

For more information about DLD College London, see page 55

Learn to sail in Greece with family RYA training courses

Sail Ionian extends an invitation to keen sailors-in-the-making

With sheltered islands, crystal clear waters, steady winds and the kind of scenery from the *Mamma Mia* films, the Ionian is a stunning part of the Mediterranean and arguably one of the finest sailing areas in the entire world. It's no wonder why the area attracts so many return visitors year on year - with seemingly more unspoiled bays and charming harbours to discover upon each visit, the Ionian and its authenticity just keep on delivering. Steeped in Ancient Greek history and home to the traditional delights of tangy tzatziki and refreshingly cold Mythos beer, what's not to love about this gem of a place.

Sail Ionian, a family-run yacht charter company based on the island of Lefkada, agree that along with some awesome sailing, you really can't go wrong! If you are a family looking to take the youngsters on an action-packed learning experience while exploring the real Greece, then an RYA training course involving the whole family could be for you. Ideal for unqualified yet keen sailors-in-the-making, an RYA course opens up a world of opportunities for future adventures by sea.

The RYA is the UK's national governing body for dinghy, yacht and motor cruising among other watersports. They provide training from recreational to professional level all over the world and are leaders in the industry. Sail Ionian Sea School's affiliation with the RYA means that their professional RYA Cruising Instructors can offer a wide range of practical sailing courses in the Greek sunshine with the most popular courses being RYA Competent Crew for beginners and RYA Day Skipper for those with some previous sailing experience. The RYA Day Skipper qualification is the minimum requirement for anyone looking to charter a yacht in Greece, the Mediterranean and many others places in the world so to say the RYA courses have become more popular in recent years would be an understatement!

So if Mum or Dad have the relevant pre course experience and theoretical knowledge for RYA Day Skipper, and the children are eager to learn a new hobby in the RYA Competent Crew course taught by a fun, friendly instructor who will feel like part of the family at the end of the course, RYA training as a family is a great way to pair a holiday with a learning experience.

The RYA Competent Crew course is a 5 day course which is aimed at those completely new to sailing or with dinghy sailing experience. During the course you will learn all of the skills required to become a useful crew member aboard a yacht anywhere in the world, with some extras in the training thrown in – you'll even have the opportunity to moor the boat and navigate each day! Sail Ionian's minimum age for this course is 8 years old and for anyone younger, they've come up with an in-house certificate for aspiring mini-pirates.

RYA Day Skipper also runs over 5 days with a night sail in there too, you'll be taught off the skills needed to safely skipper a yacht by day. Plenty of time at the helm, close-quarter handling and sail trim make for an intense yet hugely satisfying course

The fantastic thing about taking the RYA courses in the Ionian is that not only is the weather predictable with dawn-til-dusk sunshine but you'll also be island hopping at the same time! The Ionian islands of Meganisi, Kastos, Kefalonia & Ithaca are the perfect playground for newbie sailors with relatively short distances to sail between islands, calm seas and easy line of sight navigation.

But the best bit? It's got to be that the 6th and final day of the holiday is used as a free sailing day – ideal to consolidate all of your newly learned skills in a relaxed,

family environment without the instructor on board. Sail Ionian will issue the certificates and as a newly qualified family, you'll get a taste of what a real bareboat charter feels like. Stopping in a secluded bay for

With Sail Ionian's family RYA training course, you are guaranteed to come away from a fantastic and informative sailing holiday in the beautiful surroundings of the Greek Ionian islands, with a wealth of new found knowledge that will serve as a solid foundation for any further sailing that you choose to do as family. Be warned, it's extremely addictive and the children will be pestering you to rebook on the coach back to the airport!

Already qualified? Then go for a bareboat charter exploring the Ionian at your own pace over a week, 10 days or even a fortnight on board a beautifully maintained sailing yacht. Sail Ionian's assisted sailing scheme aims to brush up and refresh skills by taking a skipper with you for a day, two days or more. This is a great option for rusty sailors at the beginning of your holiday, allowing you then to sail off around the islands with confidence in your sailing and mooring ability.

Offering something for everyone, Sail Ionian's modest fleet of new and immaculate sailing yachts will not disappoint. Visit their website at www.sailionian.com, email info@sailionian.com or call 0800 321 3800 for a personalised holiday quotation.

Choosing a school – what to consider

However much a school may appeal at first sight, you still need sound information to form your judgement

Schools attract pupils by their reputations, so most go to considerable lengths to ensure that parents are presented with an attractive image. Modern marketing techniques try to promote good points and play down (without totally obscuring) bad ones. But every Head knows that, however good the school prospectus is, it only serves to attract parents through the school gates. Thereafter the decision depends on what they see and hear. Research we have carried out over the years suggests that in many cases the most important factor in choosing a school is the impression given by the Head. As well as finding out what goes on in a school, parents need to be reassured by the aura of confidence that they expect from a Head. How they judge the latter may help them form their opinion of the former. In other words, how a Head answers questions is important in itself and, to get you started, we have drawn up a list of points that you may like to consider. Some can be posed

as questions and some are points you'll only want to check in your mind. They are not listed in any particular order and their significance will vary from family to family, but they should be useful in helping you to form an opinion.

Before visiting and asking questions, **check the facts** – such as which association the school belongs to, how big it is, how many staff *etc*. Is there any form of financial pie chart showing how the school's resources are used? The answers to questions like these should be in the promotional material you've been sent. If they aren't, you've already got a good question to ask!

Check the website. Is it up-to-date? Look at the school's social media feeds and videos. What type of tone do they set? That first impression is very important.

When you get to the school you will want to judge the overall atmosphere and decide whether it will suit you and your child. Are any other members of the family going to

MPW London – see editorial on page 14

help to pay the fees? If so, their views are important and the school's attitude towards them may be instructive.

When you make it to the inner sanctum, **what do you make of the Head as a person?** Age? Family? Staying? Moving on? Retiring? Busted flush? Accessible to children, parents and staff? If you never get to see the Head, but deal with an admissions person of some sort, it may not mean you should rule the school out, but it certainly tells you something about the school's view of pupil recruitment.

Academic priorities – attitude towards league tables? This is a forked question. If the answer is 'We're most concerned with doing the best for the child', you pitch them a late-developer; if the answer is, 'Well, frankly, we have a very high entry threshold', then you say 'So we have to give you a foolproof academic winner, do we?'

Supplementary questions:

- What is the ratio of teachers to pupils?
- What are the professional qualifications of the teaching staff?
- What is the school's retention rate? In prep schools this means how many pupils do they lose at 11 when the school goes on to 13.
- How long is the school day – and week?
- What are the school's exam results?
- What are the criteria for presenting them?
- Were they consistent over the years?
- Is progress accelerated for the academically bright?
- How does the school cope with pupils who do not work?
- Where do pupils go when they leave?
- How important and well resourced are sports, extra-curricular and after school activities, music and drama?
- What cultural or other visits are arranged away from the school?

Other topics to cover:

- What is the school's mission?
- What is its attitude to religion?
- How well is the school integrated into the local community?
- How have they responded to the Charities Act initiatives?
- What are the responsibilities and obligations at weekends for parents, pupils and the school?
- Does the school keep a watching brief or reserve the option to get involved after a weekend incident?
- What is the school's attitude to discipline?
- Have there been problems with drugs, drink or sex? How have they been dealt with?
- What is the school's policy on bullying?
- How does the school cope with pupils' problems?
- What sort of academic and pastoral advice is available?
- What positive steps are taken to encourage good manners, behaviour and sportsmanship?
- What is the uniform?
- What steps are taken to ensure that pupils take pride in their personal appearance?
- How often does the school communicate with parents through reports, parent/teacher meetings or other visits?
- What level of parental involvement is encouraged both in terms of keeping in touch with staff about your own child and more generally, eg a Parents' Association?

And finally – and perhaps most importantly – what does your child make of the school, the adults met, the other children met, pupils at the school in other contexts, and the website?

Initial advice

Educational institutions often belong to organisations that encourage high standards. Here we give a brief guide to what some of the initials mean.

BSA

The Boarding Schools' Association

Since its foundation in 1966, the Boarding Schools' Association (BSA) has had the twin objectives of promoting boarding education and the development of quality boarding through high standards of pastoral care and boarding accommodation. Parents and prospective pupils choosing a boarding school can, therefore, be assured that the 560 schools in the UK and internationally that make up the membership of the BSA are committed to providing the best possible boarding environment for their pupils.

A UK boarding school can only be a full member of the BSA if it is also a member of one of the Independent Schools Council (ISC) constituent associations, or in membership of the State Boarding Forum (SBF). These two bodies require member schools to be regularly inspected by the Independent Schools' Inspectorate (ISI) or Ofsted. Other boarding schools who are not members of these organisations can apply to be affiliate members. Similar arrangements are in place for overseas members. Boarding inspection of ISC accredited independent schools has been conducted by ISI since September 2012. Ofsted retains responsibility for the inspection of boarding in state schools and non-association independent schools. Boarding inspections must be conducted every three years. Boarding is judged against the National Minimum Standards for Boarding Schools which were last revised in 2015 and is set to be updated again soon.

Relationship with government

The BSA is in regular communication with the Department for Education (DfE) on all boarding matters. The Children Act (1989) and the Care Standards Act (2001) require boarding schools to conform to national legislation and the promotion of this legislation and the training required to carry it out are matters on which the DfE and the BSA work closely.

Boarding training

The programme of training for boarding staff from BSA member schools has been supported and sponsored in the past by the DfE. The BSA maintains the high standards expected as a consequence of that support and from the BSA's Commitment to Care Charter – which all member schools must abide by.

The BSA organises five conferences and more than 90 seminars a year for governors, Heads, deputies, housemasters and housemistresses, and matrons and medical staff where further training takes place in formal sessions and in sharing good practice. The BSA provides the following range of training and information:

- Professional qualifications for both teaching and non-teaching staff in boarding schools. The BSA has been responsible for the development of a number of courses: Certificates of Professional Practice in Boarding Education, Certificate in International Boarding, Certificate in Professional Practice for Nurses and Matrons, and a Diploma for senior leaders. The certificates courses are the result of at least two years' study, and completion of the Diploma takes at least one year. Courses run across the UK.

- A rolling programme of day seminars on current boarding legislation and good practice.

- Bespoke training and consultancy on best boarding practice, particularly with regard to safeguarding.

- The Accredited Boarding Practitioner scheme, where individuals working in boarding can have their service and experience accredited by BSA.

- Centre for Boarding Education Research (CEBER) which brings together a wide variety of articles and research on all matters related to boarding.

State Boarding Forum

The BSA issues information regards its 40 state boarding school members and the BSA should be contacted for details of these schools. In these schools, parents pay for boarding but not for education, so fees are substantially lower than in an independent boarding school.

BSA Leadership Team

National Director: Robin Fletcher
Direction of Operations: Aileen Kane

Director of Training and International: Andrew Lewin
Head of Safeguarding and Standards: Dale Wilkins

Boarding Schools' Association
4th Floor, 134-136 Buckingham Palace Road
London SWIW 9SA
Tel: 020 7798 1580
Fax: 020 7798 1581
Email: bsa@boarding.org.uk
Website: www.boarding.org.uk

GSA

The Girls' Schools Association, to which Heads of leading girls' schools belong

The Girls' Schools Association represents the Heads of a diverse range of UK independent girls' schools, among which are some of the top-performing schools in the country. It is a member of the Independent Schools Council.

The GSA encourages high standards of education for girls and promotes the benefits of being taught in a largely girls-only environment. GSA schools are internationally respected and have a global reputation for excellence. Their innovative practice and academic rigour attract pupils from around the world. As a whole, students at GSA schools do well in 'difficult' modern foreign languages and STEM (science, technology, engineering, maths) subjects and a high percentage – 96% – progress to higher education. GSA schools share experience, specialisms, opportunities and facilities with state sector schools in a wide range of partnerships. Many also provide means-tested bursaries for families of limited financial means.

Twenty first century girls' schools come in many different shapes and sizes. Some cater for 100% girls, others provide a predominantly girls-only environment with boys in the nursery and/or sixth form. Some follow a diamond model, with equal numbers of boys but separate classrooms between the ages of 11 to 16. Educational provision across the Association offers a choice of day, boarding, weekly, and flexi-boarding education. Schools range in type from large urban schools of 1000 pupils to small rural schools of around 200. Many schools have junior and pre-prep departments, and can offer a complete education from 3/4 to 18. A significant proportion of schools also have religious affiliations. Heads of schools in the Girls' Day School Trust (GDST) are members of the GSA.

The Association aims to inform and influence national educational debate and is a powerful and well-respected voice within the educational establishment, advising and lobbying educational policy makers on core education issues as well as those relating to girls' schools and the education of girls. The Association liaises with the Department for Education, the Office for Standards in Education, the Qualifications and Curriculum Authority and other bodies.

The GSA also provides its members and their staff with professional development courses, conferences, advice and opportunities to debate and share best practice, ensuring that they have every opportunity to remain fully up-to-date with all aspects of their profession.

As the GSA is one of the constituent bodies of the Independent Schools' Council (ISC), its schools are required to undergo a regular cycle of inspections to ensure that these rigorous standards are being maintained. GSA schools must also belong to the Association of Governing Bodies of Independent Schools, and Heads must be in membership of the Association of School and College Leaders (ASCL).

The Association's secretariat is based in Leicester.

GSA, Suite 105, 108 New Walk, Leicester LE1 7EA
Tel: 0116 254 1619
Email: office@gsa.uk.com
Website: www.gsa.uk.com
Twitter: @GSAUK

President 2019: Sue Hincks, Bolton School Girls' Division
Chief Executive: Vivienne Durham

HMC

The Headmasters' and Headmistresses' Conference, to which the Heads of leading independent schools belong

Founded in 1869 the HMC exists to enable members to discuss matters of common interest and to influence important developments in education. It looks after the professional interests of members, central to which is their wish to provide the best possible educational opportunities for their pupils.

The Heads of some 292 leading independent schools are members of The Headmasters' and Headmistresses' Conference, whose membership now includes Heads of boys', girls' and coeducational schools. International membership includes the Heads of around 56 schools throughout the world.

The great variety of these schools is one of the strengths of HMC but all must exhibit high quality in the education provided. While day schools are the largest group, about a quarter of HMC schools consist mainly of boarders and others have a smaller boarding element including weekly and flexible boarders.

All schools are noted for their academic excellence and achieve good results, including those with pupils from a broad ability band. Members believe that good education consists of more than academic results and schools provide pupils with a wide range of educational co-curricular activities and with strong pastoral support.

Only those schools that meet with the rigorous membership criteria are admitted and this helps ensure that HMC is synonymous with high quality in education. There is a set of membership requirements and a Code of Practice to which members must subscribe. Those who want the intimate atmosphere of a small school will find some with around 350 pupils. Others who want a wide range of facilities and specialisations will find these offered in large day or boarding schools. Many have over 1000 pupils. 32 schools are for boys only, others are coeducational throughout or only in the sixth form. The first girls-only schools joined HMC in 2006. There are now 35 girls-only schools.

Within HMC there are schools with continuous histories as long as any in the world and many others trace their origins to Tudor times, but HMC continues to admit to membership recently-founded schools that have achieved great success. The facilities in all HMC schools will be good but some have magnificent buildings and grounds that are the result of the generosity of benefactors over many years. Some have attractive rural settings, others are sited in the centres of cities.

Pupils come from all sorts of backgrounds. Bursaries and scholarships provided by the schools give about a third of the 220,000 pupils in HMC schools help with their fees. These average about £34,500 per annum for boarding schools and £15,000 for day schools. About 190,000 are day pupils and 45,000 boarders.

Entry into some schools is highly selective but others are well-suited to a wide ability range. Senior boarding schools usually admit pupils after the Common Entrance examination taken when they are 13.

Most day schools select their pupils by 11+ examination. Many HMC schools have junior schools, some with nursery and pre-prep departments. The growing number of boarders from overseas is evidence of the high reputation of the schools worldwide.

The independent sector has always been fortunate in attracting very good teachers. Higher salary scales, excellent conditions of employment, exciting educational opportunities and good pupil/teacher ratios bring rewards commensurate with the demanding expectations. Schools expect teachers to have a good education culminating in a good honours degree and a professional qualification, though some do not insist on the latter especially if relevant experience is offered. Willingness to participate in the whole life of the school is essential.

Parents expect the school to provide not only good teaching that helps their children achieve the best possible examination results, but also the dedicated pastoral care and valuable educational experiences outside the classroom in music, drama, games, outdoor pursuits and community service. Over 95% of pupils go on to higher education, many of them winning places on the most highly-subscribed university courses.

All members attend the Annual Conference, usually held in a large conference centre in September/October. There are ten divisions covering England, Wales, Scotland and Ireland where members meet once a term on a

Leading Independent Schools HMC

regional basis, and a distinctive international division.

The chair and committee, with the advice of the general secretary and membership secretary, make decisions on matters referred by membership-led sub-committees, steering groups and working parties. Close links are maintained with other professional associations in membership of the Independent Schools Council and with the Association of School and College Leaders.

Membership Secretary: Ian Power
Tel: 01858 465260

Executive Director: Mike Buchanan
Tel: 01858 469059

HMC
12 The Point
Rockingham Road
Market Harborough
Leicestershire LE16 7QU
Email: gensec@hmc.org.uk
Website: www.hmc.org.uk

IAPS

The Independent Association of Preparatory Schools (IAPS) is a membership association representing leading headteachers and their prep schools in the UK and overseas

With more than 650 members, IAPS schools represent a multi-billion pound enterprise, educating more than 160,000 children and employing more than 20,000 staff.

Schools are spread throughout cities, towns and the countryside and offer pupils the choice of day, boarding, weekly and flexible boarding, in both single sex and coeducational settings. Sizes vary from 100 to more than 800 per school, with the majority between 150 and 400. Most schools are charitable trusts, some are limited companies and a few are proprietary. There are also junior schools attached to senior schools, choir schools, those with a particular religious affiliation and those that offer specialist provision as well as some schools with an age range extending to age 16 or above.

IAPS only accredits those schools that can demonstrate that they provide the highest standards of education and care. Member schools offer an all-round, values-led, broad education, which produces confident, adaptable, motivated children with a lifelong passion for learning. In order to be elected to membership, a Head must be suitably qualified and schools must be accredited through a satisfactory inspection. IAPS offers its members and their staff a comprehensive and up-to-date programme of professional development courses to ensure that high professional standards are maintained.

Pupils are offered a rich and varied school life. The targets of the National Curriculum are regarded as a basic foundation, which is greatly extended by the wider programmes of study offered. Specialist subject teaching begins at an early age and pupils are offered a range of cultural and sporting opportunities. Together with more than 30 recreational games, music, art and drama form part of curricular and extracurricular

activities. In addition, IAPS organises holiday and term-time sporting competitions for pupils to take part in, including skiing, sailing, judo, swimming, golf, fencing and squash, amongst many others.

IAPS has well-established links with senior independent schools, and experience in methods of transfer and entry to them. As the voice of independent prep school education, it has national influence and actively defends and promotes the interests of its members. It lobbies the government on their behalf and promotes prep school issues on a national and international stage. IAPS works directly with ministers and national policy advisers to ensure that the needs of the prep school sector are met.

IAPS
11 Waterloo Place
Leamington Spa
Warwickshire CV32 5LA
Tel: 01926 887833
Email: iaps@iaps.uk
Website: iaps.uk

Excellence in Education
The Independent Association

ISA

The Independent Schools Association, with membership across all types of school

The Independent Schools Association (ISA), established in 1879, is one of the oldest of the Headteachers' associations of independent schools that make up the Independent Schools' Council (ISC). It began life as the Association of Principals of Private Schools, which was created to encourage high standards and foster friendliness and cooperation among Heads who had previously worked in isolation. In 1895 it was incorporated as The Private Schools Association and in 1927 the word 'private' was replaced by 'independent'. The recently published history of the association, *Pro Liberis*, demonstrates the strong links ISA has with proprietorial schools, which is still the case today, even though boards of governors now run the majority of schools.

Membership is open to any Head or Proprietor, provided they meet the necessary accreditation criteria, including inspection of their school by a government-approved inspectorate. ISA's Executive Council is elected by members and supports all developments of the Association through its committee structure and the strong regional network of co-ordinators and area committees. Each of ISA's seven areas in turn supports members through regular training events and meetings.

ISA celebrates a wide-ranging membership, not confined to any one type of school, but including all: nursery, pre-preparatory, junior and senior, all-through schools, coeducational, single-sex, boarding, day and performing arts and special schools.

Promoting best practice and fellowship remains at the core of the ISA, as it did when it began 140 years ago. The association is growing, and its 474 members and their schools enjoy high quality national conferences and courses that foster excellence in independent education. ISA's central office also supports members and provides advice, and represents the views of its membership at national and governmental levels. Pupils in ISA schools enjoy a wide variety of competitions, in particular the wealth of sporting, artistic and academic activities at area and national level.

President: Lord Lexden
Chief Executive: Neil Roskilly, BA PGCE NPQH FRSA FRGS

ISA House, 5-7 Great Chesterford Court,
Great Chesterford, Essex CB10 1PF
Tel: 01799 523619
Email: isa@isaschools.org.uk
Website: www.isaschools.org.uk

ISA members and their schools enjoy high quality national conferences and courses that foster excellence in independent education.

ISA | INDEPENDENT SCHOOLS ASSOCIATION

The Society of Heads

The Society of Heads represents the interests of independent secondary schools.

The Society of Heads represents the interests of independent, secondary schools. The Society celebrated its 50th Anniversary in 2011. The Society has as its members 118 Heads of well-established secondary schools, many with a boarding element, meeting a wide range of educational needs. All member schools provide education up to 18, with sixth forms offering both A and AS levels and/or the International Baccalaureate. Also some offer vocational courses. Many have junior schools attached to their foundation. A number cater for pupils with special educational needs, whilst others offer places to gifted dancers and musicians. All the schools provide education appropriate to their pupils' individual requirements together with the best in pastoral care.

The average size of the schools is about 350, and all aim to provide small classes ensuring favourable pupil:teacher ratios. The majority are coeducational and offer facilities for both boarding and day pupils. Many of the schools are non-denominational, whilst others have specific religious foundations.

The Society believes that independent schools are an important part of Britain's national education system. Given their independence, the schools can either introduce new developments ahead of the maintained sector or offer certain courses specifically appropriate to the pupils in their schools. They are able to respond quickly to the needs of parents and pupils alike.

Schools are admitted to membership of the Society only after a strict inspection procedure carried out by the Independent Schools Inspectorate. Regular inspection visits thereafter ensure that standards are maintained.

The Society is a constituent member of the Independent Schools Council and every full member in the Society has been accredited to it. All the Society's Heads belong to the Association of School and College Leaders (ASCL) (or another recognised union for school leaders) and their schools are members of AGBIS.

The Society's policy is: to maintain high standards of education, acting as a guarantee of quality to parents who choose a Society school for their children; to ensure the genuine independence of member schools; to provide an opportunity for Heads to share ideas and common concerns for the benefit of the children in their care; to provide training opportunities for Heads and staff in order to keep them abreast of new educational initiatives; to promote links with higher and further education and the professions, so that pupils leaving the Society's schools are

> Schools are admitted to membership of the Society only after a strict inspection procedure carried out by the Independent Schools Inspectorate. Regular inspection visits thereafter ensure that standards are maintained.

given the best advice and opportunities for their future careers; and to help Heads strengthen relations with their local communities.

The Society of Heads Office,
12 The Point, Rockingham Road,
Market Harborough,
Leicestershire LE16 7QU
Tel: 01858 433760
Email: gensec@thesocietyofheads.org.uk
Website: www.thesocietyofheads.org.uk

The Independent Schools Council

The Independent Schools Council (ISC) works with its members to promote and preserve the quality, diversity and excellence of UK independent education both at home and abroad

What is the ISC?

ISC brings together seven associations of independent schools, their heads, bursars and governors. Through our member associations we represent over 1,300 independent schools in the UK and overseas. These schools are ranked among the best in the world and educate more than half a million children each year.

The ISC's work is carried out by a small number of dedicated professionals in our offices in central London. We are assisted by the contributions from expert advisory groups in specialist areas. Our priorities are set by the board of directors led by our Chairman, Barnaby Lenon. We are tasked by our members to protect and promote the sector in everything we do.

ISC schools

ISC schools offer a high quality, rounded education. Whilst our schools are very academically successful, their strength also lies in the extra-curricular activities offered – helping to nurture pupils' soft skills and encourage them to be self-disciplined, ambitious and curious. There are independent schools to suit every need, whether you want a day or boarding school, single sex or co-education, a large or a small school, or schools offering specialisms, such as in the arts.

Our schools are very diverse: some of our schools are selective and highly academic, while others have very strong drama or music departments full of creative opportunities in plays, orchestras and choirs. For children with special needs such as dyslexia or autism there are many outstanding independent schools that offer some of the best provision in the country.

Many schools have very strong track records of high achievement at sport, offering a wide range of facilities and excellent coaches. Independent schools excel at the traditional sports like football and rugby, but also offer more unusual sports like rowing, fencing and even rock climbing.

There is also a wealth of co-curricular opportunity available. Whether your child is into debating, sailing, the Model United Nations or is interested in army training in the Combined Cadet Force, most schools offer numerous clubs and activities. It all adds up to an exciting, broad and stimulating all-round education.

Academic results

In 2018 47% of A-level subjects taken at independent schools were graded A*/A - this is almost double the national average of 26.4%. This year also saw nearly two thirds of independent school GCSE entries being awarded an A/7 or higher, three times the national average. This is especially impressive given the fact a third of ISC schools offering GCSEs are not academically selective.

In 2018, figures demonstrated more students are following different pathways post-GCSE. There was an increase in candidates taking the Extended Project Qualification, Pre-U and BTEC qualifications compared to 2017. The average points score for pupils taking the IB Diploma was 36, roughly equivalent to 4.5 As at A-level. In the International Baccalaureate, 2% of pupils obtained 45 points, the highest mark, which is only achieved by 0.3% of candidates worldwide.

Many schools have very strong track records of high achievement at sport, offering a wide range of facilities and excellent coaches. Independent schools excel at the traditional sports like football and rugby, but also offer more unusual sports like rowing, fencing and even rock climbing.

Fee Assistance

Independent schools are very mindful that hard working families can find it difficult to pay school fees. Affordability is of course a concern for schools and they work hard to remain competitive whilst facing pressures on salaries, pensions and maintenance and utility costs. Schools are strongly committed to widening access and have made strenuous efforts to increase the amount they can offer in bursaries. This year almost £400m was provided in means-tested fee assistance for pupils at ISC schools. Currently a third of pupils at our schools benefit from reduced fees.

ISC Associations

There are seven member associations of the ISC, each with a distinctive ethos in their respective entrance criteria and quality assurance:

Girls' Schools Association (GSA) – see page 37
Headmasters' and Headmistresses' Conference (HMC) – see page 38
Independent Association of Prep Schools (IAPS) – see page 39
Independent Schools Association (ISA) – see page 40
The Society of Heads – see page 41
Association of Governing Bodies of Independent Schools (AGBIS) – www.agbis.org
Independent Schools' Bursars Association (ISBA) – www.isba.org.uk

Further organisations who are affiliated to the ISC: Boarding Schools Association (BSA), Council of British International Schools (COBIS), Scottish Council of Independent Schools (SCIS) and Welsh Independent Schools Council (WISC).

The Independent Schools Council can be contacted at:
First Floor,
27 Queen Anne's Gate,
London,
SW1H 9BU
Telephone: 020 7766 7070
Website: www.isc.co.uk

independent
schools
council

Help in finding the fees

Chris Procter, joint managing director of SFIA, outlines a planned approach to funding your child's school fees

Average school fee increases in the last year, according to the ISC census, were 3.4% which is the lowest since 1994, however this is still significantly higher than inflation.

The latest Independent Schools Council (ISC) survey, completed by all 1,326 schools in UK membership indicate that there are now a record 529,164 pupils being educated privately, the highest number since records began in 1974. 86.8% of these were day school pupils, 13.2% were boarders. The share of girls and boys at ISC schools is very nearly equal, with boys representing 51% of all pupils.

The overall average boarding fee is £11,228 per term and the overall average day fee is £4,854 per term. However, fees charged by schools vary by region – for example the average boarding fee ranges from £9,159 per term in the North East to £13,080 per term in Greater London; the average day fee ranges from £3,572 per term in the North West to £5,751 per term in Greater London.

The overall cost (including university fees) might seem daunting: the cost of educating one child privately could well be very similar to that of buying a house but, as with house buying, the school fees commitment for the majority of parents can be made possible by spreading it over a long period rather than funding it all from current resources.

It is vital that parents do their financial homework, plan ahead, start to save early and regularly. Grandparents who have access to capital could help out; by contributing to school fees they could also help to reduce any potential future inheritance tax liability.

Parents would be well-advised to consult a specialist financial adviser as early as possible, since a longterm plan for the payment of fees – possibly university as well – can prove very advantageous from a financial point of view and offer greater peace of mind. Funding fees is neither science, nor magic, nor is there any panacea. It is quite simply a question of planning and using whatever resources are available, such as income, capital, or tax reduction opportunities.

The fundamental point to recognise is that you, your circumstances and your wishes or ambitions, for your children, or grandchildren are unique. They might well be similar to those of other people but they will still be uniquely different. There will be no single solution to your problem. In fact, after a review of all your circumstances, there might not be a problem at all.

So, what are the reasons for seeking advice about education expenses?

- To reduce the overall cost?

- To get some tax benefit?

- To reduce your cash outflow?

- To invest capital to ensure that future fees are paid?

- To set aside money now for future fees?

- To provide protection for school fees?

- Or just to make sure that, as well as educating your children, you can still have a life!

Any, some, or all of the above – or others not listed – could be on your agenda, the important thing is to develop a strategy.

At this stage, it really does not help to get hung up on which financial 'product' is the most suitable. The composition of a school fees plan will differ for each family depending on a number of factors. That is why there is no one school fees plan on offer.

The simplest strategy but in most cases, the most expensive option, is to write out a cheque for the whole bill when it arrives and post it back to the school. Like most simple plans, that can work well, if you have the money. Even if you do have the money, is that really the best way of doing things? Do you know that to fund £1,000 of school fees as a higher rate taxpayer paying 40% income tax, you currently need to earn £1,667, this rises to £1,818 if you are an additional rate taxpayer where the rate is 45%.

How then do you start to develop your strategy? As with most things in life, if you can define your objective, then you will know what you are aiming at. Your objective in this case will be to determine how much money is needed and when.

You need to draw up a school fees schedule or what others may term a cash flow forecast. So, you need to identify:

- How many children?

- Which schools and therefore what are the fees? (or you could use an average school fee)

- When are they due?

- Any special educational needs?

- Inflation estimate

- Include university costs?

With this basic information, the school fees schedule/cash flow forecast can be prepared and you will have defined what it is you are trying to achieve. Remember though, that senior school fees are typically more than prep school fees – this needs to be factored in. Also, be aware that the cost of university is not restricted to the fees alone; there are a lot of maintenance and other costs involved: accommodation, books, food, to name a few. Don't forget to build in inflation, I refer you back to the data at the beginning of this article.

You now have one element of the equation, the relatively simple element. The other side is the resources you have available to achieve the objective. This also needs to be identified, but this is a much more difficult exercise. The reason that it is more difficult, of course, is that school fees are not the only drain on your resources. You probably have a mortgage, you want to have holidays, you need to buy food and clothes, you may be concerned that you should be funding a pension.

This is a key area of expertise, since your financial commitments are unique. A specialist in the area of school fees planning can help identify these commitments, to record them and help you to distribute your resources according to your priorities.

The options open to you as parents depend completely upon your adviser's knowledge of these complex personal financial issues. (Did I forget to mention your tax position, capital gains tax allowance, other tax allowances, including those of your children and a lower or zero rate tax paying spouse or partner? These could well be used to your advantage.)

A typical school fees plan can incorporate many elements to fund short, medium and long-term fees. Each plan is designed according to individual circumstances and usually there is a special emphasis on what parents are looking to achieve, for example, to maximise overall savings and to minimise the outflow of cash.

Additionally, it is possible to protect the payment of the fees in the event of unforeseen circumstances that could lead to a significant or total loss of earnings.

Short-term fees

Short-term fees are typically the termly amounts needed within five years: these are usually funded from such things as guaranteed investments, liquid capital, loan plans (if no savings are available) or maturing insurance policies, investments etc. Alternatively, they can be funded from disposable income.

Medium-term fees

Once the short-term plan expires, the medium-term funding is invoked to fund the education costs for a further five to ten years. Monthly amounts can be invested in a low-risk, regular premium investment ranging from a building society account to a friendly society savings plan to equity ISAs. It is important to understand the pattern of the future fees and to be aware of the timing of withdrawals.

Long-term fees

Longer term funding can incorporate a higher element of risk (as long as this is acceptable to the investor), which will offer higher potential returns. Investing in UK and overseas equities could be considered. Solutions may be the same as those for medium-term fees, but will have the flexibility to utilise investments that may have an increased 'equity based' content.

Finally, it is important to remember that most investments, or financial products either mature with a single payment, or provide for regular withdrawals; rarely do they provide timed termly payments.

Additionally, the overall risk profile of the portfolio should lean towards the side of caution (for obvious reasons).

There are any number of advisers in the country, but few who specialise in the area of planning to meet school and university fees. SFIA is the largest organisation specialising in school fees planning in the UK.

> Funding fees is neither science, nor magic, nor is there any panacea. It is quite simply a question of planning and using whatever resources are available, such as income, capital, or tax reduction opportunities.

This article has been contributed by SFIA and edited by Chris Procter, Managing Director.
Chris can be contacted at: SFIA, 29 High Street, Marlow, Buckinghamshire, SL7 1AU
Tel: 01628 566777
Fax: 0333 444 1550
Email: enquiries@sfia.co.uk
Web: www.schoolfeesadvice.org

Profiles

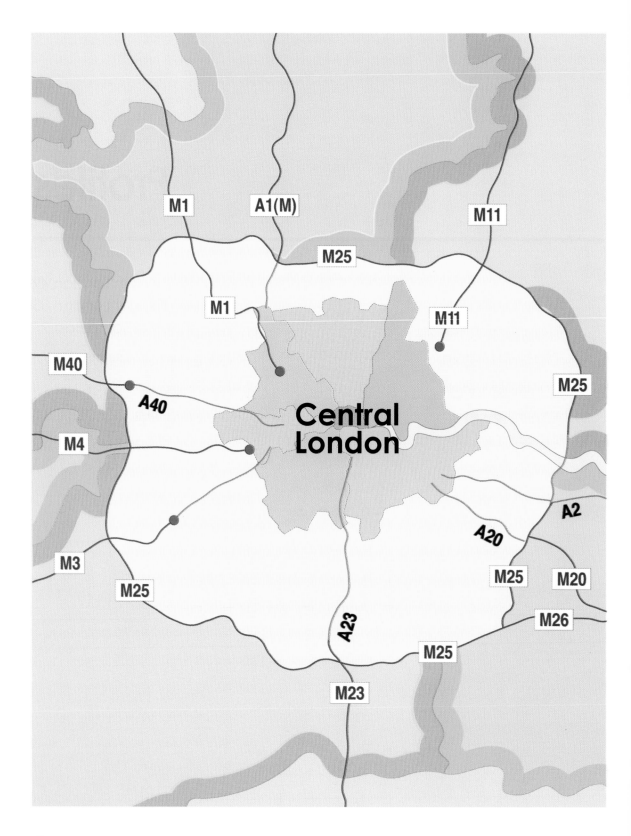

M1

A1(M)

M11

M25

M1

M11

M40

A40

M25

M4

Central
London

A2

A20

M3

M25

M25

M20

M26

A23

M25

M23

Schools in Central London

Bassett House School

BASSETT
HOUSE SCHOOL

(Founded 1947)

60 Bassett Road, London, W10 6JP

Tel: 020 8969 0313

Email: info@bassetths.org.uk

Website: www.bassetths.org.uk

Headmistress:

Mrs Philippa Cawthorne MA (Soton) PGCE Mont Cert

Appointed: January 2014

School type: Co-educational Day

Age range of pupils: 3–11

No. of pupils enrolled as at 01/09/2018: 190

Fees per annum as at 01/01/2019:

Day: £8,850–£18,450

Average class size: 20

Teacher/pupil ratio: 1:7

At Bassett House, last year we marked 71 years of educating young children to achieve their very best. The school's founder, Sylvia Rentoul, recognised children as individuals, and encouraged them to express themselves, helping to grow their achievements and self-confidence.

Focused attention remains our hallmark. We believe tailor-made teaching opens up young minds to endless

possibilities, encouraging them to think creatively. We start by ensuring high staff-to-pupil ratios and many specialist teaching staff. Our teachers know every child in their care inside out and use great teaching supported by our excellent equipment (including cutting-edge IT) to bring lessons to life for each child. Our 'sport for all' ethos encourages all our children to think of themselves as athletes, while allowing our sporting stars to shine. We offer football, netball, tag rugby, hockey, tennis, rounders, athletics, gymnastics and eurhythmics as part of the core curriculum and clubs in swimming, fencing, yoga and dance.

We don't stop there. Vibrant music and drama give our children a passion for participation and performance, fostering a sense of achievement and boosting self-confidence. Our children first take to the stage from age 3 and have many opportunities to shine throughout life at Bassett House, whether in whole-school assemblies, stage shows or concerts. We have choirs, musical ensembles and an orchestra and provide individual instrumental music lessons from specialist music teachers.

Our extra-curricular clubs, together with our weekly enrichment hour, expand our children's horizons beyond the core curriculum. Each term children can choose to add a variety of activities to the school day, be it Lego modelling, computer coding, Scottish dancing, origami, chess, geography, cookery, arts and crafts or Zumba.

Residential trips from year 3 onwards create a sense of adventure and build self-reliance. The glow of a 7-year-old's face recounting a nighttime bug-hunting expedition, a 9-year-old's thrill at working

with a friend to sail a dinghy, a 10-year-old embracing the challenge of sleeping out under a self-made shelter: we create these memorable moments, knowing that their positive effects will last a lifetime.

All of this makes not only for well-rounded individuals, it translates into excellent academic results. When they leave aged 11, Bassett House children are ready to thrive at London's best senior schools. And they do: our children win places to the cream of London's senior schools. For those who want to board, Bassett House prepares them well for life at leading boarding schools.

We collaborate closely with our sister schools, Orchard House and Prospect House, sparking off new ideas to promote ever more successful teaching practices. The three schools share a common ethos but each retains its unique personality.

The schools (brought together under the umbrella of House Schools Group) are proudly non-selective. True to our belief, children are not tested and judged at the tender age of 3 or 4 years. Our outstanding results repeatedly show all children can fulfill their potential, regardless of early learning ability. We encourage our high fliers to skyrocket, whilst children who need a little extra help are given the support they need to reach their fullest potential.

Our last full ISI inspection awarded us 'excellent' and 'outstanding' in all areas and we flew through our 2016 compliance inspection.

This year, we look forward to another year of stellar success in education.

Broomwood Hall

Upper School:
68-74 Nightingale Lane, London, SW12 8NR
Tel: 020 8682 8810

Lower School:
The Vicarage, Ramsden Road, SW12 8QR
& 50 Nightingale Lane, SW12 8TE
Tel: 020 8682 8820
Email:
admissions@northwoodschools.com
Website: www.northwoodschools.com
Headmistress: Carole Jenkinson
School type: Girls' Day (Co-ed Pre-Prep)

Religious Denomination: Church of England, all denominations welcome
Age range of boys: 4–8
Age range of girls: 4–13
No. of pupils enrolled as at 01/01/2019: 620
Fees per term as at 01/01/2019:
Day: £5,375–£6,595
Average class size: Max 20
Teacher/pupil ratio: 1:7

Broomwood Hall is a co-educational pre-prep and girls' preparatory school in South West London offering an all-round education that incorporates lots of art, music, drama and sport and most importantly, equips them with skills for life, not just the next school. Part of the family-run and family-oriented Northwood Schools which includes our sibling boys prep school, Northcote Lodge.

We are a traditional school, embracing values that promote the 'soft' skills such as kindness, collaboration, creativity, good communication, and a sense of community. But we are also a modern school; coupling the very latest in educational thinking and practice with an eye on the increasingly automated workplaces that our children will enter in the future and equipping them with the skills that they'll need to succeed in the years to come.

These include critical thinking, confidence, self-discipline, resilience, organisation, teamwork, creativity, a sense of duty and responsibility, good manners, courtesy and tolerance of others. Our motto, 'To do your best to be your best' exemplifies the ethos of our school.

We don't believe in selective entry – yet our results are equal to schools that do. We believe that a supportive but focussed environment – without undue stress or 'hot-housing' – is the best way to help children fulfil their potential, both inside and outside the classroom. We help each child develop to the best of their individual ability. We take pride in the breadth of our curriculum and get wonderful results in all areas with children regularly winning awards and scholarships in all areas to some of the country's best schools, both day and boarding.

Dallington School

Dallington School

(Founded 1978)

8 Dallington Street, Islington, London, EC1V 0BW
Tel: 020 7251 2284
Email: hercules@dallingtonschool.co.uk
Website: www.dallingtonschool.co.uk
Headteacher: Maria Blake
Appointed: 2019

School type:
Coeducational Day and Nursery
Age range of pupils: 3–11
No. of pupils enrolled as at 01/01/2019: 138
Boys: 81 **Girls:** 57
Fees per annum as at 01/01/2019:
Day: £9,978–£12,630
Teacher/pupil ratio: 1:16 (with full time TA)

A family-run, independent, co-educational day school for children aged 3 to 11, in the heart of London

"Dallington is a school that holds a unique place in the constellation of outstanding London schools – a vibrant oasis of creativity; proudly and fiercely independent. Established and led for over 40 years by Mogg Hercules MBE, it has been the school of choice for parents seeking an exceptional education for their children. Taking over the headship presents a formidable challenge – how to celebrate and develop Mogg's legacy, whilst bringing to bear my own style and experience?

"As I begin this fascinating journey, I hope to champion Outdoor Learning and to ultimately see our children fly the flag that will inspire other schools to recognise this learning as a fundamental part of the holistic education we all aim to offer."
Maria Blake, Headteacher

At Dallington, we want children to enjoy their childhood, develop a love of learning, independence of thought and retain their individuality. Our expectation is for every child to understand the part it has to play in its learning. The relationships between the staff and the children are informal, but considerate. First names are used and we do not have a school uniform.

We encourage our children to become confident, enthusiastic learners. We offer a topic-based curriculum which is broad, creative and balanced; The Arts are a strong element of our curriculum. Our school is widely creative and the children are encouraged to assume responsibility in a self-regulated, purposeful way.

Our children work and play together in a co-operative, supportive way and great emphasis is placed on nurturing the development of the powers of reasoning and reflective, critical thinking. We provide an environment where children can openly relate to others and expect to be listened to and respected for their points of view.

We have an exemplary record of attaining places prior to and at Secondary level. Children are prepared for external exams in a non-competitive, stress-free environment. A non-competitive ethos does not mean the children lack purpose in their learning.

Personal tours each day of the week. Non-selective entry policy. Early registration advised.

Devonshire House Preparatory School

(Founded 1989)
2 Arkwright Road, Hampstead,
London, NW3 6AE

Tel: 020 7435 1916
Email: enquiries@
devonshirehouseprepschool.co.uk
Website:
www.devonshirehouseschool.co.uk
Headmistress: Mrs S. Piper BA(Hons)
School type: Preparatory, Pre-preparatory
& Nursery Day School

Religious Denomination: Non-
denominational
Age range of boys: 2½–13
Age range of girls: 2½–11
No. of pupils enrolled as at 01/01/2019: 650
Boys: 350 **Girls:** 300
Fees per annum as at 01/01/2019:
Day: £10,125–£18,600

Academic & leisure facilities

The school is situated in fine premises in the heart of Hampstead with its own walled grounds. The aim is to achieve high academic standards whilst developing enthusiasm and initiative throughout a wide range of interests. It is considered essential to encourage pupils to develop their own individual interests and a good sense of personal responsibility.

Curriculum

Early literacy and numeracy are very important and the traditional academic subjects form the core curriculum. The younger children all have a class teacher and classroom assistant and their day consists of a mixture of formal lessons and learning through play. Whilst children of all ages continue to have a form teacher, as they grow older an increasing part of the curriculum is delivered by subject specialists. The combined sciences form an increasingly important part of the timetable as the children mature. The use of computers is introduced from an early stage, both as its own skill and as an integrated part of the pupils' education.

Expression in all forms of communication is encouraged, with classes having lessons in art, music, drama and French. Physical exercise and games also play a key part of the curriculum. Much encouragement is given to pupils to help widen their horizons and broaden their interests. The school fosters a sense of responsibility amongst the pupils, and individuality and personal attention for each pupil is considered essential to make progress in the modern world.

The principal areas of the National Curriculum are covered, though subjects may be taken at a higher level, or at a quicker pace. For the girls approaching the 11+ senior schools' entry examinations, special emphasis is given to the requirements for these, and in the top two years for the boys, Common Entrance curriculum is taught. The pupils achieve great success in these examinations and a number also sit successfully for senior school scholarships.

The school has its own nursery, The Oak Tree Nursery, which takes children from two-and-a-half years of age.

Entry requirements

The Oak Tree Nursery: For children entering the Oak Tree Nursery, places are offered on the basis on an informal assessment made at the nursery. Children in The Oak Tree Nursery transfer directly to the Junior School.

The Junior School: For children entering the junior school from the ages of three to five, places are offered on the basis of assessment made at the school. From the age of six places are usually subject to a written test taken at school. At eight, children transfer directly into the upper school. Parents and their children are welcome to visit for interview and to see around the school.

The Upper School: Entry to the upper school is principally from the junior school. For pupils seeking to join the school from elsewhere places are normally subject to a written entrance test.

DLD College London

DLD COLLEGE LONDON

ESTABLISHED 1931

199 Westminster Bridge Road,
London, SE1 7FX

Tel: +44 (0)20 7935 8411
Email: dld@dld.org
Website: www.dldcollege.co.uk
Principal:
Irfan H Latif BSc (Hons) PGCE FRSA FRSC
Appointed: January 2018
School type:
Co-educational Day & Boarding

No. of pupils enrolled as at 01/01/2019: 426
Boys: 210 **Girls:** 216
No. of boarders: 247
Fees per annum as at 01/01/2019:
Day: £23,500–£29,950
Full Boarding: £18,000–£28,000
Average class size: 10-12
Teacher/pupil ratio: 1:6

DLD College is a leading independent boarding and day school that offers over 400 students a wide-ranging curriculum in a superb and modern learning environment. It is delivered by teachers who are selected for their academic strength, enthusiasm and their ability to relate positively to young people. We are helping students achieve grades they often didn't believe possible and preparing them to access the university courses and destinations of their choice.

DLD College is a dynamic place to study providing high quality GCSE, A Level & BTEC courses as well as International Foundation Programmes. Our lessons are lively and encourage students to discuss ideas, ask questions and actively learn. We recognise that choosing the most appropriate programme of study is a very important part of the application process and we therefore invite all those interested in enrolling at DLD to an interview to discuss their subject choices. We believe small class sizes encourage a more purposeful learning environment and allows for a greater measure of individual attention, helping students to be more focused on their studies and building their confidence. Students learn important study skills including note taking, essay writing, time management, revision and exam techniques. On average, class sizes at DLD are around 10-12 students. Each student is allocated a Personal Tutor who monitors their progress as they move through the course. The wellbeing of students is paramount and the Personal Tutors are supported by a team of dedicated Directors of Studies.

In September 2015, DLD College relocated to brand new, purpose built premises in the heart of London, overlooking Westminster and the River Thames. DLD College London is a truly unique College campus with facilities including:

- On-site boarding accommodation. Boarding with us in an extraordinary experience, offering unique opportunities for a wide range of boarders' trips throughout London, in-house activities and special occasions.
- 55 classrooms – 60 touch screens.
- Theatre with state-of-the-art LED lighting. The theatre is also equipped with a cinema screen and surround sound.
- Dedicated Wellbeing Centre where students have access to a range of support including the Head of Wellbeing, the College Nurse, College Counsellor, Student Services as well as a Performance and Wellbeing Practitioner.
- Two music rooms fully equipped with the latest iMacs and software and a studio complex with three rooms. In addition, we have three practice rooms equipped with musical instruments.
- Three Art studios, Graphic suite and a Photography studio and classrooms.
- Separate laboratories for Biology, Chemistry and Physics.
- Dedicated learning zones with quiet booths.
- Under 16's study areas equipped with computers (supervised) and open space learning.
- The Refectory provides a multifunctional space for eating, studying and socialising, and has a mixture of long bench style tables and booths. In addition, students also have access to a Starbucks Café from 8am.
- Atrium with film projectors and surround sound.
- New Gallery workspace with seating for student group work.
- New Library space.
- New e-hub and DLD Genius Bar.
- Underground swimming pool and fitness suite available through Urbanest.

École Jeannine Manuel – London

ÉCOLE Jeannine Manuel
International understanding through a bilingual education

(Founded 2015)

43-45 Bedford Square, London, WC1B 3DN

Tel: 020 3829 5970
Email: admissions@jmanuel.uk.net
Website:
www.ecolejeanninemanuel.org.uk
Head of School: Pauline Prévot
School type: Coeducational Day

Age range of pupils: 3–18 years
No. of pupils enrolled as at 01/01/2019: 442
Fees per annum as at 01/01/2019:
Day: £17,460
Average class size: 18
Teacher/pupil ratio: 1:9

École Jeannine Manuel in London is a French, bilingual, international school which opened its doors in September 2015 in three contiguous mansions on Bedford Square, steps away from the British Museum. In 2019, the school opened additional premises on Russell Square, where it now houses its Upper School.

Our school currently welcomes pupils from all nationalities and cultural backgrounds, from Nursery to Year 11. Starting from September 2019, we will welcome pupils up to Year 12 and will open Year 13 the subsequent year. Sixth Formers will follow either the official French programmes (with an international option) or a purely International track.

École Jeannine Manuel is the young sister school of its Paris namesake, a UNESCO associated school founded in 1954 and one of France's most prestigious schools, ranked first among French high schools (public and independent) for overall academic performance for the past six years. As is the case in France, École Jeannine Manuel London's mission is "to promote international understanding through the bilingual education of a multicultural community of students, the fostering of pedagogical innovation, and the constant exploration of best practices in the context of an ever- changing global environment."

A bilingual education

École Jeannine Manuel offers an enriched, bilingual adaptation of the French national curriculum, including English, Science and Chinese programmes developed by its sister school in Paris. In History, the French national curriculum is complemented to help pupils gain coherent knowledge and understanding of Britain's past and that of the wider world. Extra-curricular activities include sports – with outdoor facilities within walking distance of the school – as well as a broad range of artistic and tech-based clubs.

English and French are spoken equally in class. Our aim is to bring pupils to a native proficiency – orally and in writing – in both languages. We welcome non French-speaking students at all levels and help them adapt to the demands of a bilingual curriculum. With respect to English, the school accommodates beginners up to Year 7. Experience shows that studying in French and in English yields a strong and mutually reinforced command of both languages as well as a deep understanding of the cultures they express. A bilingual education enhances pupils' capacity for abstract, conceptual thinking and develops a sense of nuance, nurtured by exposure to multiple perspectives.

A multicultural community of students

Looking beyond French and bi-national families, the school welcomes pupils from all nationalities, cultural traditions and native languages. École Jeannine Manuel in London is positioned, as is the case in Paris, as a unique, truly bicultural institution with a multicultural student body representing more than 40 nationalities. We attract international and internationally minded families deeply invested in the education and well being of their children. Living within this cultural melting pot every day yields a special consciousness of one's place in the world, an appreciation for the broad landscape of culture and civilizations that we learn to understand and value together.

The fostering of pedagogical innovation

The key drivers of our school's pedagogy are coherence and innovation. Whether inspired by current research in the cognitive sciences, by best practices from around the world or home-grown, our teaching methods are constantly evolving. Our international teams of teachers stimulate new ideas that lead to a creative, pioneering education. Hands-on manipulations in math, inquiry- based learning in the sciences, and teamwork are among the practices that foster pupil engagement and growth. Our aim is to have pupils think, do and share. The school's pedagogical principles are founded on four pillars: the early mastery of core academic skills; the development of autonomy; the encouragement of collaborative work; and the nurturing of curiosity, creativity and a lifelong appetite for culture.

© Paul Riddle

Eltham College

(Founded 1842)
Grove Park Road, Mottingham,
London, SE9 4QF

Tel: 0208 857 1455
Fax: 0208 857 1913
Email: mail@eltham-college.org.uk
Website: www.elthamcollege.london
Headmaster: Guy Sanderson
Appointed: 2014
School type: Coeducational Day

Age range of pupils: 7–18
No. of pupils enrolled as at 01/01/2019: 907
Sixth Form: 194
Junior: 227 *Senior:* 486
Fees per term as at 01/01/2019:
Senior School & Sixth Form: £5,925 per term
Junior School: £5,230 per term

Eltham College is a small independent school based in over 70 acres of grounds in Mottingham, south east London for children aged 7-18. The school was founded in 1842 as the School for the Sons of Missionaries, a small boarding school catering for the children of missionaries serving overseas.

It moved to its present site in 1912 and since the 1950s has been an independent day school for boys, and since the start of the 1980s has had a co-educational Sixth Form. From September 2020 the school will become fully co-educational when it begins to welcome girls in Years 3 and 7, as well as the existing co-educational Sixth Form.

When a child comes to Eltham College, whatever their age, they immediately feel part of our community. We look after every student from the moment they join us to the moment they leave. It is this sense of individual attention that sets us apart. The school is small enough to know every child well and large enough to offer an exceptional range of co-curricular activities in sport, music, art and drama.

We balance the highest academic standards with outstanding pastoral care, ensuring that students at Eltham College learn to be resourceful and resilient. We help them to discover their unique talents and give them the confidence to seize opportunities.

The Junior School is just three minutes walk along the path from the Senior School. We teach in small classes, with Form Tutors who teach the core curriculum, but use their specialist strengths to teach other subjects throughout the school. We use specialist teachers and dedicated rooms for Art and Design, Science, Music, Drama and Languages which means our students always have the best resources for learning.

Children at Eltham College Junior School become increasingly independent learners as they move through the school. By Year 6 they understand the value of hard work, perseverance, adaptability and co-operation and are ready to move smoothly into Eltham College's Senior School. We don't ask them to sit an entrance exam because by this stage we have known them for some time and are confident they will thrive in the Senior School. Year 6 is therefore an exciting time for students as we run a three-term transition programme of academic, sporting and cultural activities that prepare them for every aspect of Senior School life.

From sculpture to algorithms, and from the Industrial Revolution to the reaction of acids we offer a broad and challenging curriculum throughout the Senior School. At Eltham College education is truly personalised, so students can build on their strengths and follow their passions. In Years 7 and 8 students aren't limited to combined humanities or science. They can try out various subjects before selecting those they enjoy most for GCSE. There is a similar degree of freedom when it comes to GCSEs and A levels. Students can choose any combination of subjects, with guidance given to ensure they have a good balance of subjects that suit their study and career goals.

Our co-curriculum is built into our working day and there's a seamless flow between it and our academic curriculum. There is always plenty to do whether it's on the sports field, on stage, in a concert hall or in our art gallery. Students have the chance to stretch themselves through a rich variety of activities across art, sport, music and drama. They'll also have access to a whole range of clubs, societies and trips, as well as community service.

We expect our students to try new things and we think it is the best way to prepare for a lifetime of discovery.

Sixth Form is an important time of transition as students prepare for university and life beyond Eltham College. With small tutor groups and the support of their Sixth Form tutors, students settle in quickly. Each student has a subject mentor who guides them through their degree course choices and helps them with interviews, entrance exams, additional reading and their personal statement.

And, their Sixth Form home is a brand new building with lecture and seminar rooms, a specialist careers suite and a spacious café.

Faraday School

TRINITY BUOY WHARF

Old Gate House, 7 Trinity Buoy Wharf,
London, E14 0JW
Tel: 020 8965 7374
Email: info@newmodelschool.co.uk
Website: www.faradayschool.co.uk
Head Teacher: Claire Murdoch

School type: Coeducational Day
Age range of pupils: 4–11
No. of pupils enrolled as at 01/01/2019: 105
Fees per term as at 01/01/2019:
Day: £3,448

Founded in 2009, Faraday is a small but growing independent primary school in East London. The school's riverside location provides a magical environment and access to a stimulating, creative community that offers exciting learning opportunities for the pupils and staff.

Here at Faraday, we are committed to giving every child a first-class education, with small classes, quality teaching and a personal approach. In these formative years we hope to inspire a love of learning and that this desire to explore, grow and create will stay with our pupils for life. We place a strong focus on literacy and numeracy, with a targeted approach that enables each child to progress at their own level.

Our lessons stretch, challenge and engage pupils of all abilities and interests. We present children with the great literature, music and works of art to help them acquire an increased understanding of the world in which they live and build a thorough understanding of knowledge in each subject. As such, our curriculum is broad and stimulating, and includes specialist teaching in French, Music, Drama and Physical Education.

We also provide a wide range of after school clubs and, to help working parents, a private school bus runs before and after school from 22 different locations, including south of the river.

We were founded in 2009 and maintain strong links with our sister school, Maple Walk, in North West London. Our setting beside the River Thames, opposite the iconic O2 arena and beside the Trinity Lighthouse, gives our pupils an inspirational location in which to learn. We are fortunate enough to be surrounded by creative industries and we make the best of all that London has to offer, with regular trips to museums, historic attractions and galleries.

Our June 2014 ISI Inspection found Faraday School pupil attainment to be "well-above national age-rated expectations."

Hawkesdown House School Kensington

Hawkesdown House School
Endeavour • Courage • Truth

27 Edge Street, Kensington,
London, W8 7PN

Tel: 020 7727 9090
Email: admin@hawkesdown.co.uk
Website: www.hawkesdown.co.uk
Headmistress:
Mrs. J. A. K. Mackay B.Ed (Hons)
Appointed: April 2017
School type: Coeducational
Independent Preparatory Day

Religious Denomination:
Non-denominational
Age range of pupils: 3–11
No. of pupils enrolled as at 01/01/2019: 100
Fees per annum as at 01/01/2019:
Day: £16,350–£19,130
Average class size: 14
Teacher/pupil ratio: 1:9

Hawkesdown House is an independent prep school for girls and boys from the age of four to eleven, with a Nursery class for children of three years old. It is housed in a fine building in Edge Street just off Kensington Church Street where bright and airy classrooms provide a creative and welcoming environment.

Hawkesdown House is dedicated to providing an outstanding early education. The children are prepared for examinations at 11+ to a wide range of London's selective prep and senior schools. Pupils may also choose to sit entrance examinations at 8+ to London's prep schools and country boarding schools.

The excellence of the broad and creative educational provision enriches the pupils' lives across the curriculum and in all co-curricular and extra curricular activities, so fencing, judo, chess and coding, for example, are all included in the timetable.

The ethos and aims of the School embrace high academic standards and expectations. Hawkesdown House prides itself on its outstanding pastoral care, thoughtful teaching and individual attention. Right from the beginning, Hawkesdown House provides advice, support, reassurance and the preparation to give pupils and parents a very happy start at school.

The School's motto, "Endeavor, Courage, Truth", reflects the aspirations for the pupils; that they grow into kind, capable and considerate adults, well prepared to make sound judgements and take responsibility for themselves and others. Hawkesdown House pupils are actively encouraged to develop both their initiative and their intellectual curiosity.

Mrs Jenny Mackay, the Headmistress, has a deep commitment to pastoral care, academic excellence and the development of the individual. With a degree in Education from Oxford, she also has extensive experience of some of the best education in Britain, at some of London's most highly sought after and outstanding schools.

Hawkesdown House is a happy, nurturing and successful school. There is a fantastic, dedicated staff body and a wonderful collaborative approach which ensures that the curriculum meets the needs of each and every child. The school exudes busyness and celebrates the excellence and achievements of all.

Hill House International Junior School

HILL HOUSE
INTERNATIONAL JUNIOR SCHOOL

(Founded 1949)

17 Hans Place, Chelsea, London, SW1X 0EP

Tel: 020 7584 1331

Email: info@hillhouseschool.co.uk

Website: www.hillhouseschool.co.uk

Principals: Richard, Janet, William & Edmund Townend

Appointed: 2002

Founders: Lt Col Stuart Townend OBE & Mrs Beatrice Townend

School type: Coeducational Day

Age range of pupils: 4–13

No. of pupils enrolled as at 01/01/2019: 740

Boys: 420 **Girls:** 320

Fees per annum as at 01/01/2019:

Day: £13,200–£17,400

Average class size: 12-14

Teacher/pupil ratio: 1:7

'A child's mind is not a vessel to be filled, but a fire to be kindled.'

Hill House was founded in Switzerland in 1949 moving to La Tour-de-Peilz in 1951 when the building in Hans Place, London was opened. We hold fast to the guiding vision set by the founders that the modern child must be educated for a world community. He or she must be taught to understand that all nations depend on one another; learn to live with children of other nationalities; respect that which is unknown and often very foreign to them, and thus open the doors to a world which each day becomes smaller. Hill House became the first school

to teach in two different countries at the same time with the same children. The purpose built house in Glion, 2,500 feet above Lac Leman, hosts specialist courses throughout the year for selected pupils from London, providing experience of a boarding school environment in the setting of a mountain village in the French speaking canton of Vaud.

Hill House is the oldest London school in which every aspect of the daily administration of the school remains in the care and control of the founding family. It is a school that enables children from all over the world to have the opportunity to follow an English curriculum while learning

that every nation is equal but different and that peaceful co-existence comes from mutual respect, understanding and consideration for others from diverse backgrounds. A full academic programme, enriched by outstanding teaching in small classes, leads to pupils consistently going on to the leading day and boarding secondary schools of their choice with many scholarships awarded each year. We passionately believe in supporting and stretching all our pupils to seek the highest levels of academic achievement. There is a particular emphasis on Art, Drama, Music and Sport all of which are taught by over thirty specialist teachers. Throughout the year there are over seventy concerts, recitals and drama evenings in Founders' Hall where pupils can showcase their artistic talents and the school year ends with a celebratory Field Day culminating in the famous Gun Run.

Admissions

Children can enter Hill House at any age between four and eleven years old if places are available. There is no formal entry test at four years old. Older children will be assessed in English and Maths. Parents are invited to visit Hans Place any Monday, Tuesday, Thursday or Friday during term time at 8.30am for a tour of the school. There is no need for an appointment – please just come when it is convenient for you. After the tour, if you wish, you may complete the simple admissions form. All forms must be completed by the parents, in person, at Hans Place. We will not send forms by post.

Contacts

Mrs Janet Townend (Director of Admissions), Miss Beryl Lang (Registrar)
Tel: 020 7584 1331, registrar@ hillhouseschool.co.uk

L'Ecole de Battersea

(Founded 1977)
Trott Street, Battersea, London, SW11 3DS

Tel: 020 7371 8350
Fax: 020 7801 3297
Email: admin@lecoledespetits.co.uk
Website: www.lecoledespetits.co.uk
Principal: Mrs F Brisset
Head: Mr L Balerdi
Founder: Mrs M Otten
School type: Independent Bilingual Pre-

Prep and Primary (Partenaire AEFE)
Religious Denomination: All
denominations welcome
Age range of pupils: 3–11
No. of pupils enrolled as at 01/01/2019: 265
Fees per annum as at 01/01/2019:
Day: £12,600–£12,780
Average class size: 20

L'Ecole de Battersea opened in 2005 following on from the success of its sister school, L'Ecole des Petits.

The school is unique in that it offers a **continuous bilingual education from age three through until age eleven** at the end of primary, where both the French and English educational systems operate together.

The teaching emphasis throughout the school is fundamentally based on the French system, into which aspects of the English curriculum and methodology are integrated.

The highly motivated bilingual team of teachers are qualified in both the English and French educational systems.

This bilingual facility enables children and parents to choose to progress on to either the English private school system or on to the French Lycée system, and is also ideal for the increasingly popular International Baccalaureate.

The school welcomes bilingual pupils from a range of cultures, and so aims to generate a **truly international atmosphere**.

Partnership with the family is paramount in the school's ethos, and the school successfully seeks to **develop confident and balanced children** with experience of a wide range of activities, an appreciation of artistic and cultural heritage and a thoughtful and considerate attitude towards others.

Class sizes are small and the school occupies a recently refurbished building with **top quality facilities**, and with good outside spaces for a Central London school. The school is only **a five-minute drive from Chelsea** and operates a twice daily school bus service between South Kensington and Battersea, as well as a link to its sister school in Fulham, ten minutes distance.

The school is inspected by both the French Inspectorate and Ofsted and achieves excellent academic results.

OFSTED 2018 report said the school was "Outstanding in all categories" and it has been selected as one of the top 225 private schools in the country in *The Tatler Education Guides 2009-2019.*

L'Ecole des Petits

(Founded 1977)

2 Hazlebury Road, Fulham, London, SW6 2NB

Tel: 020 7371 8350

Fax: 020 7736 9522

Email: admin@lecoledespetits.co.uk

Website: www.lecoledespetits.co.uk

Principal: Mrs F Brisset

Deputy: Miss E Mesnage

Founder: Mrs M Otten

School type: Independent Bilingual Pre-Primary (Partenaire AEFE)

Religious Denomination: All denominations welcome

Age range of pupils: 3–6

No. of pupils enrolled as at 01/01/2019: 130

Fees per annum as at 01/01/2019:

Day: £12,300–£12,450

Average class size: Max 20

L'Ecole des Petits is a flourishing pre-primary school situated in Fulham, just **ten minutes from Chelsea**, with easy access by public transport. The school also runs its own daily morning and afternoon **bus service between South Kensington and Fulham**, and between its sister school in Battersea.

The school was founded in 1977 to cater for English and French families who want their children to **grow up in a bilingual environment**. By combining the Early Years curriculum with the French National curriculum, the school provides all aspects of education in both French and English, and today has a wonderfully **international flavour with children from 22 different countries** attending.

Children are taught by qualified and highly-motivated bilingual teachers. The school aims to provide **an education that enhances early learning skills in the controlled environment of small classes**.

The school has a warm and friendly atmosphere which encourages children to express themselves whilst following the structured bilingual curriculum. We consider maintaining **traditional family values** a very important aspect of our approach.

Our philosophy is to develop confident and happy children by providing **the best possible all-round education and care**, with an abundance of sports, drama, clubs, school outings and events as well as academic lessons.

We prepare our children to move onto both English and French schools, and many also continue their primary education at our sister school, L'Ecole de Battersea.

According to one of our parents, "This is an exceptional school that provides a nurturing environment, as well as good discipline and a wonderful education, and my child could not be happier and more confident about going to school."

OFSTED 2017 report: "Outstanding in all categories".

Lloyd Williamson Schools

LLOYD WILLIAMSON
———— S C H O O L S ————

(Founded 1999)

12 Telford Road, London, W10 5SH
Tel: 020 8962 0345
Fax: 020 8962 0345
Email: admin@lws.org.uk
Website: www.lloydwilliamson.co.uk
Co-Principals:
Ms Lucy Meyer & Mr Aaron Williams
Appointed: December 1999

School type: Coeducational Day
Age range of pupils: 4 months–14 years
(15 in 2019, 16 in 2020)
Fees per annum as at 01/01/2019:
Day: £14,400
Average class size: 12-16
Teacher/pupil ratio: 1:12

Over the past twelve years, Lloyd Williamson Schools have built an excellent reputation for being schools with high academic standards, personalised learning for individual children and a friendly, happy environment in which to learn. We foster initiative and a love for learning.

We are pleased to offer parents important extras:

- Breakfast and after-school club at no extra cost (the school and nurseries are open 7.30am – 6pm).
- Holiday clubs (we are open 50 weeks of the year).

- Small classes (max 16 to Year 6, max 18 in Secondary).
- Competitive fees.
- Home-cooked meals freshly prepared every day by our in-house chefs.

We boast an outstanding playground with excellent facilities, a homely atmosphere with school pets, and dedicated teachers who support the children to be focused, positive and enthusiastic.

'Throughout the school, relationships between staff and children are excellent, which gives the pupils security and confidence to succeed.' (Ofsted)

In the words of our children:

"I'm really happy here – the teachers really listen and if I get stuck they help!"

"There is always someone who listens to me."

"I like the way the big children look after the little children."

And the parents:

"You always know a Lloyd Williamson child – they're so polite!"

"I think the school is, beyond doubt, the best I could wish for."

"The best-kept secret in London!"

To visit the school or nurseries, please contact the school administrator, Emma Cole on: 020 8962 0345.

Lyndhurst House Prep School

LYNDHURST HOUSE
PREPARATORY SCHOOL

(Founded 1952)
24 Lyndhurst Gardens, Hampstead,
London, NW3 5NW

Tel: 020 7435 4936
Email: office@lyndhursthouse.co.uk
Website: www.lyndhursthouse.co.uk
Head of School:
Mr Andrew Reid MA (Oxon)
Appointed: September 2008
School type: Boys' Day

Age range of boys: 4–13
No. of pupils enrolled as at 01/01/2019: 150
Fees per term as at 01/01/2019:
Day: £6,190–£6,910
Average class size: 15
Teacher/pupil ratio: 1:8

Lyndhurst House Pre-Prep & Prep School for boys was founded by Vernon Davies in 1952, in a tall, handsome Willett-style building in leafy Lyndhurst Gardens, Hampstead.

For over 60 years Lyndhurst has played a full part in the range of local independent educational provision, sending on its thirteen year olds to the many renowned senior schools in London, and some to boarding further afield with an excellent record of academic success and achievement, matched by a strong participation in sports, music and art.

Pupils develop a good knowledge of their own and other cultures and traditions. Visits to theatres, museums and art galleries feature prominently throughout the year. A significant strength of the school is the way pupils from a wide range of cultural backgrounds work and play together harmoniously.

One of the smaller prep schools in the area, Lyndhurst provides a structured but individually responsive education from reception at four-plus up to Common Entrance and scholarship at 13, delivered by an experienced, well-qualified, and stable staff team, and the

abiding characteristics of its pupils seem to be a lively enthusiasm and sense of engagement and belonging. Lyndhurst House is a non-denominational school.

For all enquiries, please contact:
Mrs Dawn Lewis
Lyndhurst House Preparatory
24 Lyndhurst Gardens
Hampstead
London NW3 5NW
Tel: 020 7435 4936
Email: dlewis@lyndhursthouse.co.uk
Website: www.lyndhursthouse.co.uk
We look forward to meeting you.

Maple Walk School

62A Crownhill Road, London, NW10 4EB
Tel: 020 8963 3890
Email: admin@maplewalkschool.co.uk
Website: www.maplewalkschool.co.uk
Head Teacher: Mrs S Gillam
School type: Coeducational Day

Age range of pupils: 4–11
No. of pupils enrolled as at 01/01/2019: 200
Fees per term as at 01/01/2019:
Day: £3,349
Average class size: 20

Maple Walk is a small, independent prep school in North West London.

Maple Walk School is committed to giving every child a first-class education in the arts and sciences, drawing as a resource upon the Core Knowledge approach, which imparts knowledge through traditional academic subjects.

Although we believe in a traditional approach, our lessons reflect modern thinking on how children learn most effectively and our small classes and quality staff allow for a very personal approach to learning.

We feel literacy and numeracy are important, however, our curriculum is broad and stimulating, including specialist teaching in French, Music, Drama, Dance and Physical Education. Our aim is to educate the whole child through a rich curriculum with many stimuli, in order to support an atmosphere of life-long learning. Maple Walk is particularly proud of its most recent 11+ offers to a range of excellent secondary schools.

Our sports teams compete in a range of competitions and have seen growing success, particularly at Cross Country, Football and Gymnastics. We also provide a wide range of after school clubs and care.

Maple Walk was founded in 2004 and we maintain strong links with our sister school, Faraday School, in East London. We are easily accessible by road and public transport and make use of the local facilities, including the Green-Flag awarded Roundwood Park for PE and Willesden Sports Centre for swimming lessons. We take full advantage of the extensive cultural opportunities London has to offer, with termly trips to a wide range of museums, galleries, theatres and places of scientific, historical and religious interest.

Our March 2012 ISI Inspection found that *"the personal development of pupils is excellent"*. In 2017 we passed all categories of our first ISI Compliance Inspection.

In 2016 Maple Walk was named in *The Telegraph* newspaper as one of the Top 10 Best Value Prep Schools.

Mander Portman Woodward – London

M|P|W

Mander Portman Woodward

(Founded 1973)

90-92 Queen's Gate, London, SW7 5AB
Tel: 020 7835 1355
Fax: 020 7259 2705
Email: london@mpw.ac.uk
Website: www.mpw.ac.uk
Principal: Mr John Southworth BSc MSc
Appointed: August 2016

School type: Coeducational Day
Age range of pupils: 14–19
No. of pupils enrolled as at 01/01/2019: 620
Fees per term as at 01/01/2019:
Day: £9,529
Average class size: 6
Teacher/pupil ratio: 1:6

MPW London was founded in 1973 by three Cambridge graduates. The academic experience for students is modelled on the Oxford and Cambridge tutorial, with lessons being more relaxed and informal than those of a typical school, but also intellectually stimulating and demanding. MPW's mission is to help our students develop their confidence, maturity, knowledge and skills, turning their academic aspirations into reality.

Through our bespoke lessons, we aim to make working hard good fun and equip our alumni with the independence and aptitudes they need for success at university and beyond. With fewer than 10 students in any class, and an average student:teacher ratio more like 6:1, lessons are intensive but rewarding with plenty of opportunity for individual attention and personalised learning. Over 40 subjects are offered at A level and 25 at GCSE.

Our academic programme aims not only to enable students to achieve their best in GCSE and A level examinations but also to prepare them for life at university and beyond. We prepare students for a range of universities, including Oxford and Cambridge, University of the Arts, and competitive degree specialisms such as Medicine or Law. Each year, over 70% of our graduates head to top tier universities and our modal A level grade is consistently A/A*. We are especially proud of this given that our admissions policy is academically non-selective; MPW's 'value-add' (the distance travelled by students at A level relative to where they were at GCSE) is exceptional.

As well as expert tuition, students benefit from pastoral care, mentoring and university advice provided by a team of Directors of Studies. A student's Director of Studies provides detailed counsel

on university entrance and support for submitting the application, from personal statement critique to organising tutoring for entrance tests or mock interviews. The role of a Director of Studies only begins at UCAS and additional, day-to-day, support is provided to all students throughout their studies. *"They have put themselves out to be helpful"* said one parent to the Good Schools Guide.

Parents are invited to the college regularly to discuss progress with their child's Director of Studies and also for events such as our Art Show, Principal's lecture series or UCAS Week, where we provide advice on university applications. We also run a number of ad-hoc parental seminars throughout the year on relevant topics, such as 'how to support a teenager through exam stress'.

An extensive extra-curricular programme caters for all tastes, from sports – rugby and football are the most

popular – to creative arts, language lessons, guitar lessons, drama, journalism, chess club and everything in between. The Duke of Edinburgh award scheme is available to all students and year 10 complete the Bronze award together over the course of the year.

MPW is academically rigorous but socially relaxed and the college prides itself on maintaining a relatively informal, personalised and supportive atmosphere, allowing our students to develop the independence and responsibility that they will need in the future. Our focus on equipping students with the skills they need for life encourages success across a wide range of disciplines. Recent alumni include Harry Stebbings, Europe's youngest ever venture capitalist (*"I would not be who I am without MPW"*) and Tom Charman, CEO of KOMPAS (*"nothing could have prepared me better for the role that I play today"*).

More House School

MORE HOUSE
SCHOOL
KNIGHTSBRIDGE

(Founded 1953)
22-24 Pont Street, Knightsbridge,
London, SW1X 0AA

Tel: 020 7235 2855
Fax: 020 7259 6782
Email: office@morehouse.org.uk
Website: www.morehouse.org.uk
Co-Heads: Mrs. Amanda Leach &
Mr. Michael Keeley
Appointed: April 2014 & July 2017

School type: Independent Girls' Day
Age range of girls: 11–18
No. of pupils enrolled as at 01/01/2019: 206
Fees per term as at 01/01/2019:
Day: £6,650
Average class size: 16
Teacher/pupil ratio: 1:5

More House School provides an environment where pupils and staff are valued and supported as individuals and where their rights and dignity are maintained. Our School fosters an ethos of spiritual growth, not only for those within the Roman Catholic Church but also for those who adhere to other Christian traditions and other faiths.

The school was founded in 1953 by the Canonesses of St Augustine, at the request of a group of parents determined to send their daughters to a Catholic London day school. It occupies two interconnecting townhouses in the heart of Knightsbridge. Pupils of all faiths or none are welcome and the school has a broad cultural mix. Girls are provided with a rounded education, designed to allow individual strengths to shine through.

Academic results are good, balanced by a wide range of extra-curricular activities. Music, drama, and art are well supported and pupils regularly achieve local success in sports such as netball, football, rowing and hockey. The Duke of Edinburgh's Award is popular and there is an active commitment to fundraising for charity.

Our mission at More House is to provide an environment for pupils to not only gain the qualifications they need to pursue the courses and careers of their choice, but also the confidence and self assurance to meet the challenges that lie ahead in an ever-changing world.

Academic, music, drama, art and sport scholarships are available at 11+ entry and sixth form. Bursaries are also available.

North Bridge House

North Bridge House

(Founded 1939)

Main Site: 65 Rosslyn Hill, London, NW3 5UD
Tel: 020 7428 1520
Email: admissionsenquiries@
northbridgehouse.com

Website: www.northbridgehouse.com
Head of Nursery & Pre-Prep Schools:
Mrs. Christine McLelland
Head of Prep School: Mr. James Stenning
Head of Senior Hampstead:
Mr. Brendan Pavey
Head of Senior Canonbury:
Mr. Jonathan Taylor
School type: Co-educational Day
Age range of pupils: 2–18 years

No. of pupils enrolled as at 01/01/2019: 1375
Fees per annum as at 01/01/2019:
Nursery: £7,200 (half day)
– £14,385 (full time)
Pre-Reception & Reception: £16,800
Pre-Prep – Prep: £17,430 –18,195
Senior Hampstead: £18,150
Senior School & Sixth Form Canonbury:
£18,150 –19,355
Average class size: 20

Founded in 1939, North Bridge House shares a warm, family atmosphere across five prestigious sites in North London, providing a unique and personalised education for pupils aged 2 to 18 years. Since the addition of North Bridge House Canonbury – the first Independent Senior School and Sixth Form in Islington – in 2014, students complete their A-Levels in a stunning Grade II listed building, rated 'Outstanding' in all areas by Ofsted.

At North Bridge House, we celebrate the individual, develop their character and nurture their aspirations. As well as happy and understood, our pupils are notably high-achieving. Our Key Stage 1 standards of reading, writing and maths score well above the national average. Our Prep School is renowned for first-class results in the girls' 11+ and boys' 13+ senior school entrance exams, whilst NBH Senior Schools celebrate GCSE and A-Level results that evidence significant value added to academic performance.

All North Bridge House, pupils benefit from a rich and varied range of academic and extra-curricular activities which, together with our outstanding pastoral support, build character, confidence and independence. We focus on educating the whole child and providing a breadth of learning experience that takes pupils much further than the curriculum itself.

Pupils also enjoy a wide range of sports, with weekly PE and Games sessions designed to develop the individual's physical and emotional wellbeing, as well as essential team skills.

At the heart of the school is a highly qualified and inspirational team of teachers, dedicated to helping every child fulfil their potential. From the fundamental foundations that are established in the early years of education to the expert UCAS and careers advice that is provided at A-Level, North Bridge House is a platform to success and a gateway to the top universities. Ultimately, with excellent grades and indispensable life skills, North Bridge House prepares students for the challenges and rewards of adult life and the real world.

Our schools
North Bridge House Nursery School
33 Fitzjohn's Avenue, Hampstead,
London NW3 5JY
North Bridge House Pre-Prep School
8 Netherhall Gardens, Hampstead,
London NW3 5RR
North Bridge House Prep School
1 Gloucester Avenue, London NW1 7AB
North Bridge House Senior Hampstead
65 Rosslyn Hill, London NW3 5UD
North Bridge House Senior Canonbury
6-9 Canonbury Place, London N1 2NQ

Orchard House School

ORCHARD
HOUSE SCHOOL.

(Founded 1993)

16 Newton Grove, Bedford Park,
London, W4 1LB
Tel: 020 8742 8544
Email: info@orchardhs.org.uk
Website: www.orchardhs.org.uk
Headmistress:
Mrs Maria Edwards BEd(Beds) PGCE(Man)
Mont Cert

Appointed: September 2015
School type: Co-educational Day
Age range of pupils: 3–11
No. of pupils enrolled as at 01/01/2019: 290
Fees per annum as at 01/01/2019:
Day: £8,850–£18,450
Average class size: 20
Teacher/pupil ratio: 1:7

At Orchard House School, children are loved first and taught second. Our Pupil Pastoral Plan monitors the well-being of each child and was recently shortlisted for a TES (Times Educational Supplement) national award for educational innovation. This emphasis on a nurturing environment is not, however, at the cost of academic excellence. In fact, our outstanding results show how creating the right environment enables every child to thrive academically and emotionally. We believe learning should be exciting and fun, and the children should positively want to come to Orchard House every day. And they do: we harness the exuberance and energy of every child in our care, and instil within them a lifelong love of learning.

Orchard House's diverse curriculum creates a sense of adventure, developing the children's appetite for risk. This feeds into greater academic and creative achievements. Whether it's a whole-school skipping day, a project with Jaguar to enable our 10- and 11-year-

old mathematicians to engineer performance cars or learning archery in Normandy (taught solely in French), Orchard House children embrace novel tasks throughout their time with us. By the time they sit 11+ exams, they are past masters at tackling new challenges with verve: this shows in our stellar results.

Sport at Orchard House encourages a respectful, competitive attitude, teaching children the value of camaraderie and the buzz of going for gold, or goal. We offer football, netball, rugby, hockey, lacrosse, cross country, tennis, athletics, triathlon, cricket, rounders, swimming and gymnastics and arrange regular team-sport fixtures against other schools, often lifting the trophy but always relishing the match.

Similarly, music and drama build confidence and self-esteem, as well as many opportunities for every child to perform. Visiting music teachers offer individual instrumental tuition on a variety of instruments. We have a school orchestra, Pippin choir, chamber choir,

senior and junior choir and a parent and staff choir. There are many other instrumental groups including a pupil-led rock band.

We collaborate closely with our sister schools, Bassett House and Prospect House, sparking off new ideas to promote ever more successful teaching practices. The three schools share a common ethos but each retains its unique personality. The schools (brought together under the umbrella of House Schools Group) are proudly non-selective. True to our belief, children are not tested and judged at the tender age of 3 or 4 years. Our educational success shows all children can fulfil their potential, regardless of early learning ability.

The Independent Schools Inspectorate awarded Orchard House the highest accolades of 'excellent' in all areas and 'exceptional' in achievements and learning. These are mirrored in our first-class academic results and the scholarships our pupils win to their next schools.

Prospect House School

PROSPECT
HOUSE SCHOOL

(Founded 1991)

75 Putney Hill, London, SW15 3NT
Tel: 020 8246 4897
Email: info@prospecths.org.uk
Website: www.prospecths.org.uk
Headmaster:
Mr Michael Hodge BPED(Rhodes) QTS
Appointed: September 2017

School type: Co-educational Day
Age range of pupils: 3–11
No. of pupils enrolled as at 01/01/2019: 316
Fees per annum as at 01/01/2019:
Day: £8,850–£18,450
Average class size: 20
Teacher/pupil ratio: 1:7

At Prospect House School, we focus on making each child feel valued and secure and on making their educational experience both challenging and fun. This allows us to develop every child to their fullest potential, as our outstanding results demonstrate. Our most recent full Independent Schools Inspectorate inspection, in 2013, rated us 'excellent' against all the inspectors' criteria and we flew through our 2017 regulatory compliance inspection.

Prospect House's superb teachers provide a supportive and encouraging academic environment in which children excel. The sound of laughter is never far away, as Prospect House children discover their aptitude for sport, music, art, computing, drama or a whole host of other opportunities both within the curriculum and before and after school. Whether taking up the trombone or orienteering on Putney Heath, our children relish each new challenge and emerge better able to face the next challenge that comes their way.

Music is an integral part of life at Prospect House. We have over 200 individual music lessons taking place each week and a school orchestra, chamber choir and senior and junior choirs, as well as a number of ensembles. All children act in assemblies, school plays, musical productions and concerts throughout the year. Children in Years 1 to 6 enjoy drama lessons and our high-quality staging, lighting, sound and props give every production a professional feel.

Physical activity promotes wellbeing, so we offer a busy sports programme. This includes football, netball, hockey, cross country, judo, athletics, cricket, rounders, swimming, fencing, dance and gymnastics. Our approach to fixtures and tournaments successfully balances participation for everyone with letting our sports stars shine.

Residential trips thrill the children with the sense of adventure, encouraging risk-taking and building self-reliance, whether on a history expedition, a bushcraft adventure or a week in Normandy immersed in the French language and culture.

We encourage our children to think for themselves, to be confident and to develop a sense of responsibility for the world in which they live. By the time they leave us aged 11, Prospect House children are ready to thrive at London's best senior schools. This is reflected in our impressive 11+ results. In 2018/19, academic, sports or music scholarships made up over 12% of our overall senior school offers.

We collaborate closely with our sister schools, Bassett House and Orchard House, sparking off new ideas to promote ever more successful teaching practices. The three schools share a common ethos but each retains its unique personality.

The schools (brought together under the umbrella of House Schools Group) are proudly non-selective. True to our belief, children are not tested and judged at the tender age of 3 or 4 years. Our stellar results repeatedly show all children can fulfil their potential, regardless of early learning ability. We encourage our high-flyers to soar, whilst children who need a little extra help are given the tools they need to reach their fullest potential. At Prospect House, every child is supported to achieve their personal best.

Northcote Lodge School

26 Bolingbroke Grove, London, SW11 6EL

Tel: 020 8682 8888

Email:
admissions@northwoodschools.com

Website: www.northwoodschools.com

Headmaster: Clive Smith-Langridge

School type: Boys' Day

Religious Denomination: Church of England, all denominations welcome

Age range of boys: 8–13

No. of pupils enrolled as at 01/01/2019: 260

Fees per term as at 01/01/2019:

Day: £6,595

Average class size: 15, Max 20

Northcote Lodge is an all-boy preparatory school in South West London which offers the very best in modern education within a traditional setting to ensure that we bring out the best in boys. Part of family-owned and family-oriented Northwood Schools which includes our sibling schools, Broomwood Hall Lower and Upper schools, Northcote Lodge is unique within London; it offers all the benefits of a country education without leaving town: we're large enough to offer an education of real substance but small enough to ensure that no boy slips through the net.

Our focus is on educating the 'whole boy' so each boy can find something that excites and motivates him, whether this be drama, reading, science, maths, ICT, sports, music or art.

We have invested in Sport and the staff within the department include FA, RFU, and ECB qualified staff with a wealth of experience of playing sport to a high level. We aim to inspire our pupils to enjoy and work hard in all sports, offering a high quality and wide varied sporting programme for all. Alongside academic excellence, we also place great value on manners and respect for others. It is these

softer, but essential skills that will equip a boy for life beyond his senior school into a future workplace where collaboration, creativity and innate self-confidence will matter more than ever.

We offer plenty of extra-curricular opportunities and the benefit of doing all written homework at school so that come 6pm a boy can go home and relax, knowing his day's work is done.

Whilst some boys do leave at 11, most leave us at 13 and regularly win places and scholarships in all subjects to some of the country's leading public schools – both day and boarding.

Ravenscourt Park Preparatory School

(Founded 1991)

16 Ravenscourt Avenue, London, W6 0SL
Tel: 020 8846 9153
Fax: 020 8846 9413
Email: secretary@rpps.co.uk
Website: www.rpps.co.uk
Headmaster: Mr Carl Howes MA
(Cantab), PGCE (Exeter)

Appointed: September 2015
School type: Coeducational Day
Age range of pupils: 4–11
No. of pupils enrolled as at 01/01/2019: 419
Fees per term as at 01/01/2019:
Day: £5,857
Average class size: 20

Ravenscourt Park Preparatory School (RPPS) is a lively, co-educational, independent school for children aged 4 to 11 in West London. Owned by the Gardener Schools Group, a family founded company set up in 1991, RPPS was the first of three schools to open, followed by Kew Green Prep School and Kew House Senior School.

There is a palpable sense of community at RPPS, and visitors often comment on the warm and happy atmosphere, and the family feel that they notice around the school.

Our school is situated next to Ravenscourt Park, a twenty-acre park which provides the setting for the majority of PE and Games lessons. RPPS has specialist on- site facilities such as a multi-purpose Auditorium, Library, Music Suite, Art Studio and Science Laboratory. Additional facilities include a designated gymnasium, ICT suite and large outdoor playground space.

RPPS provides an education of the highest quality with an engaging curriculum that is varied, exciting and forward-looking, whilst also preparing pupils for transfer at the end of Year 6 to London Day Schools and 11+ boarding schools.

Our pupils engage in the excitement of learning and develop the confidence to question, analyse and express their opinions. We encourage children to develop a Growth Mindset so that they become resourceful, resilient, reflective and enthusiastic learners who are able to learn from their mistakes and build on their successes.

We form strong and trusting partnerships with our parents and we operate an 'Open Door Policy', where parents' comments, views, contributions and suggestions are valued.

The Independent Schools Inspectorate (ISI) visited RPPS in 2016 and we were delighted to have received the judgement of 'excellent' in all areas.

St Benedict's School

(Founded 1902)

54 Eaton Rise, Ealing, London, W5 2ES

Tel: 020 8862 2000

Email: admissions@stbenedicts.org.uk

Website: www.stbenedicts.org.uk

Headmaster: Mr A Johnson BA

Appointed: September 2016

School type: Co-educational Day

Age range of pupils: 3–18

No. of pupils enrolled as at 01/01/2019: 1086

Boys: 720 **Girls:** 366 **Sixth Form:** 213

Fees per annum as at 01/01/2019:

Day: £12,990–£16,845

Average class size:

Junior School: 17

Senior School: 18

Sixth Form: 7

Teacher/pupil ratio: 1:10

St Benedict's is London's leading independent Catholic co-educational school, situated in leafy Ealing. The School is a successful blend of the traditional and the progressive; proud of its heritage but also forward thinking and innovative.

Within a caring, happy community, our pupils thrive, benefiting from a seamless education which can begin at the age of 3 and continue through to the Sixth Form.

St Benedict's combines strong academic standards with excellent personal development. St Benedict's pupils achieved the school's best ever GCSE results, and the best A level results in 5 years in 2018: in GCSE, 66% of pupils were awarded grades 9 to 7, and in A level 74% achieved A* to B. Inspirational teaching, tutorial guidance and exceptional pastoral care are at the heart of the education we offer.

The Junior School and Nursery provide a supportive and vibrant environment in which to learn. Sharing excellent facilities with the Senior School and a programme of cross-curricular activities help ease the transition at 11+ to the Senior School, which is on the same site.

At St Benedict's, there is a vital focus on personal development, and our outstanding co-curricular programme helps pupils to thrive by enabling them to find and develop their unique gifts and talents. St Benedict's has a distinguished sporting tradition: while many boys and girls train and compete at county and national level, everyone is encouraged to enjoy sport, teamwork and fitness. Music and Drama are both excellent; there is a strong choral tradition, renowned Abbey Choir and many instrumental ensembles. Termly Drama productions have recently included *Les Misérables*, *Amadeus* and *West Side Story*.

We encourage principled leadership, resilience and character in our pupils, and promote the Christian values of integrity, fairness and generosity to others. This is a hallmark of the School, informed by the 1500 year-old Rule of St Benedict, and there could be no better way of equipping young people for the future.

Recent developments include a fine new Sixth Form Centre and Art Department, opened in 2015. A new Nursery and Pre-Prep Department opened in September 2017, providing our youngest pupils with a first-rate learning environment.

St Benedict's School is unique. Come and visit, and see what we have to offer. You can be sure of a warm Benedictine welcome.

St Augustine's Priory

(Founded 1634)

Hillcrest Road, Ealing, London, W5 2JL

Tel: 020 8997 2022

Fax: 020 8810 6501

Email: office@sapriory.com

Website: www.sapriory.com

Headteacher:

Mrs Sarah Raffray M.A., N.P.Q.H

Appointed: September 2012

School type:

Girls' Independent Day School

Religious Denomination: Catholic

Age range of boys: 3–4

Age range of girls: 3–18

No. of pupils enrolled as at 01/01/2019: 485

Fees per annum as at 01/01/2019:

Day: £11,031–£15,693

Average class size: 20-24

Teacher/pupil ratio: 1:10.13

We are in the top 50 London Schools and our results are quite simply excellent. Our girls go on to world class universities. But we are about much more than that. We teach long lasting habits of wellbeing like no other school. At a time when so many of us in education are concerned about the mental health of the young people in our care, we build on the most up-to-date research alongside old-fashioned common sense to teach lifelong habits of well-being. Daily, throughout the year, we build in ways to be alert to the beauty around us. We have a farm, an outdoor stage, we have a prayer garden, a meadow, a stewardship programme which involves care for the grounds, growing of plants from seeds, care for our allotment. Long before banning them became the talk of the TES we said no phones in school.

The entrance to our school leads us past sheep, bushes and trees newly planted by girls and students. We have 13 acres of land and are blessed. We have a farm with pigs as well as sheep and chickens. There aren't many schools in London where you walk to reception to the sound of the cockerel crowing and where you can buy eggs collected by girls who also tend to the animals at weekends and in the holidays. Proper pastoral care attends to the whole family.

When we are happy we learn well. They are also happy – and most unusually, many of them know what it is like to feel the wind on their face, to climb trees and to sledge freely using trays from the kitchen when it snows. Our girls and staff are game changers – they are ambitious and they are also learning deep rooted habits of establishing deep emotional wellbeing.

St John's Wood Pre-Preparatory School

(Founded 1982)
St Johns Hall, Lords Roundabout,
London, NW8 7NE
Tel: 020 7722 7149
Fax: 020 7586 6093
Email: info@sjwpre-prep.org.uk

Website: www.sjwpre-prep.org.uk
Principal: Adrian Ellis
School type: Coeducational Day
Age range of pupils: 3–7
Average class size: 16
Teacher/pupil ratio: 1:8

Happiness is at the heart of the philosophy at St Johns' Wood Pre-Prep School, and it works. This small school, described by owner and Principal, Adrian Ellis, as feeling more like a private members' club, is a 7+ specialist school. The school is immensely proud of the 2018/2019 Year 2 pupils for their outstanding entrance test results. Of the 11 children in the class two girls will go to City of London School for Girls, one to South Hampstead High School. Two boys will head to St Paul's Juniors, four to UCS and two to Westminster Under School.

With a friendly and caring environment as its strength for three-to seven year-old boys and girls, Mr Ellis believes that the excellent ratio of staff to pupils allows each child to reach their full potential. *"Of course, together with parents, we look to establish each child's unique qualities and particular talents and aim to develop them as fully as possible,"* said Mr Ellis.

Parents have high expectations of the school. Mr Ellis points out this is a two way street, *"Equally, we have high expectations of our parents. This combination is the recipe for success".*

Following this year's excellent results, St John's Wood Pre-Prep remains a recommended 'feeder' to many of London's top prep schools.

St Mary's School Hampstead

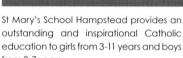

ST MARY'S SCHOOL HAMPSTEAD

(Founded 1871)

47 Fitzjohn's Avenue, Hampstead,
London, NW3 6PG

Tel: 020 7435 1868
Fax: 020 7794 7922
Email: office@stmh.co.uk
Website: www.stmh.co.uk
Head Teacher: Mrs Harriet Connor-Earl
Appointed: September 2016
School type: Coeducational Day
Religious Denomination: CISC

Age range of boys: 2 years 9 months–7 years
Age range of girls: 2 years 9 months–11 years
No. of pupils enrolled as at 01/01/2019: 300
Boys: 17 **Girls:** 283
Fees per annum as at 01/01/2019:
Day: £7,305–£13,500
Average class size: Max 20
Teacher/pupil ratio: 1:9.5

St Mary's School Hampstead provides an outstanding and inspirational Catholic education to girls from 3-11 years and boys from 3-7 years.

St Mary's School celebrates the uniqueness of every pupil and their achievements. The rigorous, challenging curriculum places a strong emphasis on high academic achievement within a culture of care and support.

The School aims to instil four key habits of learning in their pupils. The children are encouraged to be risk takers, not only in their play, but also in their learning. They are also taught to be resilient and not to fall at the first hurdle. Staff ask the children to make mistakes because in the process of challenging themselves, they make more academic progress and in turn excel not only in the classroom, but in their own self confidence. The boys and girls at St Mary's School are respectful, not just of each other, but of themselves. Finally, pupils are encouraged to be reflective, on their faith, their behaviour and their academic work.

Computer Science and digital literacy skills are integrated superbly within the classroom. Technology is used to support and enhance all curriculum areas and learning every day from Nursery to Year 6.

Music, drama, art and sports are also an essential part of life at St Mary's School and involve everyone. Children demonstrate great enthusiasm and build valuable skills that last a lifetime.

St Mary's School is an unexpected oasis amidst the bustle and activity of Hampstead. The outdoor space at St Mary's School is extensive, and the leafy playground makes it easy to forget you are in London. The children in Nursery have their own dedicated garden, aptly named 'The Secret Garden', where they can dig in the mud, play at the water tables, dress up and spend time in the sensory room.

Leavers achieve impressive results, gaining offers and Academic Scholarships from the best schools in the country, including City of London School for Girls, Francis Holland School, Highgate School, North London Collegiate, South Hampstead High School, St Mary's Ascot and St Paul's Girls' School.

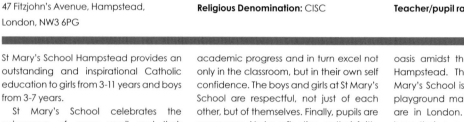

St Paul's Cathedral School

ST PAUL'S CATHEDRAL SCHOOL

(Founded 12th Century or earlier)

2 New Change, London, EC4M 9AD

Tel: 020 7248 5156

Fax: 020 7329 6568

Email: admissions@spcs.london.sch.uk

Website: www.spcslondon.com

Headmaster: Simon Larter-Evans BA (Hons), PGCE, FRSA

Appointed: September 2016

School type: Coeducational Pre-Prep, Day Prep & Boarding Choir School

Religious Denomination: Church of England, admits pupils of all faiths

Age range of pupils: 4–13

No. of pupils enrolled as at 01/01/2019: 254

Boys: 150 **Girls:** 104

No. of boarders: 30

Fees per annum as at 01/01/2019:

Day: £14,031–£15,105

Full Boarding: £8,736

Average class size: 15-20

Teacher/pupil ratio: 1:10

Curriculum

A broad curriculum, including the International Primary Curriculum, prepares all pupils for 11+, 13+, scholarship and Common Entrance examinations. There is a strong musical tradition and choristers' Cathedral choral training is outstanding. A wide variety of games and other activities is offered. At the latest ISI inspection in May 2017, the school was rated 'Excellent'.

Entry requirements

Entry at 4+, 7+ and 11+ years: Pre-prep and day pupils interview and short test; Choristers voice trials and tests held throughout the year for boys between 6 -8 years. Scholarships available at 11+ years.

St Paul's Cathedral School is a registered charity (No. 312718), which exists to provide education for the choristers of St Paul's Cathedral and for children living in the local area.

The Roche School

(Founded 1988)
11 Frogmore, London, SW18 1HW
Tel: 020 8877 0823
Email: office@therocheschool.co.uk
Website: www.therocheschool.com

Headmistress:
Mrs V Adams BA(Hons), PGCE, MA
Appointed: September 2010
School type: Co-educational Day
Religious Denomination:
Non-denominational
Age range of pupils: 2–11 years

No. of pupils enrolled as at 01/01/2019: 316
Boys: 159 **Girls:** 157
Fees per annum as at 01/01/2019:
Day: £14,970–£15,690
Average class size: 18
Teacher/pupil ratio: 1:9

Curriculum

The Roche School offers good, clear teaching well adapted to pupils' understanding in a pleasant, encouraging and homely atmosphere so that all can take pride in their progress and no one feels left behind. Classes are kept small so children benefit from the personal attention. Pupils are encouraged to respect each other sympathetically and we offer a wide variety of academic, artistic and sporting opportunities. The school seeks continually to build on its fine academic reputation. Art, Dance, Music, Languages and Sport are taught by specialists.

Entry requirements

Prospective pupils spend a morning in class during which their work is assessed. There is no testing at nursery and reception entry.

Examinations offered

Children are prepared for 11+ examinations and placed in a variety of top London schools.

Schools in Greater London

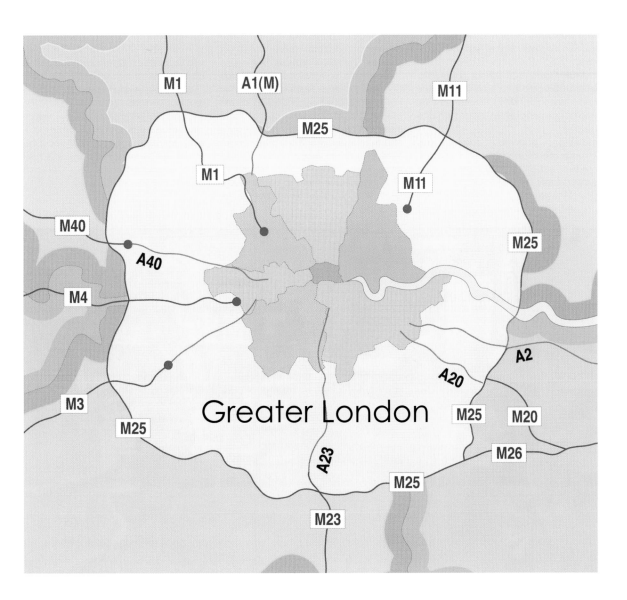

Avon House Preparatory School

AVON HOUSE
PREPARATORY SCHOOL

490 High Road, Woodford Green, Essex
IG8 0PN

Tel: 020 8504 1749
Email: registrar@ahsprep.co.uk
Website: www.avonhouseschool.co.uk
Headteacher: Mrs Amanda Campbell
Appointed: September 2011
School type: Coeducational Day
Religious Denomination: Christian

Age range of pupils: 3–11
No. of pupils enrolled as at 01/01/2019: 242
Fees per annum as at 01/01/2019:
Day: £9,750–£10,740
Average class size: 16
Teacher/pupil ratio: 1:8

As a small school we at Avon House believe we have so much to offer families who want their children to be educated in a nurturing environment with small class sizes.

Avon House is a school community where every child is valued as an individual and is encouraged to demonstrate their own unique personalities both in class and beyond.

Strong pastoral care adds immeasurable value to the success of the children and allows us to celebrate and support every child. Children enjoy being part of the House system which gives them opportunities to join with other children across the school in a number of events.

We strive to achieve academic excellence beginning with firm foundations in Early Years where our youngest children explore the world around them as well as the fundamentals of Literacy and Numeracy. Children are presented with occasions to create memorable experiences during these important years. As the children grow and develop we offer many opportunities through a broad range of co-curricular clubs, educational and residential visits that enable them to form interests which will carry them forward into senior schooling.

In recent months there have been building developments around the school campus which have enabled the school to move from one to two form entry as well as add new ICT and art and design classrooms.

We always encourage visitors to come and tour the school on a working morning so they can get a sense of how well all areas of school fit cohesively on the site. A prospectus which gives an overview of the school can be requested from the School Registrar, Mrs Best, on 020 8504 1749 opt 3 or registrar@ahsprep.co.uk

Babington House School

(Founded 1887)

Grange Drive, Chislehurst, Kent BR7 5ES

Tel: 020 8467 5537

Fax: 020 8295 1175

Email: enquiries@babingtonhouse.com

Website: www.babingtonhouse.com

Headmaster: Mr Tim Lello MA, FRSA, NPQH

Appointed: 2013

School type: Coeducational Day

Age range of pupils: 3–18

No. of pupils enrolled as at 01/01/2019: 387

Fees per term as at 01/01/2019:

Nursery: £3,180 (inclusive of lunches) based on 12 week term

Preparatory (Reception to Year 6): £4,288 per term (inclusive of lunches)

Seniors (11 to 18): £5,340 per term (inclusive of lunches)

Teacher/pupil ratio: 1:20

Inspiring Teachers, Inspiring Children

Babington House School in Chislehurst is the top small independent school in England for A level results 2018 and 3rd in the UK with 68% A* and A grades.

It is an excellent school achieving amazing results and inspiring pupils from the Sixth Form right down to the Nursery. Babington's Early Years provision is top of the Bromley Borough league tables for the second year running.

The school is an independent co-educational day school, situated in a beautiful group of buildings on Grange Drive in Chislehurst, near Bromley. It has almost 400 pupils from age 3 to 18 and from September 2019 will be accepting boys into the Senior School in Year 7.

Being a small school has BIG advantages. It has high standards of behaviour, dress and conduct, benefiting from no more than 20 pupils in a class and a strong sense of community.

Babington is an academic school. The School is committed to outstanding music, drama, sport and the arts in their broadest sense and offers a wealth of extra-curricular opportunities. Our academic, social and sporting endeavours are underpinned by core Christian values.

The co-educational Senior School is academically selective with an Entrance Examination for Year 7 entry. In Sixth Form, the focus is very much on A-level study in small sets with the opportunity for work experience, which helps university applications stand out and provides great self-confidence.

Headmaster, Tim Lello comments *"Our commitment to provide an academic and well-rounded education with small class sizes, tailored to the needs of our pupils is really paying off, our pupils and parents are happy and we are achieving excellent results."*

See for yourself –

www.babingtonhouse.com

Kew Green Preparatory School

(Founded 2004)

Layton House, Ferry Lane, Kew Green,
Richmond, Surrey TW9 3AF
Tel: 020 8948 5999
Fax: 020 8948 4774
Email: secretary@kgps.co.uk
Website: www.kgps.co.uk
Headmaster: Mr J Peck
Appointed: September 2011

School type: Coeducational Day
Age range of pupils: 4–11
No. of pupils enrolled as at 01/01/2019: 270
Fees per term as at 01/01/2019:
Day: £5,857
Average class size: 20
Teacher/pupil ratio: 1:6.4

Kew Green Prep School (KGPS) is a lively, co-educational, independent school for children aged 4 to 11 near Kew Gardens in Richmond. Owned by the Gardener Schools Group, a family founded company set up in 1991, KGPS is the sister school to Ravenscourt Prep School (RPPS) and Kew House Senior School (KHS).

Kew Green is housed in an attractive building, surrounded by mature trees and nestled in a peaceful corner of Kew Green. It is flanked by The Royal Botanical Gardens and The River Thames and we use these regularly along with the green itself.

We offer our children the opportunity to succeed, be recognised and be valued.

Our pupils grow with the faculties required to tackle the many challenges that life may have to offer. We instil tolerance and respect for others and the capacity to celebrate diversity, embrace change and understand the importance of contributing to society. Above all, we believe that children need to be nurtured, guided, motivated and inspired to allow them to blossom. We are a school of smiles, laughter and happiness where pupils fulfil their maximum potential.

We believe children thrive in an environment that is loving and supportive. Physically, socially, emotionally and intellectually – our children develop and constantly achieve during their

time with us. Our aim is that they leave as skilled and adaptable young citizens who will grow to meet the challenges of the 21st century. We believe in a broad and balanced curriculum, nurturing creativity and collaboration, resilience and determination whilst developing a strong self-esteem in each individual child. We enthusiastically share our children's education with their parents through our 'open door policy'.

Kew Green is a thriving school community where laughter and enjoyment go hand in hand with the process of delivering a first-rate education.

Kew House School

Kew House, 6 Capital Interchange Way,
London TW8 0EX

Tel: 0208 742 2038
Email: info@kewhouseschool.com
Website: www.kewhouseschool.com
Headmaster: Mr Mark Hudson
School type: Coeducational Day

Age range of pupils: 11–18
No. of pupils enrolled as at 01/01/2019: 550
Fees per term as at 01/01/2019:
Day: £7,129
Average class size: 22

Located in West London, Kew House School is a co-educational independent senior school for students aged 11-18 years. Owned by the Gardener Schools Group, a family founded company set up in 1991, Kew House is the sister school to Ravenscourt Park Prep and Kew Green Prep.

Kew House School takes a modern and pioneering approach to every aspect of school life. The school recognises and enhances the individual abilities of each child, welcoming students with varying academic profiles and placing emphasis on confidence, self-esteem and creativity.

By operating a true 'open door' policy that welcomes parents and members of the wider community to become a part of school life, Kew House has developed the feeling of a family and social hub that provides emotional support and security for all students and employees.

Sport is an important part of the Curriculum and its students achieve national and regional championship. Students benefit from using state of the art facilities at sporting locations just a stone's throw away from the school, including professional tennis courts and cricket grounds. Just a short walk from the River Thames, rowing is part of the curriculum.

In September 2017, Kew House opened a brand new Sixth Form Centre which benefits from a beautifully designed independent learning centre on the ground floor. Facilities include a Sixth Form Cafe, library, roof terrace, audio-visual suite, recording studio and Sixth Form Seminar rooms.

Following an inspection of the school in February 2018 by the Independent Schools Inspectorate (ISI) Kew House was particularly delighted to learn from the lead inspector that the results of the student and parent questionnaires were the most positive they had ever seen.

Marymount London

George Road, Kingston upon Thames
KT2 7PE

Tel: +44 (0)20 8949 0571
Fax: +44 (0)20 8336 2485
Email:
admissions@marymountlondon.com
Website: www.marymountlondon.com
Headmistress: Mrs Margaret Frazier
School type: Girls' Day & Boarding
Age range of girls: 11–18

No. of pupils enrolled as at 01/01/2019: 250
Fees per annum as at 01/01/2019:
Day: £24,985
Weekly Boarding: £40,515
Full Boarding: £42,305
Average class size: 12
Teacher/pupil ratio: 1:6

Marymount London is an independent school for girls, nurturing the limitless potential of curious, motivated students (ages 11 to 18) of diverse faiths and backgrounds. Founded in 1955 through the charism of the Religious of the Sacred Heart of Mary (RSHM), we proudly stand as the first all-girls' school in the United Kingdom to adopt the International Baccalaureate curriculum (IB MYP and Diploma), where girls are inspired to learn in a creative, collaborative, interdisciplinary, and exploratory environment.

Just 20 minutes from London, Marymount is located on a seven acre idyllic garden campus which offers outstanding facilities, including a sports hall, tennis courts, dance studio and modern dining hall. The School's challenging academic program is based on the International Baccalaureate curricula:

- The Middle Years Programme (MYP), offered in Grades 6 to 10, focuses on an integrated STEAM (Science, Technology, Engineering, Arts, Mathematics) approach, with an additional emphasis on language acquisition.
- The International Baccalaureate Diploma Programme (DP) for Grades 11 and 12 builds on the strong foundation of the MYP, leading to independent research opportunities

and exceptional university placement within the UK and around the world.
- Our results are outstanding: 100% pass rate and an average of 36 points.

Marymount's holistic approach to learning delivers a well-rounded education that encourages critical thinking, intercultural understanding, and participation in a wide array of interesting extracurricular offerings. Transport services from London and the surrounding areas as well as boarding options (weekly, full, and flexi) are available.

Admissions Process

Marymount offers year-round rolling admission. The admissions section of the website, featuring an online application portal, provides all of the information necessary to get started. Applicant families are encouraged to learn more about the School's strong tradition of excellence by exploring the website, making contact by phone/email, and scheduling a campus/Skype visit.

Mount House School

MOUNT HOUSE SCHOOL

Camlet Way, Hadley Wood, Barnet,
Hertfordshire EN4 0NJ
Tel: 020 8449 6889
Email: admissions@mounthouse.org.uk
Website: www.mounthouse.org.uk
Principal: Mr Toby Mullins
Appointed: September 2018

School type: Co-educational Day
Age range of pupils: 11–18
No. of pupils enrolled as at 01/01/2019: 190
Fees per annum as at 01/01/2019:
Day: £16,560
Average class size: 15-20

Mount House School is a non-selective, co-educational independent day school for the 21st century where children develop into confident learners.

Located in the North London suburb of Hadley Wood, Mount House School enjoys a tranquil and peaceful setting, whilst still being close to all major road and rail links.

Mount House is not a 'one size fits all' school. Here, every individual is valued and each child's unique talents will be identified and nurtured. Students leave as able, articulate, balanced, caring, and well-rounded individuals with a genuine love of learning, ready to take on life's challenges and opportunities, aware of the needs of others and confident in their ability to make a difference.

With our small class sizes and highly experienced, committed teaching staff, we are able to maximise the learning potential of every pupil.

Mount House is a happy and successful school, with an excellent record of GCSE and A level results and an outstanding record of students achieving places at top universities.

We place a high priority on personal development. Growth in moral and cultural values is encouraged as part of the everyday ethos of the school. Pastoral care is centred around our supportive tutor system, which enhances the feeling of belonging to a very special family community, where everyone feels valued.

Pupils are encouraged to become self-motivated learners, critical thinkers, to express thoughts and feelings, to write creatively and use their imaginations. They enjoy using their numeracy skills, interpreting and using data and applying their knowledge to problem solving situations. Pupils' education is supplemented through a wide variety of educational visits and visitors from the community, such as theatre groups and interactive workshops.

We believe a child's education is a shared responsibility between school and home and we positively encourage the support of parents, offering a partnership that embraces regular contact and communication, leading to the building of strong relationships that are a key factor in the school's popularity.

A significant amount of funding has already been invested in Mount House in recent months, including the provision of new music, drama and IT facilities, refurbished classrooms and the creation of a new café, which is open to parents as well as to sixth formers. And with plans for further investment, including a brand new sports hall, Mount House will become a school fit to support and develop both the curricular and extra-curricular talents of its growing pupil population.

The move to co-education (Mount House was previously the all-girls St Martha's School), together with our policy of non-selection, form the basis of our vision of making Mount House School much more inclusive and accessible to all. We believe everyone is capable of achieving, given the right tools and inspiration, and are proud that our members of staff always go the extra mile to help our pupils succeed.

Mount House School is in Camlet Way, Hadley Wood, Herts – 10 minutes walk from Hadley Wood station and three miles from J24 of the M25.

For further information, visit www.mounthouse.org.uk

Radnor House

Radnor House
—— TWICKENHAM ——
celebrating every individual

Pope's Villa, Cross Deep, Twickenham,
Middlesex TW1 4QG
Tel: 020 8891 6264

Email: admissions@radnorhouse.org
Website: www.radnor-twickenham.org
Head of School:
Darryl Wideman MA (Oxon.)
School type: Co-educational Day
Age range of pupils: 9–18
No. of pupils enrolled as at 22/03/2019: 417

Fees per annum as at 01/09/2018:
Junior School: £15,900
Year 7 & 8: £18,570
Year 9 to 13: £19,350
Average class size:
(Junior School) 20
(Senior School) 21

At Radnor House we bring a breath of fresh air to independent education in this part of the world. We are a selective co-educational day school enjoying a stunning location on the banks of the River Thames in Twickenham, easy to access with superb public transport links and three school coach routes. First rate sporting facilities with sports grounds at St Mary's university and, from September 2019, at Teddington Cricket Club in the beautiful Bushy Park, all just a few minutes away. Our pupils thrive in small classes with a strong focus on individual attention. We are a 'through school' educating and inspiring boys and girls from 9 to 18, with three main entry points in Year 5, Year 7 and Year 12.

We prefer encouragement to pressure.

We stretch, challenge and support every pupil through inspirational teaching, proactive pastoral care and a wide range of co-curricular activities. A top quality education and a genuinely friendly atmosphere combine to create an exceptional environment with proven outcomes of success, where happy children enjoy a busy, enriched school life supported by an actively involved parent community.

Our core values of courage, excellence, perseverance and respect are at the heart of our ethos and permeate everything we do. We create every opportunity for the children to develop the all-important skills of teamwork, co-operation and diplomacy, to help them fine-tune their emotional intelligence, both in the

classroom and beyond.

Recent productions of 'My Fair Lady' and 'The Witches' have showcased the strength of our performing arts, while sports tours, charity work, an enviable wide range of co-curricular activities and an engaging academic enrichment programme encourage everyone to participate and thrive. The passions and enthusiasms that children develop at school stay with them throughout their lives, and we strongly believe in the development of an active learning environment for limitless minds. Visit us on one of our Open Days, held on Saturdays in May, October and November each year, or enjoy a school tour during the school day. Booking is available via our website.

Schools in the South-East

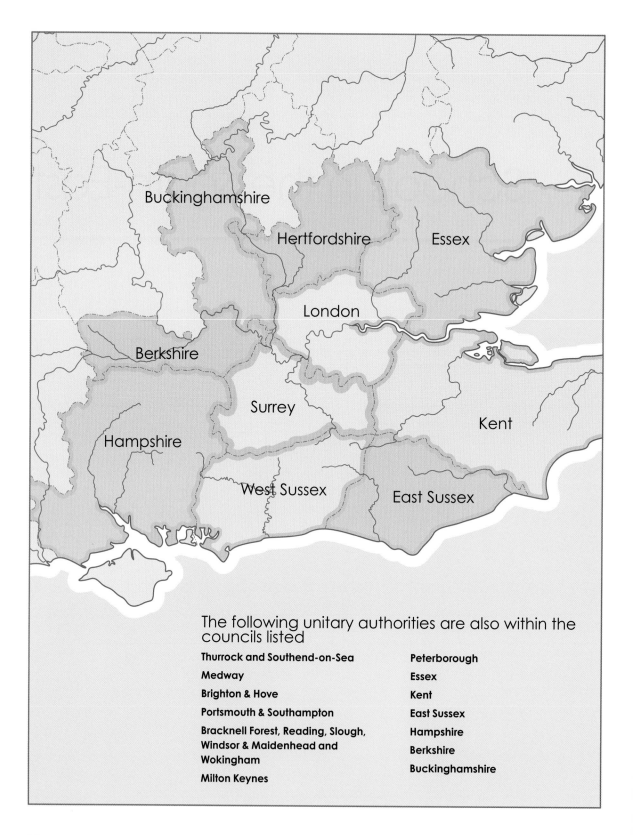

The following unitary authorities are also within the councils listed

Thurrock and Southend-on-Sea	Peterborough
Medway	Essex
Brighton & Hove	Kent
Portsmouth & Southampton	East Sussex
Bracknell Forest, Reading, Slough, Windsor & Maidenhead and Wokingham	Hampshire
	Berkshire
Milton Keynes	Buckinghamshire

Berkhamsted School

(Founded 1541)
Overton House, 131 High Street,
Berkhamsted, Hertfordshire HP4 2DJ

Tel: 01442 358001
Email: admissions@berkhamsted.com
Website: www.berkhamsted.com
Principal:
Mr Richard Backhouse MA(Cantab)
Appointed: January 2016
School type: Co-educational &
single-sex, day & boarding
Age range of pupils: 3–18

No. of pupils enrolled as at 01/01/2019: 1792
Sixth Form: 395
Pre-Prep/Prep: 548
Senior Boys: 467 **Senior Girls:** 382
Fees per annum as at 01/01/2019:
Day: £10,365–£20,640
Weekly Boarding: £27,635
Full Boarding: £32,880
Average class size: 20

With a history dating back to 1541, an excellent reputation and an accessible location, Berkhamsted School offers much to make it worthy of consideration by parents across London and the South East. Our patron, who visited in 2016 to mark the School's 475th anniversary, is Her Majesty The Queen.

Located in the historic market town of Berkhamsted, the School is a 30 minute train journey from Euston Station, and a short drive from Junction 20 of the M25. Full, weekly and flexi boarding, as well as term-time and holiday wraparound care for younger pupils, are on offer to support working parents.

Berkhamsted is one of only a small number of schools in the country to offer a 'diamond' structure that combines both single-sex and co-educational teaching. Boys and girls are taught together until the age of 11, separately from 11-16, before coming back together again in a joint Sixth Form. In senior school, boys and girls are taught separately on different sites, but share in academic trips and visits and in some co-curricular activities, such as drama productions, orchestras, Duke of

Edinburgh's Award and the Combined Cadet Force.

Academic results are consistently strong with of 80% A*- B grades at A level over the last five years. In 2018, GCSE students achieved 69% of grades 7 / A and above. Berkhamsted offers all the key components of a traditional independent school education: small class sizes, specialist staff and excellent standards of teaching throughout the school.

Alongside this, an outstanding co-curricular programme seeks to foster and develop a wide range of interests and hobbies – music, sport, drama, public speaking and a vibrant outdoor education programme. The school timetable is structured to accommodate a wide selection of clubs and societies within core school hours. Berkhamsted also has a strong tradition of undertaking service within the local community from Year 9 (13 +) onwards.

Pupils across the School enjoy the benefits of being part of a small, supportive community based in an environment appropriate to their specific educational needs, yet with access to the state-of-the

art facilities of a large school; a 500-seat theatre, a six-lane 25m swimming pool and sports centre, and one of the best art departments in the country.

The School prides itself on offering outstanding levels of pastoral care and, in an echo of its boarding roots, the House system is a key feature of Berkhamsted. Senior School pupils are allocated to Houses and the Head of House, supported by House Tutors, has the primary responsibility for the academic and pastoral progress of each student in their House. Over and above the close academic supervision and support, this structure provides an excellent social base for pupils, allowing them to mix and get to know others across the year groups. Berkhamsted offers scholarships – academic, art, drama, music and sport – and means-tested bursaries to talented pupils on entry to the school.

Parents are welcome to visit the School at any time: please call 01442 358001 for an appointment and a tour to appreciate what Berkhamsted can offer your child and how we develop remarkable people.

Cranmore School

(Founded 1968)

Epsom Road, West Horsley, Surrey KT24 6AT
Tel: 01483 280340
Fax: 01483 280341
Email: office@cranmoreprep.co.uk
Website: www.cranmoreprep.co.uk
Headmaster: Mr Michael Connolly BSc, BA, MA, MEd

Appointed: September 2006
School type: Coeducational Day
Religious Denomination: Roman Catholic
Age range of pupils: 2–13
No. of pupils enrolled as at 01/01/2019: 420
Fees per annum as at 01/01/2019:
Day: £11,850

Cranmore is a leading independent prep school in Surrey, situated in West Horsley between Guildford and Leatherhead. Its Christian ethos is central to supporting every child's development and pupils come from a variety of backgrounds with about one-third from Roman Catholic families. The majority live locally, although some come from a wider geographical area. The overall ability profile on entry is above average, and the majority of pupils start in the Cranmore Nursery and Reception with a few joining later in Year 3 or if spaces occur in other year groups. Having established a strong co-educational Nursery several years ago, Cranmore is committed to becoming fully co-educational throughout the school in planned phases.

Prior to joining Cranmore as Headmaster in 2006, Michael Connolly enjoyed twelve years' of successful experience as Headmaster at his previous school and, before that, had a rich and varied journey in education within several senior schools and a short spell working overseas.

He is a highly experienced School Inspector and has served on the Board of several national and local educational bodies and often writes articles for leading publications. He is passionate about ongoing education and is currently studying for his 5th University Degree by research in Philosophy.

Q & A with the Head:

Who/what inspired you to become a teacher?

I very much enjoyed my own time as a pupil as I had inspiring teachers who gave me a love for learning. Therefore, I decided that this would be a wonderful career.

What achievement are you most proud of as Head?

No single achievement but a satisfaction in seeing many pupils develop their talents in various aspects of school life.

What does a successful school look like to you?

Children are happy, confident, feel secure and have developed a love for learning.

What is the most important quality you want every child to have when they leave your school? And why?

Respect for others.

It is through our relationships with others that we define who we really are as a person.

Please give 5 words to describe the ethos of your school.

Nurturing, Supportive, Encouraging, Aspirational, Resilient

Davenies School

DAVENIES
Day Preparatory School for boys aged 4 to 13 years

(Founded 1940)
Station Road, Beaconsfield,
Buckinghamshire HP9 1AA

Tel: 01494 685400
Fax: 01494 685408
Email: office@davenies.co.uk
Website: www.davenies.co.uk
Headmaster: Mr Carl Rycroft BEd (Hons)
Appointed: September 2015

School type: Boys' Day
Age range of boys: 4–13
No. of pupils enrolled as at 01/01/2019: 337
Fees per annum as at 01/01/2019:
Day: £11,985–£17,400
Average class size: Max 20

Davenies is a thriving IAPS day school for boys aged 4–13. Our ethos and philosophy enable the boys to make the most of their preparatory years, supported by high-quality pastoral care, a broad and stimulating curriculum and numerous extra-curricular opportunities.

Davenies has its own distinct character and from their earliest years children are encouraged to relish the learning experience.

We are committed to an education both in and out of the classroom, thereby enabling the academic, artistic, musical, creative and physical potential of each child to flourish. This school is a warm, caring and happy one, where self-esteem is nurtured and grown; we believe that by fostering a wide range of interests and passions we provide the boys with every opportunity to develop in confidence. Our high-quality teachers have an excellent track record of preparing children for life at the country's leading senior schools and beyond.

Enterprises such as the unique Davenies Award Scheme and the permeation of technology in our teaching and learning ensure we offer a truly independent educational experience.

At Davenies, our outstanding facilities support us in providing a positive learning experience with our own language of learning that nurtures each boy's understanding of how he learns. Davenies' boys are polite and friendly with their own individual characters, personalities, passions and interests.

The School is owned by Beaconsfield Educational Trust Limited, a company limited by guarantee, whose registered office is at 73 Station Road, Beaconsfield, Bucks HP9 1AA. Registration No. 717500 Registered Charity No. 313120.

Leighton Park School

Leighton Park
School

(Founded 1890)

Shinfield Road, Reading, Berkshire RG2 7ED

Tel: 0118 987 9600

Email: admissions@leightonpark.com

Website: www.leightonpark.com

Head: Mr Matthew L S Judd BA, PGCE

Appointed: September 2018

School type:

Co-educational Day & Boarding

Religious Denomination: Quaker

Age range of pupils: 11–18

No. of pupils enrolled as at 01/01/2019: 460

Fees per term as at 01/01/2019:

£5,873–£12,190 per term

Average class size: 17

Teacher/pupil ratio: 1:8

Introduction

A vibrant learning community, our values-based education focuses on each individual – with impressive results.

At its core, a Leighton Park education offers achievement with values, character and community.

The success of our academic approach is demonstrated by the latest UK Government analysis, which showed that our Sixth Form students achieved amongst the best academic progress nationwide with the school in the top 3% of schools and colleges in England and in the top 30 boarding schools.

Academic focus

An IB World School, our emphasis on problem-solving, critical thinking and intercultural skills ensures that every student can succeed in an ever-changing, globalised world. Central to the school's approach, we have particular strengths in Science, Technology,

Engineering and Maths (STEM) as well as the Creative Arts (Music, Drama, Art and Dance). Combining these strengths, our students benefit from an interdisciplinary approach, fusing analytical skills from STEM with creative and interpersonal soft skills.

Particular examples, include the school's status as a Yamaha Flagship Music Education Partner, with excellent music and media teaching and a new Music and Media Centre opened in Spring 2018. The school is also a Lead Partner for the Network of Teaching Excellence in Computer Science. Our interdisciplinary iSTEM+ programme came runner-up in the national STEM Innovation Awards, beating 354 other schools. Our ICT Facilities won the Education Business 2018 Award.

In Sixth Form, students can choose between the International Baccalaureate Diploma Programme (IB) or A Levels, and can opt to do three or

four A Levels so that their choices are not limited so early in life.

Pastoral

All our students benefit from small class sizes. The average is 16 students per class, going down to 7 students in Sixth Form. Our dedicated teachers are able to cater lessons to each student and ensure they are kept on track both inside and out of lessons. This allows an unparalleled level of support and also a relationship between students and teachers that allows students to feel that they can speak honestly and openly to teachers about any problems they may be facing.

Boarding

Leighton Park has a thriving boarding community, offering full, weekly and flexible options for students. Co-educational, the boarding houses are split roughly 50/50 boys and girls with each group having their own wings but sharing communal spaces. Students represent 32 countries, with strong UK representation. The five houses mix boarding and day students, creating vibrant communities, with day students welcome to stay until 9pm to spend time with friends or have time and space to focus on their prep.

House parents create homely environments supported by tutors and matrons, ensuring each student feels relaxed and comfortable. With a dedicated staff and plenty of opportunity to socialise with other students, each house is very much its own community.

Hobbies and other activities

Our wrap-around provision, which welcomes day students from 7.15am to 9pm, offers all our pupils the time to discover and develop their greatest talents. Students can choose from 90 different co-curricular activities to extend

their learning, increase confidence, try new things and make new friends.

Sports

Sport plays an important role in life at Leighton Park with many individual performers and teams reaching county and regional level in sports. The school's Advanced Performer Programme supports elite athletes. While the school does very well in traditional sports such as rugby, netball, boys' cricket and hockey it also has strong teams in football and girls' cricket. The school is very supportive of individual talents and interests from rowing to gymnastics.

Music

Music and creative media is a particular strength at Leighton Park, reflected by the school's status as a Yamaha Flagship Music Education Partner – the only one in the UK. Students have so many opportunities to play or perform at Leighton Park, with the Music Department being one of the busiest places in school, catering for all musical tastes from classical to jazz, indie to rock. Opportunities to perform include regular concerts and tours abroad.

Facilities

Leighton Park has the facilities you would expect of a leading independent school, including a new Music and Media centre, an impressive library, swimming pool and a combination of high tech and historic buildings. The school's innovative use of the latest teaching and learning technologies is supported by continuous investment in technology, including Google Classroom, CleverTouch screens in classrooms and personal ChromeBook laptops.

School life

The quiet moments and the calm atmosphere of our 65 acre park, encourage students to collect their thoughts and reflect within a caring community, providing high academic standards, excellent pastoral care and a rich and diverse co-curricular programme of activities. All of this, and the focus on mutual respect, create a stable, unique and sustainable environment where children can live, learn and grow.

LVS Ascot

(Founded 1803)

London Road, Ascot, Berkshire SL5 8DR

Tel: 01344 882770

Fax: 01344 890648

Email: enquiries@lvs.ascot.sch.uk

Website: www.lvs.ascot.sch.uk

Headmistress:

Mrs Christine Cunniffe BA (Hons), MMus, MBA

Appointed: September 2010

School type:

Coeducational Day & Boarding

Religious Denomination:

Non-denominational

Age range of pupils: 4–18

No. of pupils enrolled as at 01/01/2019: 830

Fees per annum as at 01/01/2019:

Day: £10,380–£19,896

Full Boarding: £26,562–£34,953

Average class size: 18

LVS Ascot is a non-selective, co-educational day and boarding school of over 800 pupils aged 4-18. It is a through-school so pupils can begin their school career at LVS Ascot at age 4 and remain there until they complete Sixth Form.

Exam results in 2018 saw nearly 10% of GCSEs graded A* or equivalent, with 99% of students who achieved 5 or more A*-C grades gaining passes in both maths and English. LVS Ascot also recorded an increase in A* grades at A Level, with an overall pass rate of 98.3%.

The school is located on a bright and spacious site amongst 25 acres of landscaped gardens and playing fields. As one of the most modern boarding and day schools in the UK, the purpose built campus provides excellent facilities in a safe and stimulating environment, including a sports centre with indoor swimming pool, fitness centre, sports hall and all-weather sports pitch, dance studio, medical centre, a 250 seat theatre, drama studio and a music technology suite with recording studio, plus a Learning Resource Centre and over 500 networked computer workstations.

Both Infant & Junior and Senior school follow the National Curriculum, but with the added feature of a wide range of GCSE, A Level and Vocational options, catering for each individual pupil's strengths. An extensive range of activities and extra-curricular clubs and societies underpin academic studies by providing opportunities for pupils to extend their horizons in team sports, drama and music, visits, clubs, hobbies and interests.

Pastoral care is a great priority at LVS Ascot. In the Senior School each child is allocated to a house, and within that to a tutor group. House Masters and Mistresses, supported by teams of tutors, oversee the welfare and development of their pupils. In the Infant & Junior School, pastoral care is undertaken by the children's class teacher. Students are encouraged to give their best, whether the goal is university entrance, success at GCSE, honour on the sports field, artistic endeavour, or coping with the trials and tribulations of growing up. LVS Ascot aims to inspire independence.

Academic Scholarships and Bursaries are available – please request further details. Our special arrangement with the HM Forces enables us to discount our fees by 10-20% to all HM Forces and UK Diplomatic personnel.

Pangbourne College

(Founded 1917)
Pangbourne, Reading, Berkshire RG8 8LA

Tel: 0118 984 2101
Fax: 0118 984 1239
Email: admissions@pangbourne.com
Website: www.pangbourne.com
Headmaster: Thomas J C Garnier
School type:
Coeducational Boarding & Day
Age range of pupils: 11–18

No. of pupils enrolled as at 01/01/2019: 429
Boys: 274 **Girls:** 155 **Sixth Form:** 62
Fees per annum as at 01/01/2019:
Day: £17,655–£24,885
Full Boarding £24,870–£35,190
Average class size: 8-20
Teacher/pupil ratio: 1:7

Pangbourne College offers wide-ranging academic and co-curricular opportunities to girls and boys aged 11-18, with an emphasis on outstanding pastoral care and character development.

Pangbourne is a vibrant boarding and day school community, perfectly balancing strong Service values with a dynamic, modern outlook and unpretentious, inclusive attitude. The College is proud of its outstanding pastoral care, taking an integrated approach to caring for each pupil, and understanding the challenges young people face in order to improve the support it provides.

Headmaster, Mr Thomas Garnier, says: "Above all, we are a 'people place'. We are committed to the personal development of our pupils in the fullest sense. They are encouraged to work hard towards academic success with a robust and comprehensive curriculum."

"Just as important is character development: confidence and values, creative and physical skills and an appreciation of themselves and what they can contribute to the world."

The Flag Values of Kindness, Selflessness, Moral Courage, Initiative, Industry, Resilience, and Integrity underpin every aspect of life at the College. They are rooted in a Christian ethos and go a long way to preparing pupils for life's challenges and the responsibilities of adulthood. The aim is to equip Pangbournians with the strongest possible foundations for their future.

Pangbourne is set in 230 acres within an Area of Outstanding Natural Beauty, within easy reach of excellent transport connections. It is 10 minutes from Junction 12 of the M4 and served by London Paddington – Oxford Mainline rail network. Daily school transport services are available from Newbury, Basingstoke, Wantage and, as of January 2018, Henley, Twyford, Wargrave and the surrounding areas.

Entry is offered at 11+, 13+, and 16+, and occasionally into other year groups. The best way to experience Pangbourne is to come and visit, enjoy a tour of the College and speak to pupils and staff. To arrange a tour or to attend our next Open Morning, please email the Registrar.

A distinctive school that puts huge emphasis on self-discipline, teamwork and leadership. Caring and supportive, Pangbourne buzzes with activity and encourages every pupil to have a go. –
Good Schools Guide

The personal development of Pangbourne's students is outstanding, and supported by an excellent, broad curriculum which enables students to progress academically and supports the development of the whole individual. –
ISI Inspection Report

Roedean School

ROEDEAN

(Founded 1885)
Roedean Way, Brighton, East Sussex
BN2 5RQ

Tel: 01273 667500
Fax: 01273 680791
Email: info@roedean.co.uk
Website: www.roedean.co.uk
Headmaster: Mr. Oliver Bond BA(Essex), PGCE, NPQH
Appointed: 2013
School type: Girls' Boarding & Day
Age range of girls: 11–18

No. of pupils enrolled as at 01/01/2018: 607
Sixth Form: 167
No. of boarders: 317
Fees per term as at 01/01/2019:
Day: £5,480–£7,165
Weekly Boarding: £9,690–£10,805
Full Boarding: £10,620–£12,855
Average class size: 18
Teacher/pupil ratio: 1:7

The 2014 Good Schools' Guide described Roedean as 'a school that's going places', and five years later the guide's prediction has proven to be very accurate. Academic results are consistently strong, with 54% A*-A at A Level, 22.6% of GCSEs in 2018 were awarded the new elite Grade 9, and one in three leavers have gone on to study STEM subjects at university over the last 5 years.

Roedean is a wonderful school, with over 600 girls, the result of consistent annual growth – in 2014, there were 360 girls on roll. The School enjoys strong interest from those in London who are choosing to take advantage of the weekly and flexi-boarding opportunities;

they are drawn by Roedean's fantastic grounds and space, and also for a school that focuses on developing academic strengths without losing the enjoyment and delight that must be part of an all-round education. The girls are given the opportunity to grow up at their own pace, and have the freedom to develop their talents and passions.

Roedean's ethos is clearly focused on the remarkable benefits of a holistic approach to education, in which academic pursuits are complemented by a wide range of co-curricular activities. The girls love the Farm with its newly-arrived pygmy goats, and the new flood-lit all-weather pitch on site. Roedean girls

excel in a range of sports, many musicians play beyond Grade 8 level, and girls achieve at the very highest level in ballet. At Roedean, there can be no doubt that the girls' rounded education produces independent and creative young women who will make their mark in the world.

Roedean is one of the UK's leading girls' schools – the girls play sport with the sea's blue behind them and the green of the South Downs in front of them, and the boarding houses have been likened to a boutique hotel. It is not just this, but the strong academic focus with a genuine belief in the importance of creativity and an all-round education that makes Roedean unique.

St John's Beaumont Preparatory School

ST JOHN'S BEAUMONT

(Founded 1888)

Priest Hill, Old Windsor, Berkshire SL4 2JN
Tel: 01784 432428
Email: hmoffice@sjb.email
Website: www.sjbwindsor.uk
Headmaster: Mr G E F Delaney BA(Hons), PGCE, MSc
Appointed: 2006

School type: Boys' Day & Boarding
Age range of boys: 3–13
No. of pupils enrolled as at 01/09/2009: 290
Fees per term as at 01/01/2019:
Day: £3,264–£6,244
Boarding: £7,580–£9,573

St John's Beaumont is a Roman Catholic Jesuit preparatory boarding and day school for boys aged 3-13 in Old Windsor. As the oldest purpose built preparatory school in the country, founded in 1888, we combine the rich tradition of Jesuit education with the very best that modern teaching techniques and technology can offer.

At our core is the principle of cura personalis – care for each person so that boys may flourish academically, emotionally, socially, physically and spiritually. Priority is given to Roman Catholic families but we welcome boys of all backgrounds whose parents recognize

in our values and approach to education something they desire and wish to support for their own children.

With 70 acres of school grounds on site there is plenty of space for cross-country, rugby, football & cricket. A 25m indoor swimming pool and a climbing wall are also highlights of our facilities. Of equal importance to Sport is Music and the Arts, with the majority of boys learning an instrument and outstanding LAMDA results as well as a much acclaimed annual production in the outdoor theatre.

A vibrant boarding community comprising of tailored (2 or 3 nights/ week), weekly and full boarders enjoy

a full evening & weekend program making the most of the Schools facilities as well as the proximity to Windsor and London for regular trips out. Special activities for the boarders include a Diving (PADI) course, polo lessons and trips to Thorpe Park.

Our boys leave St John's aged 13 and move to some of the country's finest schools, but more importantly do so as confident, aspirational and resilient young men, aware of their own potential and their ability to leave a positive impression on the lives of others.

St Neot's School

ST NEOT'S
PREPARATORY SCHOOL

(Founded 1888)

St Neot's Road, Eversley,
Hampshire RG27 0PN
Tel: 0118 9739650
Email: admissions@stneotsprep.co.uk
Website: www.stneotsprep.co.uk
Head of School: Deborah Henderson
Appointed: September 2015

School type:
Co-educational Day, Preparatory
Age range of pupils: 2–13 years
No. of pupils enrolled as at 01/01/2019: 335
Fees per term as at 01/01/2019:
Day: £3,635–£5,200
Average class size: 18
Teacher/pupil ratio: 1:8

St Neot's, founded in 1888, is a happy, vibrant community for boys and girls from 2 to 13 years and is situated on the Hampshire/Berkshire border in 70 acres of beautiful grounds.

Our pupils develop a love of learning in a supportive and happy environment, where each individual is encouraged to achieve their full academic potential. Children are given the opportunity to embrace challenge, think creatively, develop self-confidence and foster empathy towards others, preparing them both intellectually and emotionally for success in the modern world. Forest School and Outdoor Education programmes encourage pupils to develop these attributes, which are so vital in today's world. The St Neot's journey culminates in the Years 7 and 8 leadership programme, which draws together a mix of skills through the core elements of the Pre Senior Baccalaureate (PSB).

We aim to provide the highest standards in teaching and learning, within a well rounded educational experience, and St Neot's has a very strong record of success in achieving Scholarships and Awards to numerous Senior Schools.

Physical Education is a strength of the school and our sports complex, comprising sports hall, 25m indoor pool, all-weather astro, cricket nets, hard tennis and netball courts, significantly supplements extensive playing fields. After school activities cover a wide range of interests and Holiday Clubs run in all school breaks, offering a wealth of opportunities, both sporting and creative.

St Neot's holds a Gold Artsmark award, recognising our achievements in art, music, drama and dance. Plays, concerts and recitals take place throughout the school year for all age groups.

Open Mornings take place termly – details can be found on the school website – www.stneotsprep.co.uk. We would also be delighted to arrange individual tours and meetings with the Head. Please contact Admissions on 0118 9739650 – e-mail – admissions@stneotsprep.co.uk.

St Swithun's School

St Swithun's
WINCHESTER

(Founded 1884)

Alresford Road, Winchester,
Hampshire SO21 1HA
Tel: 01962 835700
Fax: 01962 835779
Email: office@stswithuns.com
Website: www.stswithuns.com

Head of School:
Jane Gandee MA(Cantab)
Appointed: 2010
School type: Girls' Boarding & Day
Age range of girls: 11–18
No. of pupils enrolled as at 01/01/2019: 510
No. of boarders: 214

St Swithun's School is a renowned independent day, weekly and full-boarding school for girls set in 45 acres overlooking the Hampshire Downs on the outskirts of Winchester, yet only 50 minutes by train from central London. It offers excellent teaching, sporting and recreational facilities.

The school has a long-standing reputation for academic rigour and success. Girls are prepared for public examinations and higher education in a stimulating environment in which they develop intellectual curiosity, independence of mind and the ability to take responsibility for their own learning. They achieve almost one grade higher

at GCSE than their already significant baseline ability would suggest, and approximately half a grade higher at A level. St Swithun's offers a comprehensive careers and higher education support service throughout the school years. Its Oxbridge preparation is part of a whole-school academic enrichment programme providing additional challenge and stimulation.

Whilst achieving academic excellence, girls also have the opportunity to do 'something else'. There is an extensive co-curricular programme of over 100 weekly and 50 weekend activities to choose from.

As well as academic classrooms and science laboratories, there is a

magnificent performing arts centre with a 600-seat auditorium, a music school, an art and technology block, a sports hall and a full-size indoor swimming pool. There is an impressive library and ICT facility. The grounds are spacious and encompass sports fields, tennis courts and gardens.

With kindness and tolerance at the heart of its community, St Swithun's provides a civilised and caring environment in which all girls are valued for their individual gifts. By the time a girl leaves she will be courageous, compassionate, committed and self-confident with a love of learning, a moral compass and a sense of humour.

Directory

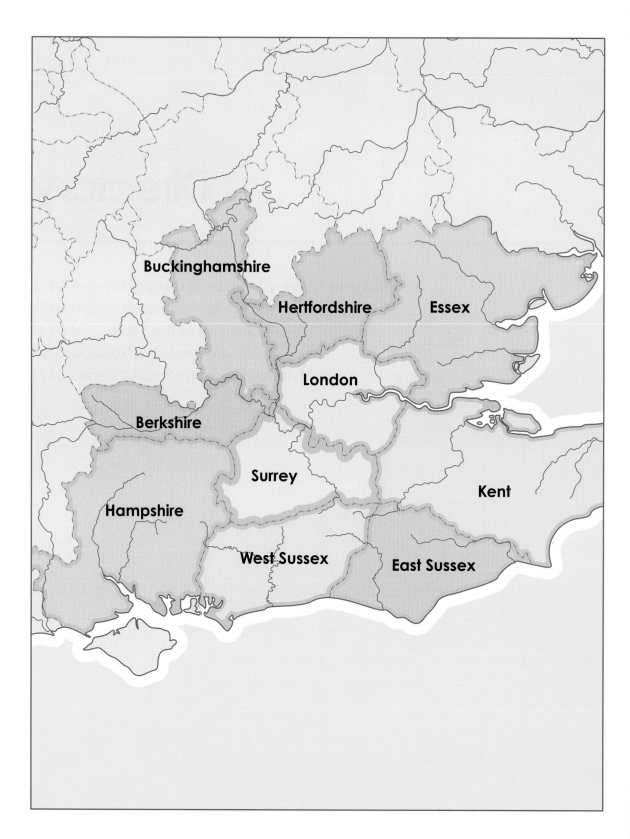

Buckinghamshire

Hertfordshire

Essex

London

Berkshire

Surrey

Kent

Hampshire

West Sussex

East Sussex

D112

Schools and Nursery Schools in Central London

KEY TO SYMBOLS

- ♀ Boys' school
- ♀ Girls' school
- 🌐 International school
- 16· Tutorial or sixth form college
- Ⓐ A levels
- 🏫 Boarding accommodation
- £ Bursaries
- ⒾⒷ International Baccalaureate
- 🖊 Learning support
- 16· Entrance at 16+
- 🎓 Vocational qualifications
- ⒾAPS Independent Association of Prep Schools
- ⒽⓂⒸ The Headmasters' & Headmistresses' Conference
- ⒾⓈⒶ Independent Schools Association
- ⒼⓈⒶ Girls' School Association
- ⒷⓈⒶ Boarding Schools' Association
- Ⓢ Society of Heads

Unless otherwise indicated, all schools are coeducational day schools. Single-sex and boarding schools will be indicated by the relevant icon.

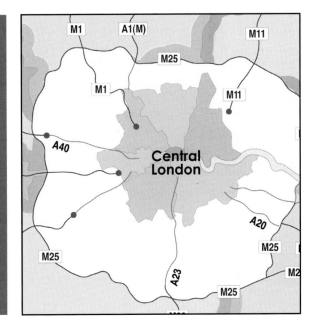

London

Central London

Accent International Consortium for Academic Programs Abroad
12 Bedford Square,
London WC1B 3JA
Tel: 020 7637 7518
Head: Natasa Blecic
16

Broadgate Day Nursery
21 Curtain Road, Hackney,
London EC2A 3LW
Tel: 020 7247 3491
Principal: Jacky Roberts NNEB
Age range: 0–5
No. of pupils: 50

CATS London
43-45 Bloomsbury Square,
London WC1A 2RA
Tel: 02078 411580
Principal: Mario Di Clemente
Age range: 15–24
🎭 Ⓐ 🏛 £ 16

Cavendish College
35-37 Alfred Place,
London WC1E 7DP
Tel: 020 7580 6043
Principal: Dr J Sanders BSc, MBA, PhD
16

Charterhouse Square School
40 Charterhouse Square,
London EC1M 6EA
Tel: 020 7600 3805
Head of School: Mrs Caroline Lloyd BEd (Hons)
Age range: 3–11
No. of pupils: 196
Fees: Day £5,680

City Lit Centre & Speech Therapy
Keeley House, Keeley Street,
London WC2B 4BA
Tel: 020 7492 2600
Principal: Mr G W Horgan
16

City of London School
Queen Victoria Street,
London EC4V 3AL
Tel: 020 3680 6300
Head: Mr A R Bird MSc
Age range: B10–18
No. of pupils: 930 VIth250
Fees: Day £17,901
🚹 Ⓐ £ ✐ 16

City of London School for Girls
St Giles' Terrace, Barbican,
London EC2Y 8BB
Tel: 020 7847 5500
Headmistress: Mrs E Harrop
Age range: G7–18
No. of pupils: 725
🚹 Ⓐ £ ✐ 16

DALLINGTON SCHOOL
For further details see p. 53
8 Dallington Street, Islington,
London EC1V 0BW
Tel: 020 7251 2284
Email: hercules@
dallingtonschool.co.uk
Website:
www.dallingtonschool.co.uk
Headteacher: Maria Blake
Age range: 3–11
No. of pupils: 138
Fees: Day £9,978–£12,630

ÉCOLE JEANNINE MANUEL – LONDON
For further details see p. 56
43-45 Bedford Square,
London WC1B 3DN
Tel: 020 3829 5970
Email: admissions@
jmanuel.uk.net
Website: www.ecolejeannine
manuel.org.uk
Head of School: Pauline Prévot
Age range: 3–18 years
No. of pupils: 442
Fees: Day £17,460
🌐 £ IB

Guildhall School of Music & Drama
Barbican, London EC2Y 8DT
Tel: 020 7382 7192
Principal: Barry Ife CBE, FKC, HonFRAM
16

Hansard Society
40-43 Chancery Lane,
London WC2A 1JA
Tel: 020 7438 1222
Head: Fiona Booth
16

Italia Conti Academy of Theatre Arts
Italia Conti House, 23 Goswell Road, London EC1M 7AJ
Tel: 020 7608 0047
Director: Chris White
Age range: 10–21
16 Ⓐ 16

Kensington College
23 Bloomsbury Square,
London WC1A 2PJ
Tel: 020 7580 1113
16

London College of International Business Studies
Surrey Quays Road,
London, SE16 2XU
Tel: 020 7242 1004
Heads: Mr Philip Moore & Ms Irene Chong
16

Royal Academy of Dramatic Art
62-64 Gower Street,
London WC1E 6ED
Tel: 020 7636 7076
Principal: Nicholas Barter MA, FRSA
16

Smithfield House Children's Nursery
14 West Smithfield,
London EC1A 9HY
Tel: 020 7236 1000
Manager: Janet MacGregor
Age range: 0–5

St Patrick's International College
London Sceptre Court Campus,
40 Tower Hill, London, EC3N 4DX
Tel: 020 7287 6664
16

ST PAUL'S CATHEDRAL SCHOOL
For further details see p. 83
2 New Change,
London EC4M 9AD
Tel: 020 7248 5156
Email: admissions@
spcs.london.sch.uk
Website: www.spcslondon.com
Headmaster: Simon Larter-Evans
BA (Hons), PGCE, FRSA
Age range: 4–13
No. of pupils: 254
Fees: Day £14,031–
£15,105 FB £8,736
🏛 £ ✐

The College of Central London
Tower Bridge Business Centre, 46-48
East Smithfield, London E1W 1AW
Tel: +44 (0) 20 3667 7607
Principal: Nicolas Kailides
Fees: Day £3,850
16 16

The Courtauld Institute of Art
Somerset House, Strand,
London WC2R 0RN
Tel: 020 7848 2777
Director: Dr Deborah Swallow
16

The London Film School
24 Shelton Street,
London WC2H 9UB
Tel: 020 7836 9642
Director: Ben Gibson
Fees: Day £0
16

The Lyceum
6 Paul Street, London EC2A 4JH
Tel: 020 7247 1588
Headteacher: Vanessa Bingham
Age range: 4–11
No. of pupils: 100
Fees: Day £16,185

The Method Studio London
Conway Hall, 25 Red Lion Square, London WC1R 4RL
Tel: 020 7831 7335
16

Urdang Academy
The Old Finsbury Town Hall, Rosebery Avenue,
London EC1R 4RP
Tel: 020 7713 7710
Principal: Stephanie Pope ARAD (dip PDTC)
Age range: 16+

Williams College
Thavies Inn House, 5 Holborn Circus, London EC1N 2HB
Tel: 020 7583 9222
Head: Mr Mujeeb Pathamanathan
16

East London

Al-Falah Primary School
48 Kenninghall Road,
Clapton, London E5 8BY
Tel: 020 8985 1059
Headteacher: Mr M A Hussain
Age range: 5–11
No. of pupils: 83
Fees: Day £7,200

Al-Mizan School
46 Whitechapel Road,
London E1 1JX
Tel: 020 7650 3070
Head: Mr Askor Ali
Age range: B7–11
No. of pupils: 200 VIth13
Fees: Day £3,400
🚹 Ⓐ 16

Alphabet House Day (Montessori) Nursery
Methodist Church, Windmill Lane, Stratford, London E15 1PG
Tel: 020 8519 2023
Principal: Ms Kemi Balogun

Alphabet House Nursery School
23 Harold Road, Upton Park, London E13 0SQ
Tel: 020 8548 9466
Principal: Ms Kemi Balogun

Ann Tayler Children's Centre
1-13 Triangle Road (off Westgate Street), Hackney, London E8 3RP
Tel: 020 7275 6022

Azhar Academy
235A Romford Road, Forest Gate, London E7 9HL
Tel: 020 8534 5959
Headteacher: Mrs R Rehman
Age range: G11–16
No. of pupils: 189

Beis Trana Girls' School
186 Upper Clapton Road, London E5 9DH
Tel: 020 8815 8003
Age range: G3–16
No. of pupils: 270

Bethnal Green Montessori School
68 Warner Place, Bethnal Green, London E2 7DA
Tel: 020 7739 4343
Head: Sidonie Winter
Age range: 2–6

Building Crafts College
Kennard Road, Stratford, London E15 1AH
Tel: 020 8522 1705
Principal: Mr John Taylor

Busy Bees at Chingford
2 Larkswood Leisure Park, 175 New Road, Chingford, London E4 9EY
Tel: 020 8524 7063
Nursery Manager: Natalie Keyes
Age range: 3 months–5 years

Busy Bees in London ExCel
5 Western Gateway, Royal Victoria Docks, London E16 1XL
Tel: 020 7474 7487
Nursery Manager: Rebecca Davy
Age range: 0–5

Chingford House School
22 Marlborough Road, Waltham Forest, London E4 9AL
Tel: 020 8527 2902; 07749 899 498
Head teacher: Helen McNulty
Age range: 0–5

City of London College
71 Whitechapel High Street, London E1 7PL
Tel: 020 7247 2166
Head: Mr David Nixon

East End Computing & Business College
149 Commercial Road, London E1 1PX
Tel: 020 7247 8447
Head: Anthony Wilkinson

East London College
Panther House, 647-661 High Road, London E11 4RD
Tel: 020 8539 2224

FARADAY SCHOOL
For further details see p. 60
Old Gate House, 7 Trinity Buoy Wharf, London E14 0JW
Tel: 020 8965 7374
Email: info@newmodelschool.co.uk
Website: www.faradayschool.co.uk
Head Teacher: Claire Murdoch
Age range: 4–11
No. of pupils: 105
Fees: Day £3,448

Forest Glade Nursery
15 Dyson Road, London E11 1NA
Tel: 020 8989 9684
Age range: 0–5

Forest School
College Place, Snaresbrook, London E17 3PY
Tel: 020 8520 1744
Warden: Mr Cliff Hodges
Age range: 4–18
No. of pupils: 1355 VIth260
Fees: Day £13,095–£18,681

Gatehouse School
Sewardstone Road, Victoria Park, London E2 9JG
Tel: 020 8980 2978
Acting Headmistress: Sevda Corby
Age range: 3–11
No. of pupils: 320
Fees: Day £11,610–£12,225

Grangewood Independent School
Chester Road, Forest Gate, London E7 8QT
Tel: 020 8472 3552
Headteacher: Mrs B A Roberts B.Ed (Hons); PG Cert (SEN)
Age range: 2–11
No. of pupils: 71
Fees: Day £5,157–£6,751.20

Happy Faces at Wisdom Kids Nursery
524 High Street, London E12 6QN
Tel: 020 8478 2805

Hyland House School
Holcombe Road, Tottenham, London N17 9AD
Tel: 020 8520 4186
Head Teacher: Mrs Gina Abbequaye
Age range: 3–11
Fees: Day £2,520

Independent Place Nursery
26/27 Independent Place, Shacklewell Lane, Hackney, London E8 2HD
Tel: 020 7275 7755
Head: Ms Dawn Pennington
Age range: 0–5
No. of pupils: 43

Kaye Rowe Nursery School
Osborne Road, London E7 0PH
Tel: 020 8534 4403

Kids Inc Day Nursery – Chingford
3 Friday Hill West, Chingford Hatch, London E4 6UP
Tel: 020 8524 6745

Kids Inc Day Nursery – South Woodford
71 Cleveland Road, South Woodford, London E18 2AE
Tel: 020 8518 8855
Manager: Sarah-Jane Smith NNEB
Age range: 3months–5

Lanterns Nursery and Pre-school
Unit D, Great Eastern Enterprise Centre, 3 Millharbour, London E14 9XP
Tel: 020 7363 0951

Little Green Man Nursery
15 Lemna Road, Waltham Forest, London E11 1HX
Tel: 020 8539 7228
Age range: 0–5
No. of pupils: 46

London East Academy
46-80 Whitechapel Road, London E1 1JX
Tel: 020 7650 3070
Headteacher: Musleh Faradhi
Age range: B11–18
No. of pupils: VIth18
Fees: Day £3,000

London School of Commerce & IT
128 Commercial Road, London E1 1NL
Tel: 020 7702 2509
Head: Dr Abul Kalam

Low Hall Nursery
Low Hall Lane, London E17 8BE
Tel: 020 8520 1689

Lubavitch House School (Junior Boys)
135 Clapton Common, London E5 9AE
Tel: 020 8800 1044
Head: Mr R Leach
Age range: B5–11
No. of pupils: 101

Madani Girls School
Myrdle Street, London E1 1HL
Tel: 020 7377 1992
Headteacher: Muhammad S. Rahman
Age range: G11–18
No. of pupils: 248 VIth11
Fees: Day £2,400

Magic Roundabout Nursery – Docklands
Jack Dash House, 2 Lawn House Close, Marsh Wall, London E14 9YQ
Tel: 020 7364 6028

Magic Roundabout Nursery – Walthamstow
161 Wadham Road, Centre Way, Walthamstow, London E17 4HU
Tel: 020 8523 5551

Market Nursery
Wilde Close, Off Pownall Road, Hackney, London E8 4JS
Tel: 020 7241 0978
Head: Ms Hazel Babb
No. of pupils: 24

Normanhurst School
68-74 Station Road, Chingford, London E4 7BA
Tel: 020 8529 4307
Headmistress: Mrs Claire Osborn
Age range: 2–16
No. of pupils: 250
Fees: Day £10,350–£13,050

Oliver Thomas Nursery School
Mathews Avenue, East Ham, London E6 6BU
Tel: 020 8552 1177
Head Teacher: Dianne Walls
Age range: 3–5

Paragon Christian Academy
233-241 Glyn Road, London E5 0JP
Tel: 020 8985 1119
Headteacher: Mrs Sharon Curry
Age range: 5–16
No. of pupils: 34

Pillar Box Montessori Nursery & Pre-Prep School
107 Bow Road, London E3 2AN
Tel: 020 8980 0700
Director: Lorraine Redknapp
Age range: 0–5
Fees: Day £12,000

PromisedLand Academy
St Cedds Hall, Webb Gardens, Plaistow, London E13 8SR
Tel: 0207 473 3229
Head: Mr A Coote
Age range: 4–16

Quwwat-ul Islam Girls School
16 Chaucer Road, Forest Gate, London E7 9NB
Tel: 020 8548 4736
Head of School: Shazia Member
Age range: G4–11
No. of pupils: 150

River House Montessori School
3-4 Shadwell Pierhead, Glamis Road, London E1W 3TD
Tel: 020 7538 9886
Headmistress: Miss S Greenwood
Age range: 3–16
Fees: Day £3,410–£3,625

Snaresbrook Preparatory School
75 Woodford Road, South Woodford, London E18 2EA
Tel: 020 8989 2394
Head of School: Mr Ralph Dalton
Age range: 3–11
Fees: Day £8,922–£11,934

St Joseph's Convent School For Girls
59 Cambridge Park, Wanstead, London E11 2PR
Tel: 020 8989 4700
Headteacher: Ms C Glover
Age range: G3–11
No. of pupils: 171
Fees: Day £6,780–£8,100

Talmud Torah Machikei Hadass School
96-98 Clapton Common, London E5 9AL
Tel: 020 8800 6599
Headteacher: Rabbi C Silbiger
Age range: B3–16
No. of pupils: 271

The Happy Nest Nursery Ltd
Fellows Court Family Centre, Weymouth Terrace, Hackney, London E2 8LR
Tel: 020 7739 3193

The Music School
59a High Street, Wanstead, London E11 2AE
Tel: 020 8502 0932

Tom Thumb Nursery
1-7 Beulah Road, London E17 9LG
Tel: 020 8520 1329
Age range: 2–5
No. of pupils: 32

Tree House Nursery & After School
35 Woodbine Place, London E11 2RH
Tel: 020 8532 2535

Whitechapel College
67 Maryland Square, Stratford, London E15 1HF
Tel: 020 8555 3355
Principal: Luke Julias Maughan-Pawsey

Winston House Preparatory School
140 High Road, London E18 2QS
Tel: 020 8505 6565
Head Teacher: Mrs Marian Kemp
Age range: 3–11

North London

5 E College of London
Selby Centre, Selby Road, London N17 8JL
Tel: 020 8885 3456/5454
Head: Mr Raj Doshi

Annemount School
18 Holne Chase, Hampstead Garden Suburb, London N2 0QN
Tel: 020 8455 2132
Principal: Mrs G Maidment BA(Hons), MontDip
Age range: 2–7
No. of pupils: 100
Fees: Day £3,275–£6,000

Asquith Nursery – Finsbury Park
Dulas Street, Finsbury Park, Islington, London N4 3AF
Tel: 020 7263 3090
Age range: 3 months–5

Asquith Nursery – Salcombe
33 The Green, Southgate, London N14 6EN
Tel: 020 8882 2136

Avenue Nursery & Pre-Preparatory School
2 Highgate Avenue, London N6 5RX
Tel: 020 8348 6815
Principal: Mrs. Mary Fysh
Age range: 2 1/2–7 1/2
No. of pupils: 79

Beis Chinuch Lebonos Girls School
Woodberry Down Centre, Woodberry Down, London N4 2SH
Tel: 020 88097 737
Headmistress: Mrs Leah Klein
Age range: G2–16
No. of pupils: 421

Beis Malka Girls School
93 Alkham Road, London N16 6XD
Tel: 020 8806 2070
Headmaster: M Dresdner
Age range: G5–16
No. of pupils: 339

Beis Rochel D'Satmar Girls School
51-57 Amhurst Park, London N16 5DL
Tel: 020 8800 9060
Headmistress: Mrs E Katz
Age range: G2–18
No. of pupils: 788

Bnois Jerusalem School
79-81 Amhurst Park, London N16 5DL
Tel: 020 8802 7470
Head: Mrs Sonnenschein
Age range: G3–16

Busy Bees at Enfield Highlands Village
2 Florey Square, Highlands Village, London N21 1UJ
Tel: 020 8360 6610
Nursery Manager: Simone Prince
Age range: 3 months–5 years

Busy Bees Nursery
c/o David Lloyd Leisure Club, Leisure Way, High Road, Finchley, London N12 0QZ
Tel: 020 8343 8500
Manager: Toni Difonzo
Age range: 3months–5
No. of pupils: 18

Channing School
The Bank, Highgate, London N6 5HF
Tel: 020 8340 2328
Head: Mrs B M Elliott
Age range: G4–18
No. of pupils: 746 VIth108
Fees: Day £17,610–£19,410

City of London Business College
Ebenezer House, 726-728 Seven Sisters Road, London N15 5NH
Tel: 020 8800 6621
Head: Mr Kwateng

Coconut Nursery
133 Stoke Newington Church Street, London N16 0UH
Tel: 020 7923 0720

Court Theatre Training Co
55 East Road, London N1 6AH
Tel: 020 7739 6868
Artistic Director: June Abbott

Dwight School London
6 Friern Barnet Lane, London N11 3LX
Tel: +44 (0)20 8920 0637
Head: Mrs Alison Cobbin BA, Dip Ed, MBA
Age range: 3–18

Finchley & Acton Yochien School
6 Hendon Avenue, Finchley, London N3 1UE
Tel: 020 8343 2191
Headteacher: J Tanabe
Age range: 2–6
No. of pupils: 145

Floral Place Day Nursery
2 Floral Place, Northampton Grove, London N1 2PL
Tel: 020 7354 9945

Grange Park Preparatory School
13 The Chine, Grange Park, Winchmore Hill, London N21 2EA
Tel: 020 8360 1469
Headteacher: Miss F Rizzo
Age range: G4–11
No. of pupils: 90
Fees: Day £10,300–£10,378

Greek Secondary School of London
Avenue Lodge, Bounds Green Road, London N22 7EU
Tel: 020 8881 9320
Headteacher: Georgia Dimitrakopoulou
Age range: 13–18
No. of pupils: 200

Hackney Care For Kids
61 Evering Road, Hackney, London N16 7PR
Tel: 020 7923 3471

Highgate
North Road, Highgate, London N6 4AY
Tel: 020 8340 1524
Head Master: Mr A S Pettitt MA
Age range: 3–18
No. of pupils: 1541 VIth312
Fees: Day £18,165–£20,970

Highgate Junior School
Cholmeley House, 3 Bishopswood Road, London N6 4PL
Tel: 020 8340 9193
Principal: Mr S M James BA
Age range: 7–11
Fees: Day £19,230

Highgate Pre-Preparatory School
7 Bishopswood Road, London N6 4PH
Tel: 020 8340 9196
Principal: Mrs Diane Hecht
Age range: 3–7
No. of pupils: 150
Fees: Day £18,165

Impact Factory
Suite 121, Business Design Centre, 52 Upper Street, London N1 0QH
Tel: 020 7226 1877
Founding Partners: Robin Chandler & Jo Ellen Grzyb

Keble Prep
Wades Hill, Winchmore
Hill, London N21 1BG
Tel: 020 8360 3359
Headmaster: Mr M J Mitchell
Age range: B4–13
No. of pupils: 228
Fees: Day £3,850–£4,930

Kerem House
18 Kingsley Way, London N2 0ER
Tel: 020 8455 7524
Headmistress: Mrs D Rose
Age range: 2–5
No. of pupils: 96
Fees: Day £2,025–£5,160

Kerem School
Norrice Lea, London N2 0RE
Tel: 020 8455 0909
Head Teacher: Miss Alyson Burns
Age range: 3–11
Fees: Day £9,435

Laurel Way Playgroup
Nansen Village, 21 Woodside
Avenue, London N12 8AQ
Tel: 020 8445 7514
Head: Mrs Susan Farber
Age range: 3–5

London Studio Centre
42-50 York Way, Kings
Cross, London N1 9AB
Tel: 020 7837 7741
Director & CEO: Mr Nic Espinosa
Age range: 18+

**Lubavitch House
School (Senior Girls)**
107-115 Stamford Hill,
Hackney, London N16 5RP
Tel: 020 8800 0022
Headmaster: Rabbi Shmuel Lew
FRSA
Age range: G11–18
No. of pupils: 102
Fees: Day £3,900

**Lubavitch Orthodox Jewish
Nursery – North London**
107-115 Stamford Hill,
Hackney, London N16 5RP
Tel: 020 8800 0022
Head: Mrs F Sudak

**MARS Montessori
Islington Green Nursery**
4 Collins Yard, Islington
Green, London N1 2XU
Tel: 020 7704 2805
Head: Angela Euesden
Age range: 2–5
No. of pupils: 24

**New Park Montessori
School**
67 Highbury New Park,
Islington, London N5 2EU
Tel: 020 7226 1109

Norfolk House School
10 Muswell Avenue, Muswell
Hill, London N10 2EG
Tel: 020 8883 4584
Head Teacher: Mr Paul Jowett
Age range: 4–11
No. of pupils: 130
Fees: Day £12,066

**North London
Grammar School**
110 Colindeep Lane, Hendon,
London NW9 6HB
Tel: 0208 205 0052
Head Teacher: Hakan Gokce
Age range: 11–18
No. of pupils: VIth20
Fees: Day £10,800–£13,500
FB £18,900–£21,600

**North London Rudolf
Steiner School**
1-3 The Campsbourne,
London N8 7PN
Tel: 020 8341 3770
Age range: 0–7
No. of pupils: 40

Palmers Green High School
Hoppers Road, Winchmore
Hill, London N21 3LJ
Tel: 020 8886 1135
Headmistress: Mrs Wendy Kempster
Age range: G3–16
No. of pupils: 300
Fees: Day £5,880–£15,930

**Pardes House
Grammar School**
Hendon Lane, Finchley,
London N3 1SA
Tel: 020 8349 4222
Headteacher: Rabbi Yitzchok Lev
Age range: B10–16
No. of pupils: 222

Pentland Day Nursery
224 Squires Lane, Finchley,
London N3 2QL
Tel: 020 8970 2441
Principal: Rachele Parker

Phoenix Academy
85 Bounces Road, Edmonton,
London N9 8LD
Tel: 020 8887 6888
Headteacher: Mr Paul Kelly
Age range: 5–18
No. of pupils: 19

**Phoenix Montessori
Nursery**
27 Stamford Hill, London N16 5TN
Tel: 020 8880 2550
Manageress: Kelly Murphy
Age range: 0–5 years

Rainbow Nursery
Yorkshire Grove Estate, 22-26
Nevill Road, London N16 8SP
Tel: 020 7254 7930
Age range: 3 months–5 years

**Rosemary Works
Independent School**
1 Branch Place, London N1 5PH
Tel: 020 7739 3950
Head: Rob Dell
Age range: 3–11
No. of pupils: 104
Fees: Day £14,097

**Salcombe Preparatory
School**
224-226 Chase Side,
Southgate, London N14 4PL
Tel: 020 8441 5356
Headmistress: Mrs Sarah-Jane
Davies BA(Hons) QTS MEd
Age range: 3–11
No. of pupils: 250
Fees: Day £11,673

Salcombe Pre-School
Green Road, Southgate,
London N14 4AD
Tel: 020 8441 5356
Headmistress: Mrs Sarah-Jane
Davies BA(Hons) QTS MEd

St Andrew's Montessori
St Andrew's Church, Thornhill
Square, London N1 1BQ
Tel: 020 7700 2961
Principal: Samantha Rawson
MontDip
Age range: 2–6
No. of pupils: 40
Fees: Day £4,200–£6,525

St Paul's Steiner School
1 St Paul's Road, Islington,
London N1 2QH
Tel: 020 7226 4454
College of Teachers: College of
Teachers
Age range: 2–14
No. of pupils: 136

**Sunrise Nursery,
Stoke Newington**
1 Cazenove Road, Stoke
Newington, Hackney,
London N16 6PA
Tel: 020 8806 6279
Principal: Didi Ananda Manika

Sunrise Primary School
55 Coniston Road, Tottenham,
London N17 0EX
Tel: 020 8806 6279 (Office); 020
8885 3354 (School)
Head: Mrs Mary-Anne Lovage
MontDipEd, BA
Age range: 2–11
No. of pupils: 30
Fees: Day £5,550

**Talmud Torah Bobov
Primary School**
87 Egerton Road, London N16 6UE
Tel: 020 8809 1025
Headmaster: Mr Chaim Weissman
Age range: B3–13
No. of pupils: 320

**Talmud Torah Chaim
Meirim School**
26 Lampard Grove, London N16 6XB
Tel: 020 8806 0017
Principal: Rabbi S Hoffman
Age range: B4–13

**Talmud Torah Yetev
Lev School**
111-115 Cazenove Road,
London N16 6AX
Tel: 020 8806 3834
Headteacher: Mr J Stauber
Age range: B2–11
No. of pupils: 567

Tawhid Boys School
21 Cazenove Road,
London N16 6PA
Tel: 020 8806 2999
Headteacher: Mr Usman Mapara
Age range: B10–15
No. of pupils: 115

Tayyibah Girls School
88 Filey Avenue, Stamford
Hill, London N16 6JJ
Tel: 020 8880 0085
Headmistress: Mrs N B Qureishi MSc
Age range: G5–18
No. of pupils: 270

**New Southgate Day
and Nursery School**
60 Beaconsfield Road, New
Soutgate, London N11 3AE
Tel: 0333 920 4841
Nursery Manager: Ms Katerina
Barotsaki
Age range: 3 months–5 years

**The Children's
House School**
77 Elmore Street, London N1 3AQ
Tel: 020 7354 2113
Head: Kate Orange
Age range: 2–4
No. of pupils: 73
Fees: Day £1,550–£1,675

**The Children's House
Upper School**
King Henry's Walk, London N1 4PB
Tel: 020 7249 6273
Headteacher: Kate Orange
Age range: 4–7
No. of pupils: 60
Fees: Day £14,730

The City College
University House, 55 East
Road, London N1 6AH
Tel: 020 7253 1133
Principal: A Andrews MCMI
Age range: 18–40
16+

The Dance Studio
2 Farm Road, Winchmore
Hill, London N21 3JA
Tel: 020 8360 5700
16+

**The Gower School
Montessori Nursery**
18 North Road, Islington,
London N7 9EY
Tel: 020 7700 2445
Principal: Miss Emma Gowers
Age range: 3 months–5 years
No. of pupils: 237

**The Gower School
Montessori Primary**
10 Cynthia Street, Barnsbury,
London N1 9JF
Tel: 020 7278 2020
Principal: Miss Emma Gowers
Age range: 4–11
No. of pupils: 237
Fees: Day £15,576

The Grove Nursery
Shepperton House, 83-
93 Shepperton Road,
Islington, London N1 3DF
Tel: 020 7226 4037
Owners: Ms Rebecca Browne & Ms
Elaine Catchpole
Age range: 0–5

**The Highgate
Activity Nurseries**
1 Church Road, Highgate,
London N6 4QH
Tel: 020 8348 9248
Head: Helena Prior
Age range: 2–5
Fees: Day £5,460–£9,620

The Sam Morris Nursery
Parkside Crescent, London N7 7JG
Tel: 020 7609 1735

TTTYY School
14 Heathland Road,
London N16 5NH
Tel: 020 8802 1348
Headmaster: Rabbi A Friesel
Age range: B2–13
No. of pupils: 187

Twinkle Stars Day Nursery
416 Seven Sisters Road,
Hackney, London N4 2LX
Tel: 020 8802 0550
Admin Officer: Noori Mohamed
Age range: 1–5

Vita et Pax School
Priory Close, Southgate,
London N14 4AT
Tel: 020 8449 8336
Headteacher: Miss Gillian
Chumbley
Age range: 3–11
Fees: Day £9,360

Woodberry Day Nursery
63 Church Hill, Winchmore
Hill, London N21 1LE
Tel: 020 8882 6917
Manager: Michelle Miller
Age range: 6 weeks–5
No. of pupils: 62

Yesodey Hatorah School
Egerton Road, London N16 6UB
Tel: 020 8826 5500
Headteacher: Rabbi Pinter
Age range: 3–16
No. of pupils: 920

North-West London

Abbey Nursery School
Cricklewood Baptist Church,
Sneyd Road, Cricklewood,
London NW2 6AN
Tel: 020 8208 2202
Head: Mrs Ruby Azam

Abercorn School
38 Portland Place, London NW8 9XP
Tel: 020 7286 4785
High Mistress: Mrs Andrea
Greystoke BA(Hons)
Age range: 2–13
No. of pupils: 360
Fees: Day £10,020–£20,055

**Al-Sadiq & Al-
Zahra Schools**
134 Salusbury Road,
London NW6 6PF
Tel: 020 7372 7706
Headteacher: Dr M Movahedi
Age range: 4–16
No. of pupils: 389

Arnold House School
1 Loudoun Road, St John's
Wood, London NW8 0LH
Tel: 020 7266 4840
Headmaster: Mr Vivian Thomas
Age range: B5–13
No. of pupils: 270
Fees: Day £6,100

**Asquith Nursery –
Golders Green**
212 Golders Green Road, Golders
Green, London NW11 9AT
Tel: 020 8458 7388
Age range: 1–5
No. of pupils: 68

Asquith Nursery – Hendon
46 Allington Road, Hendon,
London NW4 3DE
Tel: 020 8203 9020
Age range: 3 months–5

Asquith Nursery – Hill Park
5 Sunningfields Road,
Hendon, London NW4 4QR
Tel: 020 8201 5816
Age range: 3 months–5

**Asquith Nursery –
West Hampstead**
11 Woodchurch Road, West
Hampstead, London NW6 3PL
Tel: 020 7328 4787
Age range: 3 months–5

Barnet Hill Academy
10A Montagu Road, Hendon,
London NW4 3ES
Tel: 02034112660
Headteacher: Mr Shakil Ahmed
Age range: 3–11 G11–16
Fees: Day £3,000

**Beehive on Queens Park
Montessori School**
147 Chevening Rd London NW6 6DZ
Tel: 020 8969 2235
Age range: 2–5

Beis Soroh Schneirer
Arbiter House, Wilberforce
Road, London NW9 6AT
Tel: 020 8343 1190
Head: Mrs R Weiss
Age range: G2–11
No. of pupils: 150

**Belmont, Mill Hill
Preparatory School**
The Ridgeway, London NW7 4ED
Tel: 020 8906 7270
Headmaster: Mr Leon Roberts MA
Age range: 7–13
No. of pupils: 540
Fees: Day £18,099

**Beth Jacob Grammar
School for Girls**
Stratford Road, Hendon,
London NW4 2AT
Tel: 020 8203 4322
Headteacher: Mrs M Gluck
Age range: G11–17
No. of pupils: 264

Bluebells Nursery
Our Lady Help of Christians
Church Hall, Lady Margaret
Road, London NW5 2NE
Tel: 020 7284 3952
Principal: Ms Anita Pearson
Age range: 2–5
No. of pupils: 20

Brampton College
Lodge House, Lodge Road,
Hendon, London NW4 4DQ
Tel: 020 8203 5025
Principal: B Canetti BA(Hons), MSc
Age range: 15–20
Fees: Day £19,935
16+

**British American
Drama Academy**
14 Gloucester Gate,
London NW1 4HG
Tel: 020 7487 0730
Head: Paul Costello
16+

Broadhurst School
19 Greencroft Gardens,
London NW6 3LP
Tel: 020 7328 4280
Headmistress: Mrs Zoe Sylvester
Age range: 2–5
No. of pupils: 145
Fees: Day £6,480–£10,950

**Brondesbury
College for Boys**
8 Brondesbury Park,
London NW6 7BT
Tel: 020 8830 4522
Headteacher: Mr Amzad Ali
Age range: B11–16
No. of pupils: 93

Busy Bees at Mill Hill
30 Mill Way, Mill Hill,
London NW7 3RB
Tel: 0208 906 9123
Nursery Manager: Danielle Baker
Age range: 0–5

**Camden Community
Nurseries**
16 Acol Road, London NW6 3AG
Tel: 020 7624 2937

**Chaston Nursery & Pre-
preparatory School**
Chaston Place, Off Grafton
Terrace, London NW5 4JH
Tel: 020 7482 0701
Head: Mrs Sandra Witten DipEd,
DMS
Age range: 0–5
No. of pupils: 69
Fees: Day £7,020–£12,732

City Mission Nursery
2 Scrub Lane, London NW10 6RB
Tel: 0208 960 0838
Age range: 6 months–5

**College Francais
Bilingue De Londres**
87 Holmes Road, Kentish
Town, London NW5 3AX
Tel: +44 (0) 20 7993 7400
Principal: Mr François-Xavier Gabet
Age range: 5–15
No. of pupils: 210

DEVONSHIRE HOUSE PREPARATORY SCHOOL
For further details see p. 54
2 Arkwright Road, Hampstead, London NW3 6AE
Tel: 020 7435 1916
Email: enquiries@devonshire houseprepschool.co.uk
Website: www.devonshire houseschool.co.uk
Headmistress: Mrs S. Piper BA(Hons)
Age range: B2.5–13 G2.5–11
No. of pupils: 650
Fees: Day £10,125–£18,600
(£)

Fine Arts College, Hampstead
Centre Studios, 41-43 England's Lane, London NW3 4YD
Tel: 020 7586 0312
Head Teacher: Candida Cave MA
Age range: 13–19
No. of pupils: 210
Fees: Day £7,230
(16+) (A) (£) (16+)

Francis Holland School, Regent's Park, NW1
Clarence Gate, Ivor Place, Regent's Park, London NW1 6XR
Tel: 020 7723 0176
Head: Mr C B Fillingham MA (King's College London)
Age range: G11–18
No. of pupils: 495 VIth120
Fees: Day £19,260
(♦) (A) (£) (16+)

Golders Hill School
666 Finchley Road, London NW11 7NT
Tel: 020 8455 2589
Headmistress: Mrs A T Eglash BA(Hons)
Age range: 2–7
No. of pupils: 180
Fees: Day £1,575–£13,827

Goodwyn School
Hammers Lane, Mill Hill, London NW7 4DB
Tel: 020 8959 3756
Principal: Struan Robertson
Age range: 3–11
No. of pupils: 223
Fees: Day £5,120–£11,042

Grimsdell, Mill Hill Pre-Preparatory School
Winterstoke House, Wills Grove, Mill Hill, London NW7 1QR
Tel: 020 8959 6884
Head: Mrs Kate Simon BA, PGCE
Age range: 3–7
No. of pupils: 191
Fees: Day £14,895
(♦)

Hampstead Hill Pre-Prep & Nursery School
St Stephen's Hall, Pond Street, Hampstead, London NW3 2PP
Tel: 020 7435 6262
Principal: Mrs Andrea Taylor
Age range: B2–7+ G2–7+
Fees: Day £10,175–£16,830
(♦)

Heathside School
84-86 West Heath Road, London NW3 7UJ
Tel: +44 (0)20 3058 4011
Headteacher: Ms Melissa Remus MSc
Age range: 2–14
No. of pupils: 550
Fees: Day £15,000–£18,300
(♦) (♦)

Hendon Prep School
20 Tenterden Grove, Hendon, London NW4 1TD
Tel: 020 8203 7727
Head of School: Mr M. Lloyd-Williams
Age range: 2–13 years
No. of pupils: 165
Fees: Day £6,345–£14,175
(£) (♦)

Hereward House School
14 Strathray Gardens, London NW3 4NY
Tel: 020 7794 4820
Headmaster: Mr P Evans
Age range: B4–13
No. of pupils: 170
Fees: Day £15,615–£16,065
(♦)

Highgate Day Nursery and Preschool
Highgate Studios, 53-79 Highgate Road, London NW5 1TL
Tel: 020 7485 5252
Principal: Lorraine Thompson

Hill Park Pre-School
5 Sunningfields Road, Hendon, London NW4 4QR
Tel: 020 8201 5816
Age range: 1–5
No. of pupils: 92

International Community School
7B Wyndham Place, London NW1 4PT
Tel: +44 (0) 20 7298 8817
Head of School: Ms Rose Threlfall
Age range: 3–18
No. of pupils: 190
Fees: Day £19,400–£26,000
(♦) (IB) (♦) (16+)

Iranian School
100 Carlton Vale, London NW6 5HE
Tel: 020 7372 8051
Headteacher: Mr Seyed Abbas Hosseini
Age range: 6–16
No. of pupils: 53

Islamia Girls' High School
129 Salusbury Road, London NW6 6PE
Tel: 020 7372 3472
Headteacher: Mrs Fawziah Islam
Age range: G11–16 years
Fees: Day £6,900
(♦)

Joel Nursery
214 Colindeep Lane, Colindale, London NW9 6DF
Tel: 020 8200 0189
Age range: 2–5
(♦)

Kentish Town Day Nursery
37 Ryland Road, London NW5 3EH
Tel: 020 7284 3600
Manager: Carol Kewley
Age range: 3 months–5 years
No. of pupils: 55

Kentish Town Montessori School
34 Oakford Road, Kentish Town, London NW5 1AH
Tel: 020 7485 1056

Kindercare Montessori Nursery
Bridge Park Business Centre, Harrow Road, London NW10 0RG
Tel: 020 8838 1688
Age range: 2–5
Fees: Day £4,420

Lakefield Catering & Educational Centre
Maresfield Gardens, Hampstead, London NW3 5RY
Tel: 020 7794 5669
Course Director: Mrs Maria Brown
Age range: G16–24
No. of pupils: 16
Fees: FB £1,160
(♦) (16+) (♦) (£) (♦) (16+) (♦)

London Academy of Dressmaking and Design
18 Dobree Avenue, Willesden, London NW10 2AE
Tel: 020 8451 7174
Principal: Mrs P A Parkinson MA
Age range: 13+
Fees: Day £2,650
(16+) (♦) (16+) (♦)

LYNDHURST HOUSE PREP SCHOOL
For further details see p. 66
24 Lyndhurst Gardens, Hampstead, London NW3 5NW
Tel: 020 7435 4936
Email: office@ lyndhursthouse.co.uk
Website: www.lyndhursthouse.co.uk
Head of School: Mr Andrew Reid MA (Oxon)
Age range: B4–13
No. of pupils: 150
Fees: Day £6,190–£6,910
(♦) (♦)

MAPLE WALK SCHOOL
For further details see p. 67
62A Crownhill Road, London NW10 4EB
Tel: 020 8963 3890
Email: admin@ maplewalkschool.co.uk
Website: www.maplewalkschool.co.uk
Head Teacher: Mrs S Gillam
Age range: 4–11
No. of pupils: 200
Fees: Day £3,349
(£) (♦)

Maria Montessori Children's House – West Hampstead
St Mary's Community Hall, 134a Abbey Road, London NW6 4SN
Tel: 020 7624 5917

Maria Montessori Institute
26 Lyndhurst Gardens, Hampstead, London NW3 5NW
Tel: 020 7435 3646
Director of Training & School: Mrs Lynne Lawrence BA, Mont Int Dip(AMI)
Age range: 2–12
No. of pupils: 50
Fees: Day £5,580–£13,560
(16+)

Maria Montessori School – Hampstead
26 Lyndhurst Gardens, Hampstead, London NW3 5NW
Tel: +44 (0)20 7435 3646
Director of School: Miss L Kingston
Age range: 2–12
No. of pupils: 100
Fees: Day £6,270–£13,560

Mill Hill School
The Ridgeway, Mill Hill Village, London NW7 1QS
Tel: 020 8959 1176
Head: Mrs Jane Sanchez
Age range: 13–18
No. of pupils: 689 VIth259
Fees: Day £21,141 WB £28,524 FB £33,717
(♦) (A) (♦) (♦) (16+)

Naima Jewish Preparatory School
21 Andover Place, London NW6 5ED
Tel: 020 7328 2802
Headteacher: Mr Bill Pratt
Age range: 3–11
Fees: Day £7,605–£12,705
(£) (♦)

Nancy Reuben Primary School
Finchley Lane, Hendon, London NW4 1DJ
Tel: 020 82025646
Head: Anthony Wolfson
Age range: 3–11
No. of pupils: 207

Nicoll Road Nursery School
40 Nicoll Road, Harlesden,
London NW10 9AB
Tel: 020 8961 6648
Age range: 2–5
No. of pupils: 50

NORTH BRIDGE HOUSE NURSERY AND PRE-PREP SCHOOLS
8 Netherhall Gardens,
London NW3 5RR
Tel: 020 7428 1520
Head of School:
Mrs C McLelland
Age range: 2 years 9
months–7 years
No. of pupils: 380
Fees: Day £15,975–£16,575

NORTH BRIDGE HOUSE PREP SCHOOL REGENT'S PARK
1 Gloucester Avenue,
London NW1 7AB
Tel: 020 7428 1520
Head of School:
Mr James Stenning
Age range: 7–13 years
No. of pupils: 460
Fees: Day £18,195

NORTH BRIDGE HOUSE SENIOR CANONBURY
6-9 Canonbury Place,
Islington, London N1 2NQ
Tel: 020 7428 1520
Head of School: Mr J. Taylor
Age range: 11–18 years
No. of pupils: 180
Fees: Day £17,295–£18,555

NORTH BRIDGE HOUSE SENIOR HAMPSTEAD
For further details see p. 71
65 Rosslyn Hill, London NW3 5UD
Tel: 020 7428 1520
Email: admissionsenquiries@
northbridgehouse.com
Website:
www.northbridgehouse.com
Head of Senior Hampstead: Mr.
Brendan Pavey
Age range: 11–16 years
No. of pupils: 1375

NW5 Theatre School
14 Fortess Road, London NW5 2EU
Tel: 020 7482 3236
Founder: George O'Gorman
Age range: 16–30
Fees: Day £3,600

Octagon Nursery School
St Saviour's Church Hall, Eton
Road, London NW3 4SU
Tel: 020 7586 3206

Rainbow Montessori School
13 Woodchurch Road,
Hampstead, London NW6 3PL
Tel: 020 7328 8986
Head Mistress: Maggy Miller
MontDip
Age range: 5–12
Fees: Day £12,240–£12,417

Ready Steady Go – Camden
123 St Pancras Way,
London NW1 0SY
Tel: 020 7586 5862
Age range: 2–4

Ready Steady Go – Fitzroy Road
Primrose Hill Community Centre,
29 Hopkinson's Place, Fitzroy
Road, London NW1 8TN
Tel: 020 7586 5862
Age range: 2–3

Ready Steady Go – Primrose Hill
12a King Henry's Road,
London NW3 3RP
Tel: 020 7586 5862
Age range: 3–5

Ready Steady Go – St John's Wood
21 Alexandra Road,
London NW8 0DP
Tel: 020 7586 5862
Age range: 2–5

Saint Christina's School
25 St Edmunds Terrace, Regent's
Park, London NW8 7PY
Tel: 020 7722 8784
Headteacher: Miss J Finlayson
Age range: 3–11
No. of pupils: 224
Fees: Day £13,500

Sarum Hall
15 Eton Avenue, London NW3 3EL
Tel: 020 7794 2261
Headmistress: Mrs Christine Smith
Age range: G3–11
No. of pupils: 170
Fees: Day £14,025–£15,180

South Hampstead High School GDST
3 Maresfield Gardens,
London NW3 5SS
Tel: 020 7435 2899
Head of School: Mrs V Bingham
Age range: G4–18
No. of pupils: 900
Fees: Day £15,327–£18,654

Southbank International School – Hampstead
16 Netherhall Gardens,
London NW3 5TH
Tel: 020 7243 3803
Principal: Shirley Harwood
Age range: 3–11
No. of pupils: 210
Fees: Day £16,530–£25,740

St Anthony's School for Boys
90 Fitzjohn's Avenue, Hampstead,
London NW3 6NP
Tel: 020 7431 1066
Headmaster: Mr Paul Keyte
Age range: B4–13
No. of pupils: 310

St Christopher's School
32 Belsize Lane, Hampstead,
London NW3 5AE
Tel: 020 7435 1521
Head: Emma Crawford-Nash
Age range: G4–11
No. of pupils: 235
Fees: Day £14,700

ST JOHN'S WOOD PRE-PREPARATORY SCHOOL
For further details see p. 81
St Johns Hall, Lords Roundabout,
London NW8 7NE
Tel: 020 7722 7149
Email: info@sjwpre-prep.org.uk
Website:
www.sjwpre-prep.org.uk
Principal: Adrian Ellis
Age range: 3–7

St Margaret's School
18 Kidderpore Gardens,
Hampstead, London NW3 7SR
Tel: 020 7435 2439
Principal: Mr M Webster BSc, PGCE
Age range: G4–16
No. of pupils: 156
Fees: Day £12,591–£14,589

St Marks Square Nursery School
St Mark's Church, St Mark's
Square, Regents Park Road,
London NW1 7TN
Tel: +44 (0)20 7586 8383
Head: Dr Sheema Parsons B.Ed OBE
Age range: 2–6

St Martin's School
22 Goodwyn Avenue, Mill
Hill, London NW7 3RG
Tel: 020 8959 1965
Head: Dr Jason Walak
Age range: 3–11
No. of pupils: 90
Fees: Day £7,800

ST MARY'S SCHOOL HAMPSTEAD
For further details see p. 82
47 Fitzjohn's Avenue,
Hampstead, London NW3 6PG
Tel: 020 7435 1868
Email: office@stmh.co.uk
Website: www.stmh.co.uk
Head Teacher: Mrs Harriet
Connor-Earl
Age range: B2 years 9
months–7 years G2 years
9 months–11 years
No. of pupils: 300
Fees: Day £7,305–£13,500

St Nicholas School
22 Salmon Street, London NW9 8PN
Tel: 020 8205 7153
Headmaster: Mr Matt Donaldson
BA (Hons), PGCE, PGDip (Surv)
Age range: 3 months–11
No. of pupils: 80
Fees: Day £8,550–£8,850

Sue Nieto Theatre School
19 Parkside, London NW7 2LJ
Tel: 020 8201 1500
Principal: Sue Nieto
Age range: 3–18

The Academy School
3 Pilgrims Place, Rosslyn Hill,
Hampstead, London NW3 1NG
Tel: 020 7435 6621
Headteacher: Mr Garth Evans
Age range: 6–14

The American School in London
One Waverley Place,
London NW8 0NP
Tel: 020 7449 1221
Head: Robin Appleby
Age range: 4–18
No. of pupils: 1350
Fees: Day £27,050–£31,200

The Beehive Montessori on Queen's Park
147 Chevening Road,
London NW6 6DZ
Tel: 020 8969 2235
Age range: 2–5
Fees: Day £3,900–£4,300

The Cavendish School
31 Inverness Street, Camden
Town, London NW1 7HB
Tel: 020 7485 1958
Headmistress: Miss Jane Rogers
Age range: G3–11
No. of pupils: 260
Fees: Day £14,700

The Childrens Centre
Christ Church, St Albans
Road, London NW10 8UG
Tel: 020 8961 9250
Head: Denise Lepore
Age range: 18 months–5
No. of pupils: 25

The Hall School
23 Crossfield Road, Hampstead,
London NW3 4NU
Tel: 020 7722 1700
Headmaster: Mr Chris Godwin
Age range: B4–13
No. of pupils: 440
Fees: Day £17,940–£18,486

The Interior Design School
22 Lonsdale Road, Queens
Park, London NW6 6RD
Tel: 020 7372 2811
Principal: Ms Iris Dunbar

The King Alfred School
Manor Wood, North End
Road, London NW11 7HY
Tel: 020 8457 5200
Head: Robert Lobatto MA (Oxon)
Age range: 4–18
No. of pupils: 650 VIth100
Fees: Day £15,531–£18,723

The Mount, Mill Hill International
Milespit Hill, London NW7 2RX
Tel: +44 (0)20 3826 33
Head of School: Ms Sarah Bellotti
Age range: 13–17
No. of pupils: 68
Fees: Day £24,990 WB
£34,461 FB £40,539

The Mulberry House School
7 Minster Road, West
Hampstead, London NW2 3SD
Tel: 020 8452 7340
Headteacher: Ms Victoria Playford
Age range: 2–8
No. of pupils: 184

The Oak Tree Nursery
2 Arkwright Road, Hampstead,
London NW3 6AD
Tel: 020 7435 1916
Head: Mrs S Alexander
Age range: 2–3
Fees: Day £4,650

The Village School
2 Parkhill Road, Belsize
Park, London NW3 2YN
Tel: 020 7485 4673
Headmistress: Miss C E F Gay
BSc(Hons), PGCE
Age range: G3–11
No. of pupils: 106
Fees: Day £15,525

Theatretrain
69 Great North Way,
London NW4 1HS
Tel: 020 8202 2006
Director: Kevin Dowsett CertEd,
AdvDip(Drama in Education)
Age range: 6–18

Toddlers Inn Nursery School
Cicely Davies Hall, Cochrane
Street, London NW8 7NX
Tel: 020 7586 0520
Principal: Ms Laura McCole

Torah Vodaas
Julian Headon House,
West Hendon Broadway,
London NW9 7AL
Tel: 02036704670
Head of School: Rabbi S Klor
Age range: B2–11

Trevor-Roberts School
55-57 Eton Avenue,
London NW3 3ET
Tel: 020 7586 1444
Headmaster: Simon Trevor-Roberts
BA
Age range: 5–13
Fees: Day £14,700–£16,200

UCS Pre-Prep
36 College Crescent,
London NW3 5LF
Tel: 020 7722 4433
Headmistress: Dr Zoe Dunn
Age range: B4–7
No. of pupils: 100

University College School
Frognal, Hampstead,
London NW3 6XH
Tel: 020 7435 2215
Headmaster: Mr Mark J Beard MA,
MEd
Age range: B11–18 G16–18
No. of pupils: 875 VIth309
Fees: Day £20,328

University College School (Junior)
11 Holly Hill, London NW3 6QN
Tel: 020 7435 3068
Headmaster: Mr Lewis Hayward
MA (Oxon Lit. Hum), MA (OU, ED.
Management), PGCE
Age range: B7–11
No. of pupils: 250
Fees: Day £18,789

Wentworth College
6-10 Brentmead Place,
London NW11 9LH
Tel: 020 8458 8524/5
Principal: Manuel Guimaraes
Age range: 14–19
No. of pupils: 115

York Rise Nursery
St Mary Brookfield Hall, York
Rise, London NW5 1SB
Tel: 020 7485 7962
Headmistress: Miss Becca Coles
Age range: 2–5

South-East London

ABC Childrens Centre
48 Chapel Rd, West Norwood,
London SE27 0UR
Tel: 020 8766 0246
Principal: Ms E Carr

Alleyn's School
Townley Road, Dulwich,
London SE22 8SU
Tel: 020 8557 1500
Headmaster: Dr G Savage MA,
PhD, FRSA
Age range: 4–18
No. of pupils: 1252 VIth302
Fees: Day £17,361–£19,851

Alpha Meridian Colleges
Meridian House, Greenwich High
Road, Greenwich, London SE10 8TL
Tel: 020 8853 4111
Head: Mr Kudsi Tuluoglu

Anerley Montessori Nursery
45 Anerley Park, London SE20 8NQ
Tel: 020 8778 2810
Headmistress: Mrs P Bhatia
Age range: 3 months–5
Fees: Day £2,750–£4,600

Asquith Nursery – Elizabeth Terrace
18-22 Elizabeth Terrace,
Eltham, London SE9 5DR
Tel: 020 8294 0377
Age range: 3 months–5

Asquith Nursery – New Eltham
699 Sidcup Road, New
Eltham, London SE9 3AQ
Tel: 020 8851 5057
Age range: 3 months–5

Asquith Nursery – Peckham Rye
24 Waveney Avenue, Peckham
Rye, London SE15 3UE
Tel: 020 7635 5501
Age range: 4 months–5

Asquith Nursery – West Dulwich
Old Church, 226c Gipsy Road,
West Dulwich, London SE27 9RB
Tel: 0330 134 7934
Age range: 3 months–5

Bellenden Day Nursery
Faith Chapel, 198 Bellenden
Road, London SE15 4BW
Tel: 020 7639 4896
Manager: Jason Cranston

Bellerbys College London
Bounty House, Greenwich,
London SE8 3DE
Tel: +44 (0)208 694 7000
Principal: Ms Alison Baines
Age range: 15–19

Blackheath Day Nursery
The Rectory Field, Charlton,
London SE3 8SR
Tel: 020 8305 2526
Headmistress: Mrs Shipley
Age range: 0–5
No. of pupils: 61

Blackheath High School GDST
Vanbrugh Park, Blackheath,
London SE3 7AG
Tel: 020 8853 2929
Head: Mrs Carol Chandler-
Thompson BA (Hons) Exeter, PGCE
Exeter
Age range: G3–18
No. of pupils: 780

Blackheath Montessori Centre
Independents Road,
Blackheath, London SE3 9LF
Tel: 020 8852 6765
Headmistress: Mrs Jane Skillen
MontDip
Age range: 3–5
No. of pupils: 36

Blackheath Preparatory School
4 St Germans Place,
Blackheath, London SE3 0NJ
Tel: 020 8858 0692
Headmistress: Mrs P J Thompson
Age range: 3–11
No. of pupils: 390
Fees: Day £7,740–£12,930

Blake Hall College
10-11 Dock Offices, Surrey Quays
Road, London SE16 2XU
Tel: 020 7252 2033
Head: Mr Brink Gardner

Bright Horizons at Tabard Square
10-12 Empire Square, Tabard
Street, London SE1 4NA
Tel: 020 7407 2068

Broadfields Day Nursery
96 Broadfields Road, Catford,
London SE6 1NG
Tel: 020 8697 1488
Head: Elainne Dalton
Age range: 4 months–5

Clive Hall Day Nursery
rear of 54 Clive Road,
London SE21 8BY
Tel: 020 8761 9000

Colfe's Junior School
Horn Park Lane, Lee,
London SE12 8AW
Tel: 020 8463 8240
Head: Ms C Macleod
Age range: 3–11
No. of pupils: 355
Fees: Day £13,230–£13,995

Colfe's School
Horn Park Lane, Lee,
London SE12 8AW
Tel: 020 8852 2283
Head: Mr R F Russell MA(Cantab)
Age range: 3–18
No. of pupils: 1120

DLD COLLEGE LONDON
For further details see p. 55
199 Westminster Bridge
Road, London SE1 7FX
Tel: +44 (0)20 7935 8411
Email: dld@dld.org
Website: www.dldcollege.co.uk
Principal: Irfan H Latif BSc (Hons)
PGCE FRSA FRSC
No. of pupils: 426
Fees: Day £23,500–£29,950
FB £18,000–£28,000

Dulwich College
London SE21 7LD
Tel: 020 8693 3601
Master: Dr J A F Spence
Age range: B0–18
No. of pupils: 1589 VIth470
Fees: Day £20,448 WB
£40,017 FB £42,681

Dulwich College Kindergarten & Infants School
Eller Bank, 87 College
Road, London SE21 7HH
Tel: 020 8693 1538
Head: Mrs Nicky Black
Age range: 3 months–7 years
No. of pupils: 251

Dulwich Nursery
adj Sainsbury's Dulwich Store, 80
Dog Kennel Hill, London SE22 8DB
Tel: 020 7738 4007
Principal: Amanda Shead

Dulwich Prep London
42 Alleyn Park, Dulwich,
London SE21 7AA
Tel: 020 8766 5500
Headmaster: Mr M W Roulston
MBE, MEd
Age range: B3–13 G3–5
No. of pupils: 817
Fees: Day £13,074–£19,314

ELTHAM COLLEGE
For further details see p. 58
Grove Park Road, Mottingham,
London SE9 4QF
Tel: 0208 857 1455
Email: mail@eltham-
college.org.uk
Website:
www.elthamcollege.london
Headmaster: Guy Sanderson
Age range: 7–18
No. of pupils: 907 VIth194

Eltham Green Day Nursery
5 Lionel Road, Eltham,
London SE9 6DQ
Tel: 0800 085 4074
Age range: 3months–5
No. of pupils: 30

First Steps Montessori Day Nursery & Pre School
254 Upland Road, East
Dulwich, London SE22 0DN
Tel: 020 8299 6897
Principal: Karime Dinkha
Age range: 2–5
No. of pupils: 43

Five Steps Community Nursery
15 Lambourne Grove,
Rotherhithe, London SE16 2RR
Tel: 020 7237 2376

GSM London
Meridian House, Royal Hill,
Greenwich, London SE10 8RD
Tel: 020 8516 7800
Head: Dr W G Hunt

Greenwich Steiner School
Woodlands, 90 Mycenae Road,
Blackheath, London SE3 7SE
Tel: 020 8858 4404
Head of School: Mr Adrian Dow
Age range: 3–14
No. of pupils: 180
Fees: Day £7,310–£8,100

Half Moon Montessori Nursery
Methodist Church Hall, 155 Half
Moon Lane, London SE24 9HU
Tel: 020 7326 5300
Age range: 2–5
No. of pupils: 65

Heath House Preparatory School
37 Wemyss Road, Blackheath,
London SE3 0TG
Tel: 020 8297 1900
Head Teacher: Mrs Sophia Laslett
CertEd PGDE
Age range: 3–11
No. of pupils: 125
Fees: Day £13,485–£14,985

Herne Hill School
The Old Vicarage, 127 Herne
Hill, London SE24 9LY
Tel: 020 7274 6336
Headteacher: Mrs Ngaire Telford
Age range: 2–7
No. of pupils: 296
Fees: Day £6,225–£14,955

Hillyfields Day Nursery
41 Harcourt Road, Brockley,
London SE4 2AJ
Tel: 020 8694 1069
Head: Ms Lisa Reeves

James Allen's Girls' School
144 East Dulwich Grove,
Dulwich, London SE22 8TE
Tel: 020 8693 1181
Head of School: Mrs Sally-Anne
Huang MA, MSc
Age range: G4–18
No. of pupils: 1075

Kings Kids Christian School
Woodpecker Road, New
Cross, London SE14 6EU
Tel: 020 8691 5813
Headteacher: Mrs M Okenwa
Age range: 5–11
No. of pupils: 36

Lingfield Day Nursery (Blackheath)
37 Kidbrooke Grove,
Kidbrooke, London SE3 0LJ
Tel: 020 8858 1388
Manager: Sophie Campbell
Age range: 18 months–5
No. of pupils: 30
Fees: Day £9,350

Lingfield Day Nursery (Grove Park)
155 Baring Road, London SE12 0LA
Tel: 020 8851 7800
Manager: Samantha Goodwright
Age range: 18 months–5
No. of pupils: 30
Fees: Day £8,700

Little Cherubs Day Nursery
2a Bell Green Lane,
London SE26 5TB
Tel: 020 8778 3232

Lollipops Child Care Ltd
88 Southwood Road,
London SE9 3QT
Tel: 020 8859 5832
Principal: Miss L Thompson

London Bridge Business Academy
7-13 Melior Street, London SE1 3QP
Tel: 020 7378 1000
Head: Shmina Mandal

London Christian School
40 Tabard Street, London SE1 4JU
Tel: 020 3130 6430
Headmistress: Miss N Collett-White
Age range: 3–11
No. of pupils: 105
Fees: Day £9,390

Magic Roundabout Nursery – Kennington
35 Sutherland House, Sutherland
Square, London SE17 3EE
Tel: 020 7277 3643

Marathon Science School
1-9 Evelyn Street, Surrey
Quays, London SE8 5RQ
Tel: +44 (0)20 7231 3232
Headteacher: Mr Uzeyir Onur
Age range: B11–16
No. of pupils: 67

Maritime Greenwich College
4th Floor, Royal Sovereign House, 40
Beresford Street, London SE18 6BF
Tel: 0208 305 8508
Head: Mr N Kandel

McAlpine Dance Studio
Longfield Hall, 50 Knatchbull
Road, London SE5 9QY
Tel: 020 8673 4992

Mother Goose Nursery
248 Upland Road, East
Dulwich, London SE22 0NU
Tel: 020 8693 9429
Age range: 1–5

Mother Goose Nursery
34 Waveney Avenue,
Nunhead, London SE15 3UE
Tel: 020 7277 5951
Age range: 1–5

Mother Goose Nursery
The Pavilion, 65 Greendale Fields,
off Wanley Road, London SE5 8JZ
Tel: 020 7738 7700
Age range: 0–5

Mother Goose Nursery (Head Office)
133 Brookbank Road,
Lewisham, London SE13 7DA
Tel: 020 8694 8700
Age range: 1–5

Nell Gwynn Nursery
Meeting House Lane,
London SE15 2TT
Tel: 020 7252 8265

Oakfield Preparatory School
125-128 Thurlow Park Road, West
Dulwich, London SE21 8HP
Tel: 020 8670 4206
Head of School: Mr Patrick Gush
Age range: 2–11 years
No. of pupils: 420
Fees: Day £10,785

Octavia House School, Kennington
214b Kennington Road,
London SE11 6AU
Tel: 020 3651 4396 (Option:3)
Executive Head: Mr James Waite

Octavia House School, Vauxhall
Vauxhall Primary School, Vauxhall Street, London SE11 5LG
Tel: 02036 514396 (Option:1)
Executive Head: Mr James Waite
Age range: 5–14
No. of pupils: 65

Octavia House School, Walworth
Larcom House, Larcom Street, London SE17 1RT
Tel: 02036 514396 (Option:2)
Executive Head: Mr James Waite

One World Day Nursery
11 Thurlby Road, London SE27 0RN
Tel: 020 8761 3308

Riverston School
63-69 Eltham Road, Lee Green, London SE12 8UF
Tel: 020 8318 4327
Headmistress: Mrs S E Salathiel
Age range: 9 months–19 years
No. of pupils: 215
£ ✏ 16+ ❀

Rosemead Preparatory School & Nursery, Dulwich
70 Thurlow Park Road, London SE21 8HZ
Tel: 020 8670 5865
Headmaster: Mr Phil Soutar
Age range: 2–11
No. of pupils: 366
Fees: Day £10,272–£11,286
£ ✏

Skallywags Nursery
St Crispin Hall, Southwark Park Road, Rotherhithe, London SE16 2HU
Tel: 020 7252 3225
Headmistress: Miss Allison Armstrong NVQ
Age range: 3 months–5 years

St Dunstan's College
Stanstead Road, London SE6 4TY
Tel: 020 8516 7200
Headmaster: Mr Nicholas Hewlett
Age range: 3–18
No. of pupils: 870
🌐 Ⓐ £ 16+

St Olave's Preparatory School
106 Southwood Road, New Eltham, London SE9 3QS
Tel: 020 8294 8930
Headteacher: Miss Claire Holloway BEd, QTS
Age range: 3–11
No. of pupils: 220
Fees: Day £10,848–£12,300
✏

St. Patrick's Montessori Day Nursery
91 Cornwall Road, London SE1 8TH
Tel: 020 7928 5557

Sydenham High School GDST
19 Westwood Hill, London SE26 6BL
Tel: 020 8557 7000
Headmistress: Mrs Katharine Woodcock
Age range: G4–18
No. of pupils: 600 VIth70
Fees: Day £13,161–£16,737
👥 Ⓐ £ 16+

East Greenwich Day Nursery and Preschool
Chavening Road, Greenwich, London SE10 0LB
Tel: 0333 305 3679
Nursery Manager: Ms Loraine Thorpe
Age range: 3 months–5 years

West Dulwich Day Nursery and Pre-School
Old Church, 226c Gipsy Road, London SE27 9RB
Tel: 0333 122 1189
Nursery Manager: Ms Nazmin Uddin
Age range: 3 months–5 years

The Oak Tree Nursery
Tell Grove, Southwark, London SE22 8RH
Tel: 020 8693 0306
✏

The Pavilion Nursery
Catford Cricket Club Pavilion, Penerley Road, London SE6 2LQ
Tel: 020 8698 0878
Head: Mrs Karen Weller
Age range: 2–5
✏

The Pointer School
19 Stratheden Road, Blackheath, London SE3 7TH
Tel: 020 8293 1331
Headmaster: Mr R J S Higgins MA, BEd, CertEd, FCollP
Age range: 3–11
No. of pupils: 370
Fees: Day £11,415–£13,449
£ ✏

The Villa Pre-Preparatory School & Nursery
54 Lyndhurst Grove, Peckham, London SE15 5AH
Tel: 020 7703 6216
Head Teacher: Emma Champion
Age range: 2–7
No. of pupils: 210

The Village Montessori
Kingswood Hall, Kingswood Place, London SE13 5BU
Tel: 020 8318 6720
Director: Catherine Westlake MontDip
Age range: 3–5
Fees: Day £1,491

The Village Nursery
St Mary's Centre, 180 Ladywell Road, Lewisham, London SE13 7HU
Tel: 020 8690 6766
Principal: Frances Rogers

Toad Hall Montessori Nursery School
37 St Mary's Gardens, Kennington, London SE11 4UF
Tel: 020 7735 5087
Principal: Mrs V K Rees NNEB, MontDip
Age range: 2–5
No. of pupils: 40
Fees: Day £6,300

Trinity Child Care
Holy Trinity Church Hall, Bryan Road, London SE16 5HF
Tel: 020 7231 5842
Manager: Sharron Williams
Age range: 2–5
No. of pupils: 60
Fees: Day £6,240

Willow Park
19 Glenlyon Road, Eltham, London SE9 1AL
Tel: 020 8850 8753
Principal: Mrs McMahon

South-West London

345 Nursery School
Fitzhugh Community Clubroom, Fitzhugh Grove, Trinity Road, London SW18 3SA
Tel: 020 8870 8441
Principal: Mrs Annabel Dixon
Age range: 3–5
No. of pupils: 42
Fees: Day £3,555
✏

ABACUS Early Learning Nursery School – Balham Day Nursery
135 Laitwood Road, Balham, London SW12 9QH
Tel: 020 8675 8093

ABACUS Early Learning Nursery School – Stretham Day Nursery
7 Drewstead Road, Streatham Hill, London SW16 1LY
Tel: 020 8677 9117
Principals: Mrs M Taylor BEd & Ms S Petgrave
Age range: 12 mths–5 years
No. of pupils: 40

Academy of Live & Recorded Arts
Studio1, Royal Victoria Patriotic Building, John Archer Way, London SW18 3SX
Tel: 020 8870 6475
Principal: Anthony Castro
Age range: 18+
No. of pupils: 108
Fees: Day £3,000–£9,888
16+ £ ✏

Al-Muntada Islamic School
7 Bridges Place, Parsons Green, London SW6 4HW
Tel: 020 7471 8283
Headteacher: Amjad Malik
Age range: 4–11
No. of pupils: 165
Fees: Day £3,000–£7,000

Alphabet Nursery School
Chatham Hall, Northcote Road, Battersea, London SW11 6DY
Tel: 020 8871 7473
Principal: Mrs A McKenzie-Lewis
No. of pupils: 40
Fees: Day £1,500–£1,800

Al-Risalah Nursery
10A Gatton Road, Tooting, London SW17 0EE
Tel: 020 8767 0716
Head of School: Nasir Qurashi

Al-Risalah Secondary School
145 Upper Tooting Road, London SW17 7TJ
Tel: 020 8767 6057
Headteacher: Suhayl Lee
Age range: 3–16
No. of pupils: 250

Asquith Nursery – Balham
36 Radbourne Road, Balham, London SW12 0EF
Tel: 020 8673 1405

Asquith Nursery – Battersea
18/30 Latchmere Road, Battersea, London SW11 2DX
Tel: 020 7228 7008
Age range: 3 months–5

Asquith Nursery – Putney
107-109 Norroy Road, Putney, London SW15 1PH
Tel: 020 8246 5611
Age range: 3 months–5

Asquith Nursery – Raynes Park
c/o David Lloyd Leisure Club, Bushey Road, Raynes Park, London SW20 8DE
Tel: 020 8543 9005
Age range: 3 months–5

Battersea Pre-School & Nursery
Riverlight, Nine Elms Lane, Kirtling Street, Battersea, London SW8 5BP
Tel: 020 7720 9336

Beechwood School
55 Leigham Court Road, Streatham, London SW16 2NJ
Tel: 020 8677 8778
Nursery Director: Ms Bamwo
Age range: 0–5
No. of pupils: 100

Beehive Nursery School
St Margarets Church Hall, Putney
Park Lane, London SW15 5HU
Tel: 020 8780 5333
Headmistress: Lindsay Deans
Age range: 2–5
No. of pupils: 16
Fees: Day £1,140

Bees Knees Nursery School
within Brookside Community Hall,
12 Priory Lane, London SW15 5JL
Tel: 020 8876 8252
Headmistress: Jo Wood
Age range: 2–5

Bertrum House Nursery
290 Balham High Road,
London SW17 7AL
Tel: 020 8767 4051
Headteacher: Miss Vicky
Age range: 2–5
No. of pupils: 94
Fees: Day £1,775–£2,140

Bobby's Playhouse
16 Lettice Street, London SW6 4EH
Tel: 020 7384 1190
Principal: Mrs Emma Hannay
Age range: 3 months–5 years
Fees: Day £11,000

BROOMWOOD HALL
For further details see p. 52
68-74 Nightingale Lane,
London SW12 8NR
Tel: 020 8682 8810
Email: admissions@
northwoodschools.com
Website:
www.northwoodschools.com
Headmistress: Carole Jenkinson
Age range: B4–8 G4–13
No. of pupils: 620
Fees: Day £5,375–£6,595

Busy Bee Nursery School
19 Lytton Grove, Putney,
London SW15 2EZ
Tel: 020 8789 0132
Headmistress: Dr Sally Corbett
Age range: 2–5

Cameron House
4 The Vale, Chelsea,
London SW3 6AH
Tel: 020 7352 4040
Headmistress: Mrs Dina Mallett
Age range: 4–11
Fees: Day £18,465

Carmena Christian Day Nurseries
47 Thrale Road, Streatham,
London SW16 1NT
Tel: 020 8677 8231
Head: Mrs S Allen

Centre Academy London
92 St John's Hill, Battersea,
London SW11 1SH
Tel: 020 7738 2344
Headteacher: Rachel Maddison
Age range: 9–19
Fees: Day £27,600–£40,100

Chelsea Independent College
517-523 Fulham Road,
London SW6 1HD
Tel: +44 (0) 20 7610 1114
Principal: Dr Martin Meenagh
Age range: 14–19
No. of pupils: 164

Chelsea Pre-Prep
St Andrews Church, Park Walk,
Chelsea, London SW10 0AU
Tel: 020 7352 4856
Headmistress: Miss Lulu Tindall
MontDip
Age range: 2–5
Fees: Day £3,900–£6,120

Clapham Day Nursery
3 Peardon Street, London SW8 3BW
Tel: 020 7498 3165
Manager: Nicolette Warnes NNEB,
NVQ4
Age range: 3 months–5
No. of pupils: 72

Clapham Montessori
St Paul's Community Centre,
St Paul's Church, Rectory
Grove, London SW4 0DX
Tel: 020 7498 8324
Head: Mrs R Bowles BSc, IntMontDip
Age range: 2–5

Clapham Park Montessori
St James' Church House, 10 West
Road, Clapham, London SW4 7DN
Tel: 020 7627 0352
Head: Mrs R Bowles BSc, IntMontDip
Age range: 2–5

Collingham
23 Collingham Gardens,
London SW5 0HL
Tel: 020 7244 7414
Principal: Sally Powell
Age range: 14–19
No. of pupils: VIth200
Fees: Day £4,260–£22,560

Cresset Kindergarten
The Waldorf School of South
West London, 12 Ballam Park
Road, London SW12 8DR
Tel: 020 8673 4881
Principal: Pat Hague

Crown Kindergartens
Coronation House, Ashcombe
Road, Wimbledon,
London SW19 8JP
Tel: 020 8540 8820
Principal: Mrs Acres
Age range: 1–5
No. of pupils: 28

Dawmouse Montessori Nursery School
34 Haldane Road, Fulham,
London SW6 7EU
Tel: 020 7381 9385
Principal: Mrs Emma V Woodcock
NNEB, MontDip
Age range: 2–5
No. of pupils: 72

Dolphin School
106 Northcote Road,
London SW11 6QW
Tel: 020 7924 3472
Principal: Mrs. N. Baldwin
Age range: 2–11
No. of pupils: 292
Fees: Day £12,270–£13,485

Donhead
33 Edge Hill, London SW19 4NP
Tel: 020 8946 7000
Headmaster: Mr P J J Barr
Age range: B4–11
No. of pupils: 280
Fees: Day £11,175–£11,622

Eaton House Belgravia
3-5 Eaton Gate, London SW1W 9BA
Tel: 020 7924 6000
Head of School: Mr Huw May
Age range: B3–11
Fees: Day £17,850–£20,700

Eaton House The Manor
58 Clapham Common
Northside, London SW4 9RU
Tel: 020 7924 6000
Head: Mr Oliver Snowball
Age range: G4–11
Fees: Day £16,143

Eaton House The Manor Pre Prep and Nursery
58 Clapham Common
Northside, London SW4 9RU
Tel: 020 7924 6000
Head of School: Mrs Nicola
Borthwick
Age range: B3.5–8
Fees: Day £16,143

Eaton House The Manor Prep School
58 Clapham Common
Northside, London SW4 9RU
Tel: 020 7924 6000
Head: Mrs Sarah Segrave
Age range: B8–13
Fees: Day £19,743

Eaton Square Nursery School Pimlico
32a Lupus Street, London SW1V 3DZ
Age range: 2–5

Eaton Square School
79 Eccleston Square,
London SW1V 1PP
Tel: 020 7931 9469
Headmaster: Mr Sebastian Hepher
BEd(Hons)
Age range: 2–13
No. of pupils: 529
Fees: Day £20,850–£21,900

Ecole Charles De Gaulle – Wix
Clapham Common North
Side, London SW4 0AJ
Tel: +44 20 7738 0287
Headteacher: Mr Blanchard
Age range: 5–11
No. of pupils: 100

Ecole Marie D'Orliac
60 Clancarty Road,
London SW6 3AA
Tel: +44 7736 020 58 63
Principal: Mr Olivier Rauch
Age range: 4–11
No. of pupils: 50

Elm Park Nursery School
90 Clarence Avenue,
Clapham, London SW4 8JR
Tel: 020 8678 1990
Head: Ms Jacqueline Brooks
No. of pupils: 113

Emanuel School
Battersea Rise, London SW11 1HS
Tel: 020 8870 4171
Headmaster: Mr Robert Milne
Age range: 10–18
No. of pupils: 930
Fees: Day £18,372

Eveline Day & Nursery Schools
14 Trinity Crescent, Upper
Tooting, London SW17 7AE
Tel: 020 8672 4673
Headmistress: Ms Eveline Drut
Age range: 3 months–11 years
No. of pupils: 80
Fees: Day £13,859

Falkner House
19 Brechin Place, South
Kensington, London SW7 4QB
Tel: 020 7373 4501
Headteacher: Mrs Anita Griggs
BA(Hons), PGCE
Age range: B3–11 G3–11

Finton House School
171 Trinity Road, London SW17 7HL
Tel: 020 8682 0921
Head of School: Mr Ben Freeman
Age range: 4–11
No. of pupils: 300
Fees: Day £15,378–£15,588

First Steps School of Dance & Drama
234 Lillie Road, London SW6 7QA
Tel: 020 7381 5224
Age range: 3–17
Fees: Day £2,700
16+ £ ❀

Francis Holland School, Sloane Square, SW1
39 Graham Terrace,
London SW1W 8JF
Tel: 020 7730 2971
Head: Mrs Lucy Elphinstone MA(Cantab)
Age range: G4–18
No. of pupils: 520 VIth70
Fees: Day £17,760–£20,085
🏃 A £ 🧭 16+

Garden House School
Boys' School & Girls' School,
Turk's Row, London SW3 4TW
Tel: 020 7730 1652
Boys' Head: Mr Christian Warland BA(Hons), LLB.
Age range: 3–11
No. of pupils: 490
Fees: Day £17,700–£22,800
£ 🧭

Gateway House Nursery School
St Judes Church Hall, Heslop
Road, London SW12 8EG
Tel: 020 8675 8258
Principal: Miss Elizabeth Marshall
Age range: 2–4
No. of pupils: 30
Fees: Day £1,010–£1,060
🧭

Glendower School
86/87 Queen's Gate,
London SW7 5JX
Tel: 020 7370 1927
Headmistress: Mrs Sarah Knollys BA, PGCE
Age range: G4–11+
No. of pupils: 206
Fees: Day £19,200
🏃 A £ 🧭

Hall School Wimbledon
Beavers Holt, Stroud Crescent,
Putney Vale, London SW15 3EQ
Tel: 020 8788 2370
Headmaster: Timothy J Hobbs MA
Age range: 4–16
No. of pupils: 520
Fees: Day £13,126–£17,336
🧭

Hall School Wimbledon Senior School
17 The Downs, Wimbledon,
London SW20 8HF
Tel: 020 8879 9200
Headmaster: Timothy J Hobbs MA
Age range: 11–16
No. of pupils: 520
Fees: Day £17,336
🧭

Happy Nursery Days
Valens House, 132a Uppertulse
Hill, London SW2 2RX
Tel: 020 8674 7804
Age range: 3 months–5

HILL HOUSE INTERNATIONAL JUNIOR SCHOOL
For further details see p. 62
17 Hans Place, Chelsea,
London SW1X 0EP
Tel: 020 7584 1331
Email: info@
hillhouseschool.co.uk
Website:
www.hillhouseschool.co.uk
Principals: Richard, Janet,
William & Edmund Townend
Age range: 4–13
No. of pupils: 740
Fees: Day £13,200–£17,400
🌐 £ 🧭

Hornsby House School
Hearnville Road, Balham,
London SW12 8RS
Tel: 020 8673 7573
Headmaster: Mr Edward Rees
Age range: 4–11
Fees: Day £14,280–£15,345
£ 🧭

Hurlingham Nursery and Pre-Prep
The Old Methodist Hall, Gwendolen
Avenue, London SW15 6EH
Tel: 020 8780 9446
Head: Jane Appleby
Age range: 2–7
No. of pupils: 115
🧭

Hurlingham School
122 Putney Bridge Road,
Putney, London SW15 2NQ
Tel: 020 8874 7186
Headteacher: Mr Jonathan Brough
Age range: 4–11
No. of pupils: 326
Fees: Day £15,540–£16,185
£ 🧭

Hyde Park School, Queen's Gate
24 Elvaston Place, South
Kensington, London SW7 5NL
Tel: 020 7225 3131
Head of School: Dr Ronald Pritchard
Age range: 2–11
No. of pupils: 110
Fees: Day £11,280–£16,875
🧭

Ibstock Place School
Clarence Lane, London SW15 5PY
Tel: 020 8876 9991
Head: Mrs Anna Sylvester-Johnson BA(Hons), PGCE
Age range: 4–18
No. of pupils: 970
Fees: Day £16,290–£20,880
A £ 16+

Inchbald School of Design
Interior Design Faculty, 7 Eaton
Gate, London SW1W 9BA
Tel: 020 7730 5508
Principal: Mrs Jacqueline Duncan FIIDA, FIDDA
Age range: 18–50
No. of pupils: 120
16+

JJAADA Interior Design Academy
28 Abbeville Mews, 88 Clapham
Park Road, London SW4 7BX
Tel: 020 7494 3363
16+

Judith Blacklock Flower School
4/5 Kinnerton Place South,
London SW1X 8EH
Tel: 020 7235 6235
Head: Judith Blacklock
16+

Kensington Prep School
596 Fulham Road, London SW6 5PA
Tel: 0207 731 9300
Head of School: Mrs Caroline Hulme-McKibbin
Age range: G4–11
No. of pupils: 289
Fees: Day £17,193
🏃

Kids Inc Day Nursery – East Sheen
459b Upper Richmond Road West,
East Sheen, London SW14 7PR
Tel: 020 8876 8144

King's College Junior School
Southside, Wimbledon
Common, London SW19 4TT
Tel: 020 8255 5335
Headmaster: Dr. G A Silverlock
Age range: B7–13
No. of pupils: 437
🏃 £

King's College School
Southside, Wimbledon
Common, London SW19 4TT
Tel: 020 8255 5300
Head Master: A D Halls MA
Age range: B11–18 G16–18
No. of pupils: 967
Fees: Day £19,530–£21,600
🏃 🌐 A £ IB 16+

Knightsbridge School
67 Pont Street, Knightsbridge,
London SW1X 0BD
Tel: 020 7590 9000
Head: Ms Shona Colaco MA, PGCE, MSB, CBiol
Age range: 3–13
No. of pupils: 400
Fees: Day £18,756–£19,965
£ 🧭

Ladybird Nursery School
9 Knowle Close, London SW9 0TQ
Tel: 020 7924 9505

L'ECOLE DE BATTERSEA
For further details see p. 63
Trott Street, Battersea,
London SW11 3DS
Tel: 020 7371 8350
Email: admin@
lecoledespetits.co.uk
Website:
www.lecoledespetits.co.uk
Principal: Mrs F Brisset
Age range: 3–11
No. of pupils: 265
Fees: Day £12,600–£12,780

L'ECOLE DES PETITS
For further details see p. 64
2 Hazlebury Road, Fulham,
London SW6 2NB
Tel: 020 7371 8350
Email: admin@
lecoledespetits.co.uk
Website:
www.lecoledespetits.co.uk
Principal: Mrs F Brisset
Age range: 3–6
No. of pupils: 130
Fees: Day £12,300–£12,450

L'Ecole du Parc
12 Rodenhurst Road,
London SW4 8AR
Tel: 020 8671 5287
Headteacher: Mrs E Sicking-Bressler
Age range: 1–5
No. of pupils: 55
Fees: Day £4,000–£7,500

Little People of Fulham
250a Lillie Road, Fulham,
London SW6 7PX
Tel: 020 7386 0006
Owner: Miss Jane Gleasure
Age range: 4 months–5

Little Red Hen Nursery School
Cabul Road, London, SW11 2NU
Tel: 020 7738 0321
Age range: 2–5
Fees: Day £1,470–£1,740

London Film Academy
The Old Church, 52a Walham
Grove, London SW6 1QR
Tel: 020 7386 7711
Founders & Joint Principals: Daisy
Gili & Anna Macdonald
16+

London Steiner School
9 Weir Road, Balham,
London SW12 0LT
Tel: 0208 772 3504
Age range: 3–14
£

Lycée Français Charles de Gaulle
35 Cromwell Road,
London SW7 2DG
Tel: 020 7584 6322
Head of School: Mr Olivier Rauch
Age range: 5–19
No. of pupils: 4000
🌐 A £ 🧭 16+

Magic Roundabout Nursery – Stockwell
Surrey Hall, Binfield Road, Stockwell, London SW4 6TB
Tel: 020 7498 1194

MANDER PORTMAN WOODWARD – LONDON
For further details see p. 68
90-92 Queen's Gate, London SW7 5AB
Tel: 020 7835 1355
Email: london@mpw.ac.uk
Website: www.mpw.ac.uk
Principal: Mr John Southworth BSc MSc
Age range: 14–19
No. of pupils: 620
Fees: Day £9,529
16 (A) (£) ✎

Melrose House Nursery School
39 Melrose Road, London SW18 1LX
Tel: 020 8874 7769
Age range: 2–5

Melrose House Nursery School
55 Finlay Street, London SW6 6HF
Tel: 020 7736 9296

Mini Stars Day Nursery
St Margarets Church, Barcombe Avenue, London SW2 3HH
Tel: 020 8678 8600
Age range: 6 months–5
No. of pupils: 26

Miss Daisy's Nursery School
Fountain Court Club Room, Ebury Square, London SW1W 9SU
Tel: 020 7730 5797
Head: Daisy Harrison
Age range: 2–5
No. of pupils: 30
Fees: Day £1,050–£5,550

Montessori School
St Paul's Community Centre, Rectory Grove, Clapham, London SW4 0DX
Tel: 020 7498 8324
Age range: 6 months–6

MORE HOUSE SCHOOL
For further details see p. 70
22-24 Pont Street, Knightsbridge, London SW1X 0AA
Tel: 020 7235 2855
Email: office@morehouse.org.uk
Website: www.morehouse.org.uk
Co-Heads: Mrs. Amanda Leach & Mr. Michael Keeley
Age range: G11–18
No. of pupils: 206
Fees: Day £6,650
(🧍) (A) (£) ✎ 16

Newton Prep
149 Battersea Park Road, London SW8 4BX
Tel: 020 7720 4091
Headmistress: Mrs Alison Fleming BA, MA Ed, PGCE
Age range: 3–13
No. of pupils: 632
Fees: Day £9,300–£19,695
(£) ✎

Nightingale Montessori Nursery
St Lukes Community Hall, 194 Ramsden Road, London SW12 8RQ
Tel: 020 8675 8070
Principal: Mrs Tejas Earp
Age range: 2–5

Noah's Ark Nursery Schools (Dolphin School Trust)
St Michael's Church Hall, Cobham Close, London SW11 6SP
Tel: 020 7924 3472 opt 2
Head: Miss Annette Miller
Age range: 2–5
No. of pupils: 40
Fees: Day £4,725

Noah's Ark Nursery Schools (Dolphin School Trust)
Endlesham Church Hall, 48 Endlesham Road, London SW12 8JL
Tel: 020 924 3472 opt 2
Head: Miss Annette Miller
Age range: 2–5
No. of pupils: 32
Fees: Day £4,725

Noddy's Nursery School
Trinity Church Hall, Beaumont Road, Wimbledon, London SW19 6SP
Tel: 020 8785 9191
Principal: Mrs Sarah Edwards NNEB, Mont Dip
Age range: 2–5

NORTHCOTE LODGE SCHOOL
For further details see p. 76
26 Bolingbroke Grove, London SW11 6EL
Tel: 020 8682 8888
Email: admissions@northwoodschools.com
Website: www.northwoodschools.com
Headmaster: Clive Smith-Langridge
Age range: B8–13
No. of pupils: 260
Fees: Day £6,595
(🧍) ✎

Oliver House Preparatory School
7 Nightingale Lane, London SW4 9AH
Tel: 020 8772 1911
Headteacher: Mr Rob Farrell
Age range: 3–11
No. of pupils: 144
Fees: Day £6,600–£15,090

Paint Pots Montessori School – The Boltons
St Mary The Boltons Church Hall, The Boltons, London SW10 9TB
Tel: 07794 678 537
Head Teacher: Georgie Scully
Age range: 2 years 6 months–5 years
✎

Parkgate House School
80 Clapham Common North Side, London SW4 9SD
Tel: +44 (0)20 7350 2461
Principal: Miss Catherine Shanley
Age range: 2.5–11 years
No. of pupils: 220
Fees: Day £5,940–£15,600

Parsons Green Prep School
1 Fulham Park Road, Fulham, London SW6 4LJ
Tel: 020 7371 9009
Headmaster: Tim Cannell
Age range: 4–11
No. of pupils: 200
Fees: Day £16,857–£18,201
✎

Peques Anglo-Spanish School
St John's Church, North End Road, Fulham, London SW6 1PB
Tel: 020 7385 0055
Managing Director: Margarita Morro Beltran
Age range: 3 months–5

Playdays Nursery School Wimbledon
58 Queens Road, Wimbledon, London SW19 8LR
Tel: 020 8946 8139
Nursery Manager: Charline Baker

Pooh Corner Kindergarten
St Stephen's Church Hall, 48 Emperor Gate, London SW7 4HJ
Tel: 020 7373 6111
Headmistress: Sarah Crowther

PROSPECT HOUSE SCHOOL
For further details see p. 74
75 Putney Hill, London SW15 3NT
Tel: 020 8246 4897
Email: info@prospecths.org.uk
Website: www.prospecths.org.uk
Headmaster: Mr Michael Hodge BPED(Rhodes) QTS
Age range: 3–11
No. of pupils: 316
Fees: Day £8,850–£18,450
(£) ✎

Putney High School GDST
35 Putney Hill, London SW15 6BH
Tel: 020 8788 4886
Headmistress: Mrs Suzie Longstaff BA, MA, PGCE
Age range: G4–18
No. of pupils: 976 VIth150
(🧍) (A) (£) ✎ 16

Queen's Gate School
131-133 Queen's Gate, London SW7 5LE
Tel: 020 7589 3587
Principal: Mrs R M Kamaryc BA, MSc, PGCE
Age range: G4–18
No. of pupils: VIth94
(🧍) (A) (£) ✎ 16

Redcliffe School Trust Ltd
47 Redcliffe Gardens, Chelsea, London SW10 9JH
Tel: 020 7352 9247
Head: Sarah Lemmon
Age range: 3–11
Fees: Day £6,660–£17,730
(£)

Ringrose Kindergarten Chelsea
St Lukes Church Hall, St Lukes Street, London SW3 3RP
Tel: 020 7352 8784
Age range: 2–5

Royal Academy of Dance
36 Battersea Square, London SW11 3RA
Tel: 020 7326 8000
Chief Executive: Luke Rittner
16

Royal College of Art
Kensington Gore, London SW7 2EU
Tel: 020 7590 4444
Rector & Vice-Provost: Professor Christopher Frayling
16

Sinclair House Preparatory School
59 Fulham High Street, Fulham, London SW6 3JJ
Tel: 0207 736 9182
Principal: Mrs Carlotta T M O'Sullivan
Age range: 2–11
No. of pupils: 120
Fees: Day £5,280–£17,025

Square One Nursery School
Lady North Hall, 12 Ravenna Road, Putney, London SW15 6AW
Tel: 020 8788 1546
Principal: Mrs King

St Mary Magdalen Montessori Nursery School
61 North Worple Way, London SW14 8PR
Tel: 020 8878 0756
Head: Liz Maitland NNEB, RSH, MontDip
Age range: 2–5
(£)

St Mary's Summerstown Montessori
46 Wimbledon Road, Tooting, London SW17 0UQ
Tel: 020 8947 7359
Head: Liz Maitland NNEB, RSH, MontDip
Age range: 18 months–5 years
No. of pupils: 30
Fees: Day £1,300

St Michael's Montessori Nursery School
St Michael's Church, Elm Bank Gardens, Barnes, London SW13 0NX
Tel: 020 8878 0116
Head Teacher: Debbie Goldberg
Age range: 2 1/2–5

St Nicholas Preparatory School
23 Princes Gate, Kensington, London SW7 1PT
Tel: 020 7225 1277
Headmistress: Jill Walker
Age range: 3–11
No. of pupils: 200

St Paul's Juniors
St Paul's School, Lonsdale Road, London SW13 9JT
Tel: 020 8748 3461
Head of School: Maxine Shaw
Age range: B7–13
No. of pupils: 436
Fees: Day £20,010

St Paul's School
Lonsdale Road, Barnes, London SW13 9JT
Tel: 020 8748 9162
High Master: Prof Mark Bailey
Age range: B13–18
No. of pupils: 897
Fees: Day £25,032 FB £37,611

St Philip's School
6 Wetherby Place, London SW7 4NE
Tel: 020 7373 3944
Headmaster: Mr Wulffen-Thomas
Age range: B7–13
No. of pupils: 110
Fees: Day £16,200

Streatham & Clapham High School GDST
42 Abbotswood Road, London SW16 1AW
Tel: 020 8677 8400
Headmaster: Dr Millan Sachania
Age range: G3–18
No. of pupils: 603 VIth70
Fees: Day £10,431–£19,743

Streatham Montessori Nursery & Day Care
66 Blairderry Road, Streatham Hill, London SW2 4SB
Tel: 020 8674 2208
Nursery Manager: Mrs Fehmida Gangji
Age range: 1–5

Sussex House School
68 Cadogan Square, London SW1X 0EA
Tel: 020 7584 1741
Headmaster: Mr N P Kaye MA(Cantab), ACP, FRSA, FRGS
Age range: B8–13
No. of pupils: 182
Fees: Day £19,770

Swedish School
82 Lonsdale Road, London SW13 9JS
Tel: 020 8741 1751
Head of School: Ms. Annika Simonsson Bergqvist
Age range: 3–18
No. of pupils: 300 VIth145
Fees: Day £8,600–£9,100

Raynes Park Day Nursery and Pre-School
3 Spencer Road, Raynes Park, Wimbledon, London SW20 0QN
Tel: 0333 920 1909
Nursery Manager: Ms Leanne Eustace
Age range: 3 months–5 years

Southfields Day Nursery and Pre-School
Duntshill Mill, 21 Riverdale Drive, London SW18 4UR
Tel: 0330 057 6434
Nursery Manager: Ms Lydia Howards
Age range: 3 months–5 years

Streatham Day Nursery and Preschool
113 Blegborough Road, Streatham, London SW16 6DL
Tel: 0330 057 6267
Nursery Manager: Ms Nadia Kiani
Age range: 3 months–5 years

Thames Christian College
Wye Street, Battersea, London SW11 2HB
Tel: 020 7228 3933
Executive Head: Stephen Holsgrove PhD
Age range: 11–16
No. of pupils: 120
Fees: Day £15,780

The Boltons Nursery School
262b Fulham Road, Chelsea, London SW10 9EL
Tel: 020 7351 6993
Age range: 2–5
No. of pupils: 60
Fees: Day £2,370–£4,200

The Bumble Bee Nursery School
Church of Ascension, Pountney Road, London SW11 5TU
Headmistress: Deepti Bansal

The Castle Kindergarten
20 Henfield Road, London SW19 3HU
Tel: 020 8544 0089
Headmistress: Mrs Beverley Davis DipEd
Age range: 2–5

The Crescent I Kindergarten
Flat 1, No 10 Trinity Crescent, London SW17 7AE
Tel: 020 8767 5882
Principal: Philip Evelegh

The Crescent II Kindergarten
Holy Trinity Church Hall, Trinity Road, London SW17 7SQ
Tel: 020 8682 3020

The Crescent III Kindergarten
Grafton Tennis Club, 70A Thornton Road, London SW12 0LF
Tel: 020 8675 9659

The Eveline Day Nursery Schools, Furzedown
Seeley Hall, Chillerton Road, Furzedown, London SW17 9BE
Tel: 020 8672 0501

The Eveline Day Nursery Schools, Tooting
30 Ritherdon Road, Upper Tooting, London SW17 8QD
Tel: 020 8672 7549
Principal: Mrs T Larche

The Eveline Day Nursery Schools, Wandsworth
East Hill United Reformed Church Hall, Geraldine Road, Wandsworth, London SW18 2NR
Tel: 020 8870 0966

The Eveline Day Nursery Schools, Wimbledon
89a Quicks Road, Wimbledon, London SW19 1EX
Tel: 020 8545 0699

The Falcons School for Girls
11 Woodborough Road, Putney, London SW15 6PY
Tel: 020 8992 5189
Head of School: Mrs Sophia Ashworth Jones
Age range: G3–11
No. of pupils: 102
Fees: Day £8,580–£15,705

The Hampshire School, Chelsea
15 Manresa Road, Chelsea, London SW3 6NB
Tel: 020 7352 7077
Principal: Mr Donal Brennan
Age range: 3–13
No. of pupils: 300
Fees: Day £16,965–£17,955

The Harrodian School
Lonsdale Road, London SW13 9QN
Tel: 020 8748 6117
Headmaster: James R Hooke
Age range: 4–18
No. of pupils: 890 VIth95
Fees: Day £15,000–£23,040

The Knightsbridge Kindergarten
St Peter's Church, 119 Eaton Square, London SW1W 0HQ
Tel: 020 7235 5305
Headmistress: Mrs P Powell-Harper
Age range: 2–5
Fees: Day £4,000

The Laurels School
126 Atkins Road, Clapham, London SW12 0AN
Tel: 020 8674 7229
Headmistress: Linda Sanders BA Hons (Bristol), MA (Madrid)
Age range: G11–18

The Maria Montessori Children's House
St John's Ambulance Hall, 122-124 Kingston Road, London SW19 1LY
Tel: 020 8543 6353
Age range: 2–5

The Marmalade Bear Nursery School
St. Magdalene Church Hall, Trinity Road, Tooting, London SW17 7HP
Tel: 0208 265 5224
Principal: Ms Rozzy Hyslop
Age range: 2–5
Fees: Day £3,270–£3,450

The Merlin School
4 Carlton Drive, Putney Hill, London SW15 2BZ
Tel: 020 8788 2769
Principal: Mrs Kate Prest
Age range: 4–8
No. of pupils: 170

The Moat School
Bishops Avenue, Fulham, London SW6 6EG
Tel: 020 7610 9018
Head: Ms Clare King
Age range: 9–16
Fees: Day £30,000

The Montessori Childrens House Ltd
St John's Church, 1 Spencer Hill, London SW19 4NZ
Tel: 020 8971 9135
Age range: 2–5

The Montessori Pavilion – The Kindergarten School
Vine Road, Barnes, London SW13 0NE
Tel: 020 8878 0288
Headmistress: Ms Georgina Dashwood
Age range: 3–8
No. of pupils: 50

The Mouse House Nursery School
27 Mallinson Road, London SW11 1BW
Tel: 020 7924 1893
Headmistress: Amanda White-Spunner
Age range: 2–5
Fees: Day £1,650–£4,125

The Norwegian School
28 Arterberry Road, Wimbledon, London SW20 8AH
Tel: 020 8947 6617
Head: Mr Ivar Chavannes
Age range: 3–16

The Oval Montessori Nursery School
within Vauxhall Park, Fentiman Road, London SW8 1LA
Tel: 020 7735 4816
Head: Ms Louise Norwood
Age range: 2–5
Fees: Day £3,000

The Park Kindergarten
St Saviours Church Hall, 351 Battersea Park Road, London SW11 4LH
Tel: 020 7627 5125
Principal: Miss Lisa Neilsen MontDip
Age range: 2–5
Fees: Day £2,370

The Rainbow Playgroup
St Luke's Church Hall, St Luke's Street, London SW3 3RR
Tel: 020 7352 8156
Age range: 2–5

THE ROCHE SCHOOL
For further details see p. 84
11 Frogmore, London SW18 1HW
Tel: 020 8877 0823
Email: office@therocheschool.co.uk
Website: www.therocheschool.com
Headmistress: Mrs V Adams BA(Hons), PGCE, MA
Age range: 2–11 years
No. of pupils: 316
Fees: Day £14,970–£15,690

The Rowans School
19 Drax Avenue, Wimbledon, London SW20 0EG
Tel: 020 8946 8220
Head Teacher: Mrs Joanna Hubbard
Age range: 3–8
Fees: Day £7,905–£13,170

The Study Preparatory School
Wilberforce House, Camp Road, Wimbledon Common, London SW19 4UN
Tel: 020 8947 6969
Headmistress: Mrs Susan Pepper MA Oxon, PGCE
Age range: G4–11
No. of pupils: 315

The White House Preparatory School & Woodentops Kindergarten
24 Thornton Road, London SW12 0LF
Tel: 020 8674 9514
Principal: Mrs. Mary McCahery
Age range: 2–11
Fees: Day £4,436–£4,740

The Willow Nursery School
55 Grafton Square, Clapham Old Town, London SW4 0DE
Tel: 020 7498 0319
Head: Mrs Harriet Baring MontDip
Age range: 2–5
Fees: Day £3,000–£3,100

The Zebedee Nursery School
4 Parsons Green, London SW6 4TN
Tel: 020 7371 9224
Headmistress: Miss Su Gahan NNEB, RSH
Age range: 2–5
No. of pupils: 32
Fees: Day £3,900

Thomas's Kindergarten – Battersea
St Mary's Church, Battersea Church Road, London SW11 3NA
Tel: 020 7738 0400
Headmistress: Miss Iona Jennings
Age range: 2–5
Fees: Day £1,365–£2,100

Thomas's Kindergarten – Pimlico
14 Ranelagh Grove, London SW1W 8PD
Tel: 020 7730 3596
Headmistress: Miss Tamara Spierenburg HBO

Thomas's Preparatory School – Battersea
28-40 Battersea High Street, London SW11 3JB
Tel: 020 7978 0900
Head: Simon O'Malley
Age range: 4–13
No. of pupils: 547
Fees: Day £18,747–£20,868

Thomas's Preparatory School – Clapham
Broomwood Road, London SW11 6JZ
Tel: 020 7326 9300
Headmaster: Mr Philip Ward BEd(Hons)
Age range: 4–13
No. of pupils: 647
Fees: Day £17,262–£19,518

Thomas's Preparatory School – Fulham
Hugon Road, London SW6 3ES
Tel: 020 7751 8200
Head: Miss Annette Dobson BEd(Hons), PGCertDys
Age range: 4–11
Fees: Day £17,880–£20,016

Tiggers Nursery School
87 Putney Bridge Road, London SW15 2PA
Tel: 020 8874 4668
Headmistress: Natasha Green MontDip
Age range: 2–5
Fees: Day £1,425–£1,725

Toots Day Nursery
214 Totterdown Street, Tooting, London SW17 8TD
Tel: 020 8767 7017
Principal: Angela Duffell
Age range: 1–5

Tower House School
188 Sheen Lane, London SW14 8LF
Tel: 020 8876 3323
Head: Mr Gregory Evans
Age range: B4–13
No. of pupils: 180
Fees: Day £13,089–£14,838

Ursuline Preparatory School
18 The Downs, London SW20 8HR
Tel: 020 8947 0859
Headmaster: Mr Chris McGrath
Age range: B3–4 G3–11
Fees: Day £6,615–£10,815

Wandsworth Nursery & Pre-School Academy
Dolphin House, Riverside West, Smugglers Way, Wandsworth, London SW18 1DE
Tel: 020 8877 1135
Nursery Manager: Evelyn Herrera
Age range: 0–5

Wandsworth Preparatory School
The Old Library, 2 Allfarthing Lane, London SW18 2PQ
Tel: 0208 870 4133
Head of School: Miss Bridget Saul BA (Hons), PGCE, MA
Age range: 4–11
No. of pupils: 115
Fees: Day £4,570

Westminster Abbey Choir School
Dean's Yard, London SW1P 3NY
Tel: 0207 654 4918
Headmaster: Jonathan Milton BEd
Age range: B8–13
No. of pupils: 35
Fees: FB £8,571

Westminster Cathedral Choir School
Ambrosden Avenue, London SW1P 1QH
Tel: 020 7798 9081
Headmaster: Mr Neil McLaughlan
Age range: B4–13
No. of pupils: 150
Fees: Day £16,350–£19,233 FB £10,086

Westminster School
Little Dean's Yard, Westminster, London SW1P 3PF
Tel: 020 7963 1003
Headmaster: Mr Patrick Derham
Age range: B13–18 G16–18
No. of pupils: 744
Fees: Day £26,130–£28,566 FB £37,740

Westminster Tutors
86 Old Brompton Road, South Kensington, London SW7 3LQ
Tel: 020 7584 1288
Principal: Virginia Maguire BA, MA, MLitt
Age range: 14–mature
No. of pupils: VIth40
Fees: Day £4,000–£25,000

Westminster Under School
Adrian House, 27 Vincent Square, London SW1P 2NN
Tel: 020 7821 5788
Headteacher: Mr Mark O'Donnell
Age range: B7–13
No. of pupils: 265
Fees: Day £19,344

Willington School
Worcester Road, Wimbledon, London SW19 7QQ
Tel: 020 8944 7020
Acting Headmaster: Mr Marcus Tattersal
Age range: B4–13
No. of pupils: 250
Fees: Day £12,150–£14,640

Wiltshire Nursery
85 Wiltshire Road, Brixton, London SW9 7NZ
Tel: 020 7274 4446

Wimbledon Common Preparatory
113 Ridgway, Wimbledon, London SW19 4TA
Tel: 020 8946 1001
Head Teacher: Mrs Tracey Buck
Age range: B4–8
No. of pupils: 160
Fees: Day £13,185

Wimbledon High School GDST
Mansel Road, Wimbledon, London SW19 4AB
Tel: 020 8971 0900
Headmistress: Mrs Jane Lunnon
Age range: G4–18
No. of pupils: 900 VIth155
Fees: Day £14,622–£18,810

Wimbledon Park Montessori School
206 Heythorp Street, Southfields, London SW18 5BU
Tel: 020 8944 8584
Head: Ms Clare Collins
Age range: 2–5
Fees: Day £830–£950

Wimbledon School of Art
Merton Hall Road, London SW19 3QA
Tel: 020 8408 5000
Principal: Professor Roderick Bugg

**Young England
Kindergarten**
St Saviour's Hall, St George's
Square, London SW1V 3QW
Tel: 020 7834 3171
Principal: Mrs Kay C King MontDip
Age range: 2.5–5
Fees: Day £3,300–£4,950

West London

Acorn Nursery School
2 Lansdowne Crescent,
London W11 2NH
Tel: 020 7727 2122
Principal: Mrs Jane Cameron
BEd(Hons)
Age range: 2–5
Fees: Day £2,400

**Acton Yochien
Nursery School**
The Pavilion, Queens Drive Playing
Fields, Acton, London W3 0HT
Tel: 020 8343 2192

**Alan D Hairdressing
Education**
4 West Smithfield, London EC1A 9JX
Tel: 020 7580 1030
Director of Education: Alan
Hemmings
Fees: Day £200 FB £12,400

**Albemarle Independent
College**
18 Dunraven Street,
London W1K 7FE
Tel: 020 7409 7273
Co-Principals: Beverley Mellon &
James Eytle
Age range: 16–19
No. of pupils: 160
Fees: Day £7,000–£24,000

**Arts Educational Schools
London Sixth Form**
Cone Ripman House, 14 Bath
Road, Chiswick, London W4 1LY
Tel: 020 8987 6666
Head Teacher: Mr Chris Hocking
Age range: 16–18
No. of pupils: 85
Fees: Day £16,830–£16,990

**Arts Educational Schools
London Years 7-11**
Cone Ripman House, 14 Bath
Road, Chiswick, London W4 1LY
Tel: 020 8987 6666
Head Teacher: Mr Chris Hocking
Age range: 11–16
No. of pupils: 141
Fees: Day £15,390–£15,540

**Ashbourne Independent
Sixth Form College**
17 Old Court Place,
Kensington, London W8 4PL
Tel: 020 7937 3858
Principal: M J Kirby MSc, BApSc
Age range: 16–19
No. of pupils: 170
Fees: Day £24,750–£26,250

Ashbourne Middle School
17 Old Court Place,
Kensington, London W8 4PL
Tel: 020 7937 3858
Principal: M J Kirby MSc, BApSc
Age range: 13–16
No. of pupils: VIth150
Fees: Day £24,750–£26,250

Avenue House School
70 The Avenue, Ealing,
London W13 8LS
Tel: 020 8998 9981
Headteacher: Mr J Sheppard
Age range: 3–11
No. of pupils: 135
Fees: Day £11,250

Bales College
742 Harrow Road, Kensal
Town, London W10 4AA
Tel: 020 8960 5899
Principal: William Moore
Age range: 11–19
No. of pupils: 90
Fees: Day £11,550–£12,750

**Barbara Speake
Stage School**
East Acton Lane, East
Acton, London W3 7EG
Tel: 020 8743 1306
Headteacher: Mr David Speake
BA (Hons)
Age range: 3–16
Fees: Day £7,500–£9,000

BASSETT HOUSE SCHOOL
For further details see p. 50
60 Bassett Road,
London W10 6JP
Tel: 020 8969 0313
Email: info@bassetths.org.uk
Website: www.bassetths.org.uk
Headmistress: Mrs Philippa
Cawthorne MA (Soton) PGCE
Mont Cert
Age range: 3–11
No. of pupils: 190
Fees: Day £8,850–£18,450

Blake College
162 New Cavendish Street,
London W1W 6YS
Tel: 020 7636 0658
Course Director: D A J Cluckie
BA, BSc
Fees: Day £4,720–£5,310

BPP University
Aldine Place, 142-144 Uxbridge
Road, London W12 8AA
Tel: (+44) 03331 226478
Head: Martin Taylor

Bright Futures
63-65 Portland Place,
Westminster, London W1B 1QR
Tel: 020 7580 8096
Principal: Dawn Savage

**Busy Bees at Ealing
Northfields**
283-287 Windmill Road,
Ealing, London W5 4DP
Tel: 020 8567 2244

Age range: 3 months–5**Busy
Bees at Hammersmith**
30-40 Dalling Road,
London, W6 0JD
Tel: 020 8741 5382
Age range: 3 months–5 years

**Bute House Preparatory
School for Girls**
Bute House, Luxemburg
Gardens, London W6 7EA
Tel: 020 7603 7381
Head: Mrs Helen Lowe
Age range: G4–11
No. of pupils: 306
Fees: Day £16,458

Buttercups Day Nursery
38 Grange Road, Chiswick,
London W4 4DD
Tel: 020 8995 6750

Buttercups Day Nursery
9 Florence Road, Ealing,
London W5 3TU
Tel: 020 8840 4838

Buttercups Day Nursery
9 Florence Road, Ealing,
London W5 3TU
Tel: 020 8840 4838

**Buttons Day
Nursery School**
99 Oaklands Road, London W7 2DT
Tel: 020 8840 3355
Head: Julie Parhar BSc, NVQ3
Age range: 3 months–5
No. of pupils: 62

Campbell Harris Tutors
185 Kensington High Street,
London W8 6SH
Tel: 020 7937 0032
Principals: Mr Mark Harris & Ms
Claire Campbell
Age range: 13+
Fees: Day £4,000–£9,000

**Caterpillar Montessori
Nursery School**
St Albans Church Hall, South
Parade, Chiswick, London W4 3HY
Tel: 020 8747 8531
Head: Mrs Alison Scott
Age range: 2–5
Fees: Day £2,700

Chepstow House School
108a Lancaster Road,
London W11 1QS
Tel: 0207 243 0243
Headteacher: Angela Barr
Age range: 2.5–12 years

**Chiswick & Bedford
Park Prep School**
Priory House, Priory Avenue,
London W4 1TX
Tel: 020 8994 1804
Headmistress: Mrs S Daniell
Age range: B4–7+ G4–11
No. of pupils: 180
Fees: Day £13,275

**Chiswick Nursery
and Pre-School**
4 Marlborough Road,
Chiswick, London W4 4ET
Tel: 020 8742 0011
Nursery Manager: Roxane Lovell
Age range: 0–5

**Chiswick Park Nursery
and Pre-School**
Evershed Walk, London W4 5BW
Tel: 0333 920 0404
Nursery Manager: Ms Rebecca
Fergus

Age range: 3 months–5
years**Christie's Education**
42 Portland Place, Marylebone,
London, W1B 1NB
Tel: 020 7665 4350

Clifton Lodge
8 Mattock Lane, Ealing,
London W5 5BG
Tel: 020 8579 3662
Executive Head: Mr. Floyd
Steadman
Age range: 3–13
No. of pupils: 140
Fees: Day £12,240–£14,010

**College of Naturopathic
& Complementary
Medicine Ltd**
41 Riding House Street,
London W1W 7BE
Tel: 01342 410 505
Head: Hermann Keppler

Connaught House School
47 Connaught Square,
London W2 2HL
Tel: 020 7262 8830
Principal: Mrs V Hampton
Age range: 4–11
No. of pupils: 75
Fees: Day £16,650–£18,300

David Game College
31 Jewry Street, London EC3N 2ET
Tel: 020 7221 6665
Principal: D T P Game MA, MPhil
Age range: 14–19
No. of pupils: 200 VIth150
Fees: Day £3,680–£30,630
16· A £ 16·

Devonshire Day Nursery
The Vicarage, Bennet Street,
Chiswick, London W4 2AH
Tel: 020 8995 9538
Manager: Dawn Freeman
Age range: 6 weeks–5
No. of pupils: 70

Durston House
12-14 Castlebar Road,
Ealing, London W5 2DR
Tel: 020 8991 6530
Headmaster: Mr Ian Kendrick MA,
BEd(Hons)
Age range: B4–13
No. of pupils: 376
Fees: Day £4,160–£5,060
♦ £ ✆

Ealing Independent College
83 New Broadway, Ealing,
London W5 5AL
Tel: 020 8579 6668
Principal: Dr Ian Moores
Age range: 13–19
No. of pupils: 100 VIth70
Fees: Day £2,910–£18,120
16· A 16·

Ecole Francaise Jacques Prevert
59 Brook Green, London W6 7BE
Tel: 020 7602 6871
Headteacher: Delphine Gentil
Age range: 4–11
🌐

Elmwood Montessori School
St Michaels Centre, Elmwood
Road, London W4 3DY
Tel: 020 8994 8177/995 2621
Headmistress: Mrs S Herbert BA
Age range: 2–5
Fees: Day £3,480–£4,440
✆

Fulham Prep School
200 Greyhound Road,
London W14 9SD
Tel: 020 7386 2444
Head of School: Mr Neill Lunnon
Age range: 4–18
No. of pupils: 647
Fees: Day £16,869–£19,749
🌐 A ✆

Great Beginnings Montessori School
The Welsh Church Hall, 82a
Chiltern Street, Marylebone,
London W1H 5JE
Tel: 020 7486 2276
Head: Mrs Wendy Innes
Age range: 2–6
Fees: Day £1,095–£1,650
✆

Greek Primary School of London
3 Pierrepoint Road, Acton,
London W3 9JR
Tel: 020 8992 6156
Age range: 1–11

Halcyon London International School
33 Seymour Place, London W1H 5AU
Tel: +44 (0)20 7258 1169
Headteacher: Mr Barry Mansfield
Age range: 11–18
No. of pupils: 172
🌐 £ IB

Hammersmith Day Nursery & Pre-School
50 Richford Gate, 61-69 Richford
Street, London W6 7HZ
Tel: 0207 622 0484
Manager: Marion Bones NVQ
Age range: 3 months–5 years
No. of pupils: 70

Harvington School
20 Castlebar Road, Ealing,
London W5 2DS
Tel: 020 8997 1583
Headmistress: Mrs Anna Evans
Age range: B3–4 G3–11
No. of pupils: 140
Fees: Day £6,525–£12,615
♦ £ ✆

HAWKESDOWN HOUSE SCHOOL KENSINGTON
For further details see p. 61
27 Edge Street, Kensington,
London W8 7PN
Tel: 020 7727 9090
Email: admin@
hawkesdown.co.uk
Website:
www.hawkesdown.co.uk
Headmistress: Mrs. J. A. K.
Mackay B.Ed (Hons)
Age range: 3–11
No. of pupils: 100
Fees: Day £16,350–£19,130
✆

Heathfield House School
Heathfield Gardens,
Chiswick, London W4 4JU
Tel: 020 8994 3385
Headteacher: Mrs Goodsman
Age range: 4–11
No. of pupils: 197
Fees: Day £2,471–£3,676

Holland Park Day Nursery and Pre-School
34 Ladbroke Grove, Notting
Hill, London W11 3BQ
Tel: 0333 363 4009
Age range: 3 months–5

Holland Park Pre Prep School and Day Nursery
5, Holland Road, Kensington,
London W14 8HJ
Tel: 020 7602 9066/020
7602 9266
Head Mistress: Mrs Kitty Mason
Age range: 3 months–8 years
No. of pupils: 39
Fees: Day £9,180–£18,12

Hyde Park School, Marble Arch
The Long Garden, St
George's Fields, Albion
Street, London W2 2AX
Tel: 020 7262 1190
Head of School: Mrs Karen Dapson
Age range: 2–7
No. of pupils: 74
Fees: Day £11,280–£16,875

Instituto Español Vicente Cañada Blanch
317 Portobello Road,
London W10 5SZ
Tel: +44 (0) 20 8969 2664
Principal: Carmen Pinilla Padilla
Age range: 4–19
No. of pupils: 405
🌐

International School of London (ISL)
139 Gunnersbury Avenue,
London W3 8LG
Tel: +44 (0)20 8992 5823
Principal: Mr Richard Parker
Age range: 3–18 years
No. of pupils: 450
Fees: Day £19,000–£26,300
🌐 IB ✆ 16·

James Lee Nursery School
Gliddon Road, London W14 9BH
Tel: 020 8741 8877

King Fahad Academy
Bromyard Avenue, Acton,
London W3 7HD
Tel: 020 8743 0131
Director General: Dr Abdulghani
Alharbi
Age range: 3–19
No. of pupils: 500
Fees: Day £3,300–£4,300
🌐 A £ IB 16·

La Petite Ecole Francais
73 Saint Charles Square,
London W10 6EJ
Tel: +44 208 960 1278
Principal: Mme Marjorie
Lacassagne
Age range: 3–11

Ladbroke Square Montessori School
43 Ladbroke Square,
London W11 3ND
Tel: 020 7229 0125
Head Teacher: Lucy Morley
Age range: 3–5
Fees: Day £850–£1,350
✆

Latymer Prep School
36 Upper Mall, Hammersmith,
London W6 9TA
Tel: 020 7993 0061
Principal: Ms Andrea Rutterford
B.Ed (Hons)
Age range: 7–11
No. of pupils: 165
Fees: Day £18,330
✆

Latymer Upper School
King Street, Hammersmith,
London W6 9LR
Tel: 020862 92024
Head: Mr D Goodhew MA(Oxon)
Age range: 11–18
No. of pupils: 1200
Fees: Day £20,130
A £ ✆ 16·

Le Herisson
River Court Methodist
Church, Rover Court Road,
Hammersmith, London W6 9JT
Tel: 020 8563 7664
Director: Maria Frost
Age range: 2–6
Fees: Day £8,730–£8,970
✆

L'Ecole Bilingue
St David's Welsh Church, St
Mary's Terrace, London W2 1SJ
Tel: 020 7224 8427
Headteacher: Ms Veronique
Ferreira
Age range: 3–11
No. of pupils: 68
Fees: Day £9,960–£10,770

Leiths School of Food & Wine
16-20 Wendell Road, Shepherd's
Bush, London W12 9RT
Tel: 020 8749 6400
Managing Director: Camilla
Schneideman
Age range: 17–99
No. of pupils: 96
16· ✆

Little Cherubs Nursery School
The Carmelite Priory, Pitt Street,
Kensington, London W8 4JH
Tel: 020 7376 4460/07810
712241
Principal: Mrs M Colvin MontDip
Age range: 2–5

Little People of Shepherds Bush
61 Hadyn Park Road, Shepherds
Bush, London W12 9AQ
Tel: 020 8749 5080
Owner: Miss Jane Gleasure
Age range: 4 months–5

Little People of Willow Vale
9 Willow Vale, London W12 0PA
Tel: 020 8749 2877
Head: Miss Jane Gleasure
Age range: 4 months–5

Little Sweethearts Montessori
St Saviours Church Hall, Warwick Avenue, London W9 2PT
Tel: 020 7266 1616

LLOYD WILLIAMSON SCHOOLS
For further details see p. 65
12 Telford Road, London W10 5SH
Tel: 020 8962 0345
Email: admin@lws.org.uk
Website: www.lloydwilliamson.co.uk
Co-Principals: Ms Lucy Meyer & Mr Aaron Williams
Age range: 4 months–14 years (15 in 2019, 16 in 2020)
Fees: Day £14,400

London Academy of Music & Dramatic Art
155 Talgarth Road, London W14 9DA
Tel: 020 8834 0500
Head of Examinations: Dawn Postans
Age range: 17+

Maria Montessori Children's House – Notting Hill
28 Powis Gardens, London W11 1JG
Tel: 020 7221 4141
Head: Mrs L Lawrence
Age range: 2–6
No. of pupils: 20
Fees: Day £4,500

Maria Montessori Nursery School
Church of the Ascension Hall, Beaufort Road, Ealing, London W5 3EB
Tel: 07717 050761

Maria Montessori School – Bayswater
St Matthew's Church, St Petersburgh Place, London W2 4LA
Tel: +44 (0)20 7435 3646

Melrose Nursery School
St Gabriel's Church, Noel Road, Acton, London W3 0JE
Tel: 020 8992 0855
Age range: 6 months–5

Norland Place School
162-166 Holland Park Avenue, London W11 4UH
Tel: 020 7603 9103
Headmaster: Mr Patrick Mattar MA
Age range: B4–8 years G4–11 years
Fees: Day £16,107–£18,072

Notting Hill & Ealing High School GDST
2 Cleveland Road, West Ealing, London W13 8AX
Tel: (020) 8799 8400
Headmaster: Mr Matthew Shoults
Age range: G4–18
No. of pupils: 903 VIth150
Fees: Day £14,313–£18,561

Notting Hill Preparatory School
95 Lancaster Road, London W11 1QQ
Tel: 020 7221 0727
Headmistress: Mrs Jane Cameron
Age range: 4–13
No. of pupils: 325
Fees: Day £6,355

One World Montessori Nursery & Pre-Prep
56 Minford Gardens, London, W14 0AW
Tel: 020 7603 6065
Age range: 2–8
No. of pupils: 21

One World Preparatory School
10 Stanley Gardens, Acton, London W3 7SZ
Tel: 020 87433300
Head: Ms Lisa Manser
Age range: 3–11
No. of pupils: 52
Fees: Day £3,000

ORCHARD HOUSE SCHOOL
For further details see p. 72
16 Newton Grove, Bedford Park, London W4 1LB
Tel: 020 8742 8544
Email: info@orchardhs.org.uk
Website: www.orchardhs.org.uk
Headmistress: Mrs Maria Edwards BEd(Beds) PGCE(Man) Mont Cert
Age range: 3–11
No. of pupils: 290
Fees: Day £8,850–£18,450

Oxford House College – London
24 Great Chapel Street, London, W1F 8FS
Tel: 020 7580 9785
Principal: Ms Muberra Orme

Paint Pots Montessori School – Bayswater
St Stephens Church, Westbourne Park Road, London W2 5QT
Tel: 07527 100534
Head Teacher: Vinni Lewis
Age range: 2 years 6 months–5 years

Pembridge Hall
18 Pembridge Square, London W2 4EH
Tel: 020 7229 0121
Headteacher: Mr Henry Keighley-Elstub
Age range: G4–11
No. of pupils: 413

Playhouse Day Nursery
Leighton Hall, Elthorne Park Road, London W7 2JJ
Tel: 020 8840 2851
Head of Nursery: Mrs Priti Patel

Portland Place School
56-58 Portland Place, London W1B 1NJ
Tel: 0207 307 8700
Head: Mr David Bradbury
Age range: 9–18
No. of pupils: 300 VIth50
Fees: Day £21,030

Queen's College
43-49 Harley Street, London W1G 8BT
Tel: 020 7291 7000
Principal: Mr Richard Tillet
Age range: G11–18
No. of pupils: 360 VIth90

Queen's College Preparatory School
61 Portland Place, London W1B 1QP
Tel: 020 7291 0660
Headmistress: Mrs Emma Webb
Age range: G4–11

RAVENSCOURT PARK PREPARATORY SCHOOL
For further details see p. 77
16 Ravenscourt Avenue, London W6 0SL
Tel: 020 8846 9153
Email: secretary@rpps.co.uk
Website: www.rpps.co.uk
Headmaster: Mr Carl Howes MA (Cantab), PGCE (Exeter)
Age range: 4–11
No. of pupils: 419
Fees: Day £5,857

Ray Cochrane Beauty School
118 Baker Street, London W1U 6TT
Tel: 02033224738
Principal: Miss Baljeet Suri
Age range: 16–50
No. of pupils: 30
Fees: Day £650–£8,495

Rolfe's Nursery School
34A Oxford Gardens, London W10 5UG
Tel: 020 7727 8300
Headteacher: Mrs Victoria O'Brien
Age range: 2–5
Fees: Day £4,950–£8,595

Sassoon Academy
58 Buckingham Gate, Westminster, London SW1E 6AJ
Tel: 020 7399 6902

Southbank International School – Kensington
36-38 Kensington Park Road, London W11 3BU
Tel: +44 (0)20 7243 3803
Principal: Siobhan McGrath
Age range: 3–11
No. of pupils: 210
Fees: Day £16,530–£25,740

Southbank International School – Westminster
63-65 Portland Place, London W1B 1QR
Tel: 020 7243 3803
Principal: Dr Paul Wood
Age range: 11–19

ST AUGUSTINE'S PRIORY
For further details see p. 80
Hillcrest Road, Ealing, London W5 2JL
Tel: 020 8997 2022
Email: office@sapriory.com
Website: www.sapriory.com
Headteacher: Mrs Sarah Raffray M.A., N.P.Q.H
Age range: B3–4 G3–18
No. of pupils: 485
Fees: Day £11,031–£15,693

ST BENEDICT'S SCHOOL
For further details see p. 78
54 Eaton Rise, Ealing, London W5 2ES
Tel: 020 8862 2000
Email: admissions@stbenedicts.org.uk
Website: www.stbenedicts.org.uk
Headmaster: Mr A Johnson BA
Age range: 3–18
No. of pupils: 1086 VIth213
Fees: Day £12,990–£16,845

St James Preparatory School
Earsby Street, London W14 8SH
Tel: 020 7348 1777
Headmistress: Mrs Catherine Thomlinson BA(Hons)
Age range: B4–11 G4–11
Fees: Day £16,425–£17,910

St James Senior Girls' School
Earsby Street, London W14 8SH
Tel: 020 7348 1777
Headmistress: Mrs Sarah Labram BA
Age range: G11–18
No. of pupils: 295 VIth67
Fees: Day £20,100

St Matthews Montessori School
St Matthews Church Hall, North Common Road, London W5 2QA
Tel: 07495 898 760
Head Teacher: Mrs Farah Virani M.A, B.A., PGCE – Primary, Mont. Dip.Adv.
Age range: 2–5

St Paul's Girls' School
Brook Green, London W6 7BS
Tel: 020 7603 2288
High Mistress: Mrs Sarah Fletcher
Age range: G11–18 years
No. of pupils: 750 VIth200
Fees: Day £24,891–£26,760

St Peter's Nursery
59a Portobello Road, London W11 3DB
Tel: 020 7243 2617
Head of Nursery: Tracey Lloyd

Sylvia Young Theatre School
1 Nutford Place, London W1H 5YZ
Tel: 020 7258 2330
Headteacher: Mrs Frances Chave
Age range: 10–16

Tabernacle School
32 St Anns Villas, Holland Park, London W11 4RS
Tel: 020 7602 6232
Headteacher: Mrs P Wilson
Age range: 3–16
Fees: Day £6,500–£9,500

The Ark Montessori and Forest School
The Scout Hall, Rugby Road, Chiswick, London W4 1AL
Tel: 020 8995 3391

The Falcons School for Boys
2 Burnaby Gardens, Chiswick, London W4 3DT
Tel: 020 8747 8393
Head of Pre-Preparatory School: Mr Andrew Forbes
Age range: B3–13
No. of pupils: 225
Fees: Day £8,475–£17,475

The Godolphin and Latymer School
Iffley Road, Hammersmith, London W6 0PG
Tel: +44 (0)20 8741 1936
Head Mistress: Dr Frances Ramsey
Age range: G11–18
No. of pupils: 800
Fees: Day £21,615

The Japanese School
87 Creffield Road, Acton, London W3 9PU
Tel: 020 8993 7145
Headteacher: Mrs Kiyoe Tsuruoka
Age range: 6–16
No. of pupils: 500

The Jordans Montessori Nursery School
Holy Innocents Church, Paddenswick Road, London W6 0UB
Tel: 0208 741 3230
Principal: Ms Sara Green
Age range: 2–5
Fees: Day £1,356–£3,270

The Meadows Montessori School
Dukes Meadows Community Centre, Alexandra Gardens, London W4 2TD
Tel: 020 8742 1327/8995 2621
Headmistress: Mrs S Herbert BA
Age range: 2–5
Fees: Day £3,030–£3,870

The Minors Nursery School
10 Pembridge Square, London W2 4ED
Tel: 020 7727 7253
Headteacher: Ms Jane Ritchie
Age range: 2–5

The Square Montessori School
18 Holland Park Avenue, London W11 3QU
Tel: 020 7221 6004
Principal: Mrs V Lawson-Tancred
No. of pupils: 20
Fees: Day £2,220

Thomas's Preparatory School – Kensington
17-19 Cottesmore Gardens, London W8 5PR
Tel: 020 7361 6500
Headmistress: Miss Joanna Ebner MA, BEd(Hons)(Cantab), NPQH
Age range: 4–11
Fees: Day £20,526–£21,789

Treetops Preschool
2A The Grove, Ealing, London W5 5LH
Tel: 020 8566 1546
Age range: 1–5

Treetops Ealing Common
Woodgrange Avenue, Ealing Common, London W5 3NY
Tel: 020 8992 0209
Age range: 3 months–5

Treetops West Ealing
Green Man Passage, Ealing, London W13 0TG
Tel: 020 8566 5515
Age range: 3 months–5

West London College
Gliddon Road, Hammersmith, London W14 9BL
Tel: 020 8741 1688

Wetherby Preparatory School
48 Bryanston Square, London W1H 2EA
Tel: 020 7535 3520
Headteacher: Mr Nick Baker
Age range: B8–13
No. of pupils: 192
Fees: Day £21,660

Wetherby Pre-Preparatory School
11 Pembridge Square, London W2 4ED
Tel: 020 7727 9581
Headmaster: Mr Mark Snell
Age range: B2 1/2–8
No. of pupils: 350
Fees: Day £21,600

Wetherby Senior School
100 Marylebone Lane, London W1U 2QU
Tel: 020 7535 3530
Headmaster: Mr Seth Bolderow
Age range: B11–18
Fees: Day £22,995

World of Children
Log Cabin Childrens Centre, 259 Northfield Avenue, London W5 4UA
Tel: 020 8840 3400

Young Dancers Academy
25 Bulwer Street, London W12 8AR
Tel: 020 8743 3856
Head: Mrs K Williams
Age range: 11–16
Fees: Day £12,237–£12,690

Ysgol Gymraeg Llundain London Welsh School
Hanwell Community Centre, Westcott Crescent, London W7 1PD
Tel: 020 8575 0237
Leadteacher: Miss Sioned Jones
Age range: 3–11
No. of pupils: 30
Fees: Day £3,345

Schools in Greater London

KEY TO SYMBOLS
- (†) Boys' school
- (♀) Girls' school
- (🌐) International school
- (16-) Tutorial or sixth form college
- (A) A levels
- (🏛) Boarding accommodation
- (£) Bursaries
- (IB) International Baccalaureate
- (✐) Learning support
- (16+) Entrance at 16+
- (🏵) Vocational qualifications
- (IAPS) Independent Association of Prep Schools
- (HMC) The Headmasters' & Headmistresses' Conference
- (ISA) Independent Schools Association
- (GSA) Girls' School Association
- (BSA) Boarding Schools' Association
- (S) Society of Heads

Unless otherwise indicated, all schools are coeducational day schools. Single-sex and boarding schools will be indicated by the relevant icon.

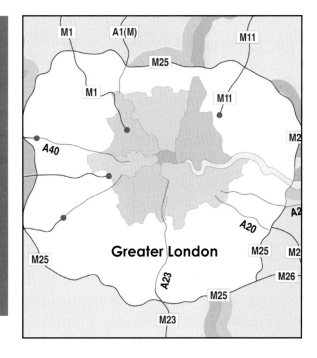

Greater London

Essex

AVON HOUSE PREPARATORY SCHOOL
For further details see p. 86
490 High Road, Woodford
Green, Essex IG8 0PN
Tel: 020 8504 1749
Email: registrar@ahsprep.co.uk
Website:
www.avonhouseschool.co.uk
Headteacher: Mrs Amanda
Campbell
Age range: 3–11
No. of pupils: 242
Fees: Day £9,750–£10,740

BANCROFT'S SCHOOL
For further details see p. 88
High Road, Woodford
Green, Essex IG8 0RF
Tel: 020 8505 4821
Email: office@bancrofts.org
Website: www.bancrofts.org
Head: Mr Simon Marshall MA,
PGCE (Cantab), MA, MPhil
(Oxon)
Age range: 7–18
No. of pupils: 1130 VIth235

Beehive Preparatory School
233 Beehive Lane, Redbridge,
Ilford, Essex IG4 5ED
Tel: 020 8550 3224
Headteacher: Miss Richards
Age range: 4–11
Fees: Day £5,685

Braeside School for Girls
130 High Road, Buckhurst
Hill, Essex IG9 5SD
Tel: 020 8504 1133
Headmistress: Claire Osborn
Age range: G3–16
No. of pupils: 199
Fees: Day £8,700–£12,750

Chigwell School
High Road, Chigwell, Essex IG7 6QF
Tel: 020 8501 5700
Headmaster: Mr M E Punt MA, MSc
Age range: 4–18
No. of pupils: 915 VIth185
Fees: Day £11,985–£17,985
FB £30,885

Daiglen School
68 Palmerston Road, Buckhurst
Hill, Essex IG9 5LG
Tel: 020 8504 7108
Headteacher: Mrs P Dear
Age range: 3–11
No. of pupils: 130
Fees: Day £9,300–£9,450

Eastcourt Independent School
1 Eastwood Road, Goodmayes,
Ilford, Essex IG3 8UW
Tel: 020 8590 5472
Headmistress: Mrs Christine
Redgrave BSc(Hons), DipEd, MEd
Age range: 3–11
Fees: Day £7,200

Gidea Park College
2 Balgores Lane, Gidea Park,
Romford, Essex RM2 5JR
Tel: 01708 740381
Headmistress: Mrs Katherine
Whiskerd
Age range: 3–11
No. of pupils: 177
Fees: Day £9,675

Goodrington School
17 Walden Road, Hornchurch,
Essex RM11 2JT
Tel: 01708 448349
Head Teacher: Mrs J R Ellenby
Age range: 3–11
Fees: Day £6,915

Guru Gobind Singh Khalsa College
Roding Lane, Chigwell,
Essex IG7 6BQ
Tel: 020 8559 9160
Principal: Mr Amarjit Singh Toor
BSc(Hons), BSc, BT
Age range: 3–19
Fees: Day £5,892–£6,720

Immanuel School
Havering Grange Centre,
Havering Road North,
Romford, Essex RM1 4HR
Tel: 01708 764449
Principal: Simon Reeves
Age range: 3–16

Loyola Preparatory School
103 Palmerston Road,
Buckhurst Hill, Essex IG9 5NH
Tel: 020 8504 7372
Headteacher: Mrs Kirsty Anthony
Age range: B3–11
No. of pupils: 183
Fees: Day £9,330

Maytime Montessori Nursery – Cranbrook Road
341 Cranbrook Road,
Ilford, Essex IG1 4UF
Tel: 020 8554 3079

Maytime Montessori Nursery – Eastwood Road
2 Eastwood Road,
Goodmayes, Essex IG3 8XB
Tel: 020 8599 3744

Maytime Montessori Nursery – York Road
87 York Road, Ilford, Essex IG1 3AF
Tel: 020 8553 1524
Age range: 0–6

Oakfields Montessori School
Harwood Hall, Harwood Hall
Lane, Upminster, Essex RM14 2YG
Tel: 01708 220117
Headmistress: Katrina Carroll
Age range: 2–11
No. of pupils: 201
Fees: Day £9,720–£10,500

Oaklands School
8 Albion Hill, Loughton,
Essex IG10 4RA
Tel: 020 8508 3517
Group Managing Principal: Mr M
Hagger
Age range: 2–16
No. of pupils: 243
Fees: Day £10,350–£10,575

Park School for Girls
20-22 Park Avenue,
Ilford, Essex IG1 4RS
Tel: 020 8554 2466
Headmistress: Mrs Androulla
Nicholas
Age range: G4–16
No. of pupils: 230 VIth19
Fees: Day £6,795–£10,260

Raphael Independent School
Park Lane, Hornchurch,
Essex RM11 1XY
Tel: 01708 744735
Head of School: Mrs C Salmon
Age range: 4–16
No. of pupils: 135
Fees: Day £6,285–£9,045

St Aubyn's School
Bunces Lane, Woodford
Green, Essex IG8 9DU
Tel: 020 8504 1577
Headmaster: Mr Leonard Blom
BEd(Hons) BA NPQH
Age range: 3–13
No. of pupils: 525
Fees: Day £5,370–£12,195

St Mary's Hare Park School & Nursery
South Drive, Gidea Park,
Romford, Essex RM2 6HH
Tel: 01708 761220
Head Teacher: Mrs K Karwacinski
Age range: 2–11
No. of pupils: 180
Fees: Day £8,775

Stratford College of Management
1-7 Hainault Street,
Ilford, Essex IG1 4EL
Tel: 020 8553 0205
Head: Dr Raza

The Ursuline Preparatory School Ilford
2-8 Coventry Road,
Ilford, Essex IG1 4QR
Tel: 020 8518 4050
Headteacher: Mrs Victoria
McNaughton
Age range: G3–11
No. of pupils: 159
Fees: Day £7,320–£9,828

Woodford Green Preparatory School
Glengall Road, Woodford
Green, Essex IG8 0BZ
Tel: 020 8504 5045
Headmaster: Mr J P Wadge
Age range: 3–11
No. of pupils: 384
Fees: Day £3,390

Hertfordshire

Lyonsdown School
3 Richmond Road, New Barnet,
Barnet, Hertfordshire EN5 1SA
Tel: 020 8449 0225
Head: Mr C Hammond BA (Hons)
PGCE
Age range: B3–7 G3–11
No. of pupils: 185
Fees: Day £4,080–£10,200

MOUNT HOUSE SCHOOL
For further details see p. 95
Camlet Way, Hadley Wood,
Barnet, Hertfordshire EN4 0NJ
Tel: 020 8449 6889
Email: admissions@
mounthouse.org.uk
Website:
www.mounthouse.org.uk
Principal: Mr Toby Mullins
Age range: 11–18
No. of pupils: 190
Fees: Day £16,560

Norfolk Lodge Montessori
Nursery & Pre-Prep School
Dancers Hill Road, Barnet,
Hertfordshire EN5 4RP
Tel: 020 8447 1565
Nursery Manager: Suzanne Clarke
Age range: 6 months–7 years
No. of pupils: 140

Susi Earnshaw
Theatre School
68 High Street, Barnet,
Hertfordshire EN5 5SJ
Tel: 020 8441 5010
Head of School: Julia VanEllis-
Hammond BA Hons
Age range: 9–16
No. of pupils: 60
Fees: Day £9,000–£12,000

The Royal Masonic
School for Girls
Rickmansworth Park,
Rickmansworth,
Hertfordshire WD3 4HF
Tel: 01923 773168
Headmaster: Mr Kevin Carson
M.Phil (Cambridge)
Age range: G4–18
No. of pupils: 930 VIth165
Fees: Day £11,475–£17,475 WB
£20,115–£27,495 FB £21,225–£29,835

Kent

Ashgrove School
116 Widmore Road,
Bromley, Kent BR1 3BE
Tel: 020 8460 4143
Principal: Patricia Ash CertEd,
BSc(Hons), PhD, CMath, FIMA
Age range: 4–11
No. of pupils: 106
Fees: Day £8,730

BABINGTON HOUSE
SCHOOL
For further details see p. 87
Grange Drive, Chislehurst,
Kent BR7 5ES
Tel: 020 8467 5537
Email: enquiries@
babingtonhouse.com
Website:
www.babingtonhouse.com
Headmaster: Mr Tim Lello MA,
FRSA, NPQH
Age range: 3–18
No. of pupils: 387

Beckenham College
The Clockhouse Business Centre,
Unit 2, Thayers Farm Road,
Beckenham, Kent BR3 4LZ
Tel: 020 8650 3321
Principal: Mrs E Wakeling
Age range: 16+
Fees: Day £100–£3,500

Benedict House
Preparatory School
1-5 Victoria Road, Sidcup,
Kent DA15 7HD
Tel: 020 8300 7206
Headteacher: Mr Malcolm Gough
Age range: 3–11
Fees: Day £3,807–£7,929

Bickley Park School
24 Page Heath Lane, Bickley,
Bromley, Kent BR1 2DS
Tel: 020 8467 2195
Headmaster: Mr Patrick Wenham
Age range: B3–13 G3–4
No. of pupils: 370
Fees: Day £6,990–£14,940

Bird College
The Centre, 27 Station Road,
Sidcup, Kent DA15 7EB
Tel: 020 8300 6004/3031
Principal & Chief Executive: Ms
Shirley Coen BA(Hons), FSRA
Fees: Day £0

Bishop Challoner School
228 Bromley Road, Shortlands,
Bromley, Kent BR2 0BS
Tel: 020 8460 3546
Headteacher: Ms Paula Anderson
Age range: 3–18
No. of pupils: 363
Fees: Day £8,331–£11,547

Breaside Preparatory
School
41-43 Orchard Road,
Bromley, Kent BR1 2PR
Tel: 020 8460 0916
Executive Principal: Mrs Karen A
Nicholson B.Ed, NPQH, Dip EYs
Age range: 2 1/2–11
No. of pupils: 360
Fees: Day £11,070–£12,900

BROMLEY HIGH
SCHOOL GDST
For further details see p. 89
Blackbrook Lane, Bickley,
Bromley, Kent BR1 2TW
Tel: 020 8781 7000/1
Email: bhs@bro.gdst.net
Website:
www.bromleyhigh.gdst.net
Head: Mrs A M Drew BA(Hons),
MBA (Dunelm)
Age range: G4–18
No. of pupils: 892
Fees: Day £13,782–£17,091

Darul Uloom London
Foxbury Avenue, Perry Street,
Chislehurst, Kent BR7 6SD
Tel: 020 8295 0637
Principal: Mufti Mustafa
Age range: B11–18
No. of pupils: 160
Fees: FB £2,400

Farringtons School
Perry Street, Chislehurst,
Kent BR7 6LR
Tel: 020 8467 0256
Head: Mrs Dorothy Nancekievill
Age range: 3–18
No. of pupils: 700 VIth100
Fees: Day £15,120 WB
£29,850 FB £31,680

Merton Court
Preparatory School
38 Knoll Road, Sidcup,
Kent DA14 4QU
Tel: 020 8300 2112
Headmaster: Mr Dominic Price
BEd, MBA
Age range: 3–11
Fees: Day £8,670–£12,765

St Christopher's
The Hall School
49 Bromley Road,
Beckenham, Kent BR3 5PA
Tel: 020 8650 2200
Headmaster: Mr A Velasco MEd,
BH(Hons), PGCE
Age range: 3–11
No. of pupils: 305
Fees: Day £3,750–£9,165

St. David's Prep
Justin Hall,, Beckenham Road,
West Wickham, Kent BR4 0QS
Tel: 020 8777 5852
Principal: Mrs J Foulger
Age range: 4–11
No. of pupils: 155
Fees: Day £5,850–£8,550

West Lodge School
36 Station Road, Sidcup,
Kent DA15 7DU
Tel: 020 8300 2489
Head Teacher: Mr Robert Francis
Age range: 3–11
No. of pupils: 163
Fees: Day £5,475–£9,150

Wickham Court School
Schiller International,
Layhams Road, West
Wickham, Kent BR4 9HW
Tel: 020 8777 2942
Head: Mrs Lisa Harries
Age range: 2–16
No. of pupils: 121
Fees: Day £6,983.40–£12,344.55

Middlesex

360 GSP College
6th Floor, Wembley Point,
1 Harrow Road, Wembley,
Middlesex HA9 6DE
Tel: 020 8672 4151/0845
6034709
Head: Mr Yassin Sayfoo
⑯

Acorn House College
39-47 High Street, Southall,
Middlesex UB1 3HF
Tel: 020 8571 9900
Principal: Dr Francis Choi
Age range: 13–19
No. of pupils: 121 VIth85
Fees: Day £4,100–£15,525
⑯ Ⓐ

**ACS Hillingdon
International School**
Hillingdon Court, 108 Vine
Lane, Hillingdon, Uxbridge,
Middlesex UB10 0BE
Tel: +44 (0) 1895 259 771
Head: Martin Hall
Age range: 4–18
No. of pupils: 520
Fees: Day £10,640–£24,400
🌐 Ⓔ ⓘ ✐ ⑯

Alpha Preparatory School
21 Hindes Road, Harrow,
Middlesex HA1 1SH
Tel: 020 8427 1471
Head: C.J.W Trinidad BSc(Hons),
PGCE
Age range: 3–11
No. of pupils: 154
Fees: Day £3,400–£3,750

Ashton House School
50-52 Eversley Crescent,
Isleworth, Middlesex TW7 4LW
Tel: 020 8560 3902
Headteacher: Mrs Angela Stewart
Age range: 3–11
Fees: Day £7,986–£11,586
✐

**Buckingham
Preparatory School**
458 Rayners Lane, Pinner,
Harrow, Middlesex HA5 5DT
Tel: 020 8866 2737
Head of School: Mrs Sarah Hollis
Age range: B3–11 G3–4
Fees: Day £9,600–£12,300
🚹 Ⓔ ✐

Buxlow Preparatory School
5/6 Castleton Gardens,
Wembley, Middlesex HA9 7QJ
Tel: 020 8904 3615
Headteacher: Mr Ralf Furse
Age range: 2–11
Fees: Day £8,970–£9,330

**Edgware Jewish Girls
– Beis Chinuch**
Yeshurun Synagogue,
Fernhurst Gardens, Edgware,
Middlesex HA8 7PH
Tel: 020 8951 0239
Headteacher: Mr M Cohen
Age range: G3–7
🚹

Halliford School
Russell Road, Shepperton,
Middlesex TW17 9HX
Tel: 01932 223593
Head: Mr James Davies BMus
(Hons) LGSM FASC ACertCM PGCE
Age range: B11–18 G16–18
No. of pupils: 402
Fees: Day £15,960
🚹 Ⓐ Ⓔ ✐ ⑯

**Hampton Prep and
Pre-Prep School**
Gloucester Road, Hampton,
Middlesex TW12 2UQ
Tel: 020 8979 1844
Headmaster: Mr Tim Smith
Age range: 3–11
Fees: Day £6,030–£13,935
✐

Hampton School
Hanworth Road, Hampton,
Middlesex TW12 3HD
Tel: 020 8979 9273
Headmaster: Mr Kevin Knibbs MA
(Oxon)
Age range: B11–18
No. of pupils: 1200
Fees: Day £6,390
🚹 Ⓐ Ⓔ ✐ ⑯

Harrow School
5 High Street, Harrow on the
Hill, Middlesex HA1 3HT
Tel: 020 8872 8000
Interim Head Master: Mr Mel
Mrowiec
Age range: B13–18
No. of pupils: 830 VIth320
Fees: FB £40,050
🚹 Ⓐ 🏛 Ⓔ ✐ ⑯

Holland House School
1 Broadhurst Avenue, Edgware,
Middlesex HA8 8TP
Tel: 020 8958 6979
Headmistress: Mrs H Stanton-Tonner
BEd(Hons) PGCE
Age range: 4–11
No. of pupils: 150
Fees: Day £8,100
Ⓔ

Jack and Jill School
30 Nightingale Road, Hampton,
Middlesex TW12 3HX
Tel: 020 8979 3195
Principal: Miss K Papirnik BEd(Hons)
Age range: B2–5 G2–7
No. of pupils: 155
Fees: Day £4,608–£13,143
🚹

KEW HOUSE SCHOOL
For further details see p. 93
Kew House, 6 Capital
Interchange Way, London,
Middlesex TW8 0EX
Tel: 0208 742 2038
Email: info@
kewhouseschool.com
Website:
www.kewhouseschool.com
Headmaster: Mr Mark Hudson
Age range: 11–18
No. of pupils: 550
Fees: Day £7,129
Ⓐ ✐ ⑯

**Kids Inc Day
Nursery – Enfield**
8 Glyn Road, Southbury,
Enfield, Middlesex EN3 4JL
Tel: 020 8805 1144

Lady Eleanor Holles
Hanworth Road, Hampton,
Middlesex TW12 3HF
Tel: 020 8979 1601
Head of School: Mrs Heather
Hanbury
Age range: G7–18
No. of pupils: 875
Fees: Day £16,731–£20,196
🚹 Ⓐ Ⓔ ✐ ⑯

**Lady Nafisa Independent
Secondary School for Girls**
83A Sunbury Road, Feltham,
Middlesex TW13 4PH
Tel: 020 8751 5610
Headteacher: Ms Fouzia Butt
Age range: G11–16
🚹

Menorah Grammar School
Abbots Road, Edgware,
Middlesex HA8 0QS
Tel: 020 8906 9756
Headteacher: Rabbi A M Goldblatt
Age range: B11–17
No. of pupils: 203
🚹

Merchant Taylors' School
Sandy Lodge, Northwood,
Middlesex HA6 2HT
Tel: 01923 820644
Head: Mr S J Everson MA (Cantab)
Age range: B11–18
No. of pupils: 865 VIth282
Fees: Day £19,998
🚹 Ⓐ Ⓔ ✐ ⑯

Newland House School
Waldegrave Park, Twickenham,
Middlesex TW1 4TQ
Tel: 020 8865 1234
Headmaster: Mr D A Alexander
Age range: B3–13 G3–11
No. of pupils: 425
Fees: Day £3,848–£4,306
Ⓔ

**North London
Collegiate School**
Canons, Canons Drive,
Edgware, Middlesex HA8 7RJ
Tel: +44 (0)20 8952 0912
Headmistress: Mrs Sarah Clark
Age range: G4–18
No. of pupils: 1080
Fees: Day £5,641–£6,676
🚹 🌐 Ⓐ Ⓔ ⓘ ⑯

**Northwood College
for Girls GDST**
Maxwell Road, Northwood,
Middlesex HA6 2YE
Tel: 01923 825446
Head Mistress: Miss Jacqualyn Pain
MA, MA, MBA
Age range: G3–18
No. of pupils: 840 VIth100
🚹 Ⓐ Ⓔ ✐ ⑯

Oak Heights
3 Red Lion Court, Alexandra Road,
Hounslow, Middlesex TW3 1JS
Tel: 020 8577 1827
Head: Mr S Dhillon
Age range: 11–16
No. of pupils: 48
Fees: Day £6,000

Orley Farm School
South Hill Avenue, Harrow,
Middlesex HA1 3NU
Tel: 020 8869 7600
Headmaster: Mr Tim Calvey
Age range: 4–13
No. of pupils: 497
Fees: Day £14,160–£16,335
Ⓔ ✐

**Quainton Hall
School & Nursery**
91 Hindes Road, Harrow,
Middlesex HA1 1RX
Tel: 020 8861 8861
Headmaster: S Ford BEd (Hons),
UWE Bristol
Age range: B2–13 G2–11
Fees: Day £11,025–£12,150
Ⓔ

RADNOR HOUSE
For further details see p. 96
Pope's Villa, Cross
Deep, Twickenham,
Middlesex TW1 4QG
Tel: 020 8891 6264
Email: admissions@
radnorhouse.org
Website:
www.radnor-twickenham.org/
Head of School: Darryl Wideman
MA (Oxon.)
Age range: 9–18
No. of pupils: 417
🌐

Rambert School of Ballet & Contemporary Dance
Clifton Lodge, St Margaret's Drive, Twickenham, Middlesex TW1 1QN
Tel: 020 8892 9960
Principal: R McKim
Age range: 16+

16⁺

Reddiford School
36-38 Cecil Park, Pinner, Middlesex HA5 5HH
Tel: 020 8866 0660
Headteacher: Mrs J Batt CertEd, NPQH
Age range: 3–11
No. of pupils: 320
Fees: Day £4,860–£11,565

£

Regent College
Sai House, 167 Imperial Drive, Harrow, Middlesex HA2 7HD
Tel: 020 8966 9900
Principal: Mrs Tharshiny Pankaj
Age range: 11–19
No. of pupils: 167
Fees: Day £4,100–£15,525

16⁺ A 16⁺

Roxeth Mead School
Buckholt House, 25 Middle Road, Harrow, Middlesex HA2 0HW
Tel: 020 8422 2092
Headmistress: Mrs A Isaacs
Age range: 3–7
No. of pupils: 54
Fees: Day £4,800–£10,665

St Catherine's Prep
Cross Deep, Twickenham, Middlesex TW1 4QJ
Tel: 020 8891 2898
Headmistress: Mrs Johneen McPherson MA
Age range: G3–11
No. of pupils: 127
Fees: Day £10,794–£12,456

St Catherine's School
Cross Deep, Twickenham, Middlesex TW1 4QJ
Tel: 020 8891 2898
Headmistress: Mrs Johneen McPherson MA
Age range: G3–18
No. of pupils: 430
Fees: Day £10,795–£14,910

 A £ 16⁺

St Christopher's School
71 Wembley Park Drive, Wembley, Middlesex HA9 8HE
Tel: 020 8902 5069
Headteacher: Mr G. P. Musetti
Age range: 4–11
Fees: Day £9,006–£9,906

St Helen's College
Parkway, Hillingdon, Uxbridge, Middlesex UB10 9JX
Tel: 01895 234371
Head: Mrs. Shirley Drummond BA, PGCert, MLDP
Age range: 2–11
No. of pupils: 383
Fees: Day £9,600–£11,850

St Helen's School
Eastbury Road, Northwood, Middlesex HA6 3AS
Tel: +44 (0)1923 843210
Headmistress: Dr Mary Short BA, PhD
Age range: G3–18
No. of pupils: VIth165

   A £ 16⁺

St John's School
Potter Street Hill, Northwood, Middlesex HA6 3QY
Tel: 020 8866 0067
Headmaster: Mr M S Robinson BSc
Age range: B3–13 years
No. of pupils: 350
Fees: Day £10,420–£15,110

 £

St John's Senior School
North Lodge, The Ridgeway, Enfield, Middlesex EN2 8BE
Tel: 020 8366 0035
Headmaster: Mr Andrew Tardios LLB(Hons), BA(Hons), CertEd
Age range: 11–18 years
No. of pupils: 309 VIth95
Fees: Day £13,170

A 16⁺

St Martin's School
40 Moor Park Road, Northwood, Middlesex HA6 2DJ
Tel: 01923 825740
Headmaster: Mr D T Tidmarsh BSc(Wales)
Age range: B3–13
No. of pupils: 400
Fees: Day £5,775–£15,135

 £

Tashbar Primary School
Mowbray Road, Edgware, Middlesex HA8 8JL
Tel: 020 8958 5162
Headteacher: Mr N Jaffe
Age range: B3–11
No. of pupils: 88

The Hall Pre-Preparatory School & Nursery
The Grange Country House, Rickmansworth Road, Northwood, Middlesex HA6 2RB
Tel: 01923 822807
Headmistress: Mrs S M Goodwin
Age range: 1–7
Fees: Day £4,650–£9,900

£

The John Lyon School
Middle Road, Harrow on the Hill, Middlesex HA2 0HN
Tel: 020 8515 9400
Head: Miss Katherine Haynes BA, MEd, NPQH
Age range: B11–18
No. of pupils: 600

 A £ 16⁺

The Mall School
185 Hampton Road, Twickenham, Middlesex TW2 5NQ
Tel: 0208 977 2523
Headmaster: Mr D C Price BSc, MA
Age range: B4–13
No. of pupils: 320
Fees: Day £12,240–£13,767

 £

The St Michael Steiner School
Park Road, Hanworth Park, London, Middlesex TW13 6PN
Tel: 0208 893 1299
Age range: 3–16 (17 from Jul 2014)
No. of pupils: 101
Fees: Day £3,850–£9,500

£

Twickenham Preparatory School
Beveree, 43 High Street, Hampton, Middlesex TW12 2SA
Tel: 020 8979 6216
Head: Mr David Malam BA(Hons) (Southampton), PGCE(Winchester)
Age range: B4–13 G4–11
No. of pupils: 273
Fees: Day £10,470–£11,340

£

Surrey

Al-Khair School
109-117 Cherry Orchard Road, Croydon, Surrey CR0 6BE
Tel: 020 8662 8664
Headteacher: Mr Mohammad R Chaudhry
Age range: 5–16
No. of pupils: 126

Broomfield House School
Broomfield Road, Kew Gardens, Richmond, Surrey TW9 3HS
Tel: 020 8940 3884
Head Teacher: Mr N O York BA(Hons), MA, MPhil, FRSA
Age range: 3–11
No. of pupils: 160
Fees: Day £7,104–£14,319

Cambridge Tutors College
Water Tower Hill, Croydon, Surrey CR0 5SX
Tel: 020 8688 5284/7363
Principal: Dr Chris Drew
Age range: 15–19
No. of pupils: 215 VIth200
Fees: Day £10,400–£22,995

16⁺ A £ 16⁺

Canbury School
Kingston Hill, Kingston upon Thames, Surrey KT2 7LN
Tel: 020 8549 8622
Headmistress: Ms Louise Clancy
Age range: 11–18
No. of pupils: 58
Fees: Day £16,401

£

Collingwood School
3 Springfield Road, Wallington, Surrey SM6 0BD
Tel: 020 8647 4607
Headmaster: Mr Leigh Hardie
Age range: 3–11
No. of pupils: 120
Fees: Day £4,980–£8,925

Croydon High School GDST
Old Farleigh Road, Selsdon, South Croydon, Surrey CR2 8YB
Tel: 020 8260 7500
Headmistress: Mrs Emma Pattison
Age range: G3–18
No. of pupils: 580 VIth75

 A £ 16⁺

Cumnor House Nursery
91 Pampisford Road, South Croydon, Surrey CR2 6DH
Tel: +44 (0)20 8660 3445
Headmaster: Mr Daniel Cummings
Age range: 2–4
No. of pupils: 200
Fees: Day £4,980–£10,635

CUMNOR HOUSE SCHOOL FOR BOYS
For further details see p. 90
168 Pampisford Road, South
Croydon, Surrey CR2 6DA
Tel: 020 8645 2614
Email: admissions@
cumnorhouse.com
Website:
www.cumnorhouse.com
Headmaster: Mr Daniel
Cummings
Age range: B2–13
No. of pupils: 423
Fees: Day £3,715–£4,460

CUMNOR HOUSE SCHOOL FOR GIRLS
For further details see p. 91
1 Woodcote Lane, Purley,
Surrey CR8 3HB
Tel: 020 8645 2614
Email: admissions@
cumnorhouse.com
Website:
www.cumnorhouse.com
Headmistress: Mrs Amanda
McShane
Age range: G2–11
No. of pupils: 138
Fees: Day £3,715–£4,460

Educare Small School
12 Cowleaze Road, Kingston
upon Thames, Surrey KT2 6DZ
Tel: 020 8547 0144
Head Teacher: Mrs E Steinthal
Age range: 3–11
No. of pupils: 46
Fees: Day £6,240

Elmhurst School
44-48 South Park Hill Rd, South
Croydon, Surrey CR2 7DW
Tel: 020 8688 0661
Headmaster: Mr Tony Padfield
Age range: B3–11
No. of pupils: 207
Fees: Day £6,129–£11,403

Holy Cross Preparatory School
George Road, Kingston upon
Thames, Surrey KT2 7NU
Tel: 020 8942 0729
Headteacher: Mrs S Hair BEd(Hons)
Age range: G4–11
No. of pupils: 285
Fees: Day £12,996

Homefield Preparatory School
Western Road, Sutton,
Surrey SM1 2TE
Tel: 0208 642 0965
Headmaster: Mr John Towers
Age range: B3–13
No. of pupils: 350
Fees: Day £6,210–£13,320

Kew College
24-26 Cumberland Road,
Kew, Surrey TW9 3HQ
Tel: 020 8940 2039
Head: Mrs Marianne Austin
BSc(Hons), MA(Hons), ACA, PGCE
Age range: 3–11
No. of pupils: 296

KEW GREEN PREPARATORY SCHOOL
For further details see p. 92
Layton House, Ferry Lane,
Kew Green, Richmond,
Surrey TW9 3AF
Tel: 020 8948 5999
Email: secretary@kgps.co.uk
Website: www.kgps.co.uk
Headmaster: Mr J Peck
Age range: 4–11
No. of pupils: 270
Fees: Day £5,857

King's House School
68 King's Road, Richmond,
Surrey TW10 6ES
Tel: 020 8940 1878
Head: Mr Mark Turner BA, PGCE,
NPQH
Age range: B3–13 G3–4
No. of pupils: 460
Fees: Day £2,370–£5,560

Kingston Grammar School
70 London Rd, Kingston upon
Thames, Surrey KT2 6PY
Tel: 020 8456 5875
Head: Mr Stephen Lehec
Age range: 11–18
No. of pupils: 829
Fees: Day £6,225

Laleham Lea School
29 Peaks Hill, Purley, Surrey CR8 3JJ
Tel: 020 8660 3351
Headteacher: Ms K Barry
Age range: 3–11
Fees: Day £7,110–£7,830

MARYMOUNT INTERNATIONAL SCHOOL LONDON
For further details see p. 94
George Road, Kingston upon
Thames, Surrey KT2 7PE
Tel: +44 (0)20 8949 0571
Email: admissions@
marymountlondon.com
Website:
www.marymountlondon.com
Headmistress: Mrs Margaret
Frazier
Age range: G11–18
No. of pupils: 250
Fees: Day £24,985 WB
£40,515 FB £42,305

Oakwood Independent School
Godstone Road, Purley,
Surrey CR8 2AN
Tel: 020 8668 8080
Headmaster: Mr Ciro Candia
BA(Hons), PGCE
Age range: 3–11
No. of pupils: 176
Fees: Day £9,030–£9,840

Old Palace of John Whitgift School
Old Palace Road, Croydon,
Surrey CR0 1AX
Tel: 020 8686 7347
Head: Mrs. C Jewell
Age range: B3 months–4
years G3 months–19 years
No. of pupils: 740 VIth120
Fees: Day £11,316–£15,366

Old Vicarage School
48 Richmond Hill, Richmond,
Surrey TW10 6QX
Tel: 020 8940 0922
Headmistress: Mrs G D Linthwaite
Age range: G4–11
No. of pupils: 200
Fees: Day £4,740

Park Hill School
8 Queens Road, Kingston upon
Thames, Surrey KT2 7SH
Tel: 020 8546 5496
Headmaster: Mr Alistair Bond
Age range: 2–11
No. of pupils: 100
Fees: Day £10,440

Reedham Park School
71A Old Lodge Lane,
Purley, Surrey CR8 4DN
Tel: 020 8660 6357
Headteacher: Mrs Katie Shah
Age range: 4–11
No. of pupils: 122
Fees: Day £5,385

Rokeby School
George Road, Kingston upon
Thames, Surrey KT2 7PB
Tel: 020 8942 2247
Head: Mr J R Peck
Age range: B4–13
No. of pupils: 370
Fees: Day £13,377–£16,656

Royal Russell Junior School
Coombe Lane, Croydon,
Surrey CR9 5BX
Tel: 020 8651 5884
Junior School Headmaster: Mr
James C Thompson
Age range: 3–11
No. of pupils: 300
Fees: Day £11,160–£14,220

Royal Russell School
Coombe Lane, Croydon,
Surrey CR9 5BX
Tel: 020 8657 3669
Headmaster: Christopher
Hutchinson
Age range: 11–18
No. of pupils: 590 VIth180
Fees: Day £18,480 FB £36,525

Seaton House School
67 Banstead Road South,
Sutton, Surrey SM2 5LH
Tel: 020 8642 2332
Headmistress: Mrs Debbie Morrison
Higher Diploma in Education (RSA)
Age range: B3–5 G3–11
No. of pupils: 164
Fees: Day £10,188

Shrewsbury House School
107 Ditton Road, Surbiton,
Surrey KT6 6RL
Tel: 020 8399 3066
Headmaster: Mr K Doble BA, PDM,
PGCE
Age range: B7–13
No. of pupils: 320
Fees: Day £18,060

St David's School
23/25 Woodcote Valley Road,
Purley, Surrey CR8 3AL
Tel: 020 8660 0723
Headmistress: Cressida Mardell
Age range: 3–11
No. of pupils: 167
Fees: Day £6,375–£10,650

St James Senior Boys School
Church Road, Ashford,
Surrey TW15 3DZ
Tel: 01784 266930
Headmaster: Mr David Brazier
Age range: B11–18
No. of pupils: 403 VIth65
Fees: Day £18,930

Staines Preparatory School
3 Gresham Road, Staines upon
Thames, Surrey TW18 2BT
Tel: 01784 450909
Head of School: Ms Samantha
Sawyer B.Ed (Hons), M.Ed, NPQH
Age range: 3–11
No. of pupils: 364
Fees: Day £9,810–£11,460

Surbiton High School
13-15 Surbiton Crescent, Kingston
upon Thames, Surrey KT1 2JT
Tel: 020 8546 5245
Principal: Mrs Rebecca Glover
Age range: B4–11 G4–18
No. of pupils: 1210 VIth186
Fees: Day £10,857–£17,142

Sutton High School GDST
55 Cheam Road, Sutton,
Surrey SM1 2AX
Tel: 020 8642 0594
Headmistress: Mrs Katharine
Crouch
Age range: G3–18
No. of pupils: 600 VIth60
Fees: Day £10,095–£17,043

The Cedars School
Coombe Road, Lloyd Park,
Croydon, Surrey CR0 5RD
Tel: 020 8185 7770
Headmaster: Robert Teague Bsc
(Hons)
Age range: B11–18

The Falcons Preparatory School for Boys
41 Few Foot Road, Richmond,
Surrey TW9 2SS
Tel: 0844 225 2211
Headmistress: Franciska Bayliss
Age range: B7–13
No. of pupils: 100
Fees: Day £17,835

The Royal Ballet School
White Lodge, Richmond,
Surrey TW10 5HR
Tel: 020 7836 8899
Artistic Director: Christopher
Powney
Age range: 11–19
No. of pupils: VIth80
Fees: Day £18,939–£24,885
FB £29,328–£33,567

The Secretary College
123 South End, Croydon,
Surrey CR0 1BJ
Tel: 0208 688 4440
Principal: Mr J E K Safo

The Study School
57 Thetford Road, New
Malden, Surrey KT3 5DP
Tel: 020 8942 0754
Head of School: Mrs Donna
Brackstone-Drake
Age range: 3–11
No. of pupils: 134
Fees: Day £4,860–£11,388

Trinity School
Shirley Park, Croydon,
Surrey CR9 7AT
Tel: 020 8656 9541
Head: Alasdair Kennedy MA
(Cantab)
Age range: B10–18 G16–18
No. of pupils: 1007
Fees: Day £16,656

Unicorn School
238 Kew Road, Richmond,
Surrey TW9 3JX
Tel: 020 8948 3926
Headmaster: Mr Kit Thompson
Age range: 3–11
Fees: Day £6,930–£12,720

Westbury House
80 Westbury Road, New
Malden, Surrey KT3 5AS
Tel: 020 8942 5885
Head of School: Rosalyn Holiday
Age range: 3–11
Fees: Day £4,860–£11,115

Whitgift School
Haling Park, South Croydon,
Surrey CR2 6YT
Tel: +44 (0)20 8688 9222
Headmaster: Mr Christopher
Ramsey
Age range: B10–18
No. of pupils: 1464
Fees: Day £20,136 WB
£32,274 FB £37,866

Schools in the South-East

KEY TO SYMBOLS

- 🏃 Boys' school
- 🏃 Girls' school
- 🌐 International school
- 16ᵗ Tutorial or sixth form college
- Ⓐ A levels
- 🏛 Boarding accommodation
- £ Bursaries
- IB International Baccalaureate
- 🏊 Learning support
- 16ᵗ Entrance at 16+
- 🎓 Vocational qualifications
- IAPS Independent Association of Prep Schools
- HMC The Headmasters' & Headmistresses' Conference
- ISA Independent Schools Association
- GSA Girls' School Association
- BSA Boarding Schools' Association
- S Society of Heads

Unless otherwise indicated, all schools are coeducational day schools. Single-sex and boarding schools will be indicated by the relevant icon.

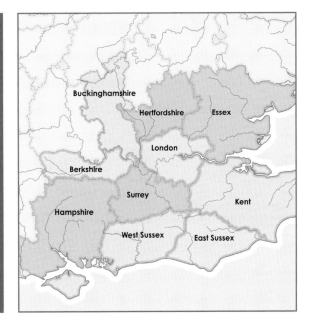

Berkshire

ABI College
Reading Campus, 80 London
Street, Reading, Berkshire RG1 4SJ
Tel: 0118 956 9111
Head: Alan McColm
16+

Alder Bridge School
Bridge House, Mill Lane, Padworth,
Reading, Berkshire RG7 4JU
Tel: 0118 971 4471
Age range: 0–14 years
No. of pupils: 65
Fees: Day £6,015–£8,880

Bradfield College
Bradfield, Berkshire RG7 6AU
Tel: 0118 964 4516
Headmaster: Dr Christopher
Stevens
Age range: 13–18
No. of pupils: 800
Fees: Day £29,925 FB £37,404

Caversham School
16 Peppard Road, Caversham,
Reading, Berkshire RG4 8JZ
Tel: 01189 478 684
Head: Mr Chris Neal
Age range: 4–11
No. of pupils: 60
Fees: Day £9,900

Chiltern College
16 Peppard Road, Caversham,
Reading, Berkshire RG4 8JZ
Tel: 0118 947 1847
Head: Christine Lawrence
16+

Claires Court Junior Boys
Maidenhead Thicket,
Maidenhead, Berkshire SL6 3QE
Tel: 01628 327700
Head: J M E Spanswick
Age range: B4–11
No. of pupils: 248
Fees: Day £9,270–£15,930

Claires Court Nursery,
Girls and Sixth Form
1 College Avenue, Maidenhead,
Berkshire SL6 6AW
Tel: 01628 327700
Head of School: Mrs M Heywood
Age range: B16–18 G3–18
No. of pupils: 495 VIth111
Fees: Day £9,270–£16,740

Claires Court Senior Boys
Ray Mill Road East, Maidenhead,
Berkshire SL6 8TE
Tel: 01628 327700
Headmaster: Mr J M Rayer BSc,
PGCE
Age range: B11–16
No. of pupils: 335 VIth112
Fees: Day £15,930–£16,740

Crosfields School
Shinfield, Reading,
Berkshire RG2 9BL
Tel: 0118 987 1810
Headmaster: Mr Craig Watson
Age range: 3–13
No. of pupils: 510
Fees: Day £10,314–£15,159

Dolphin School
Waltham Road, Hurst, Reading,
Berkshire RG10 0FR
Tel: 0118 934 1277
Head: Mr Adam Hurst
Age range: 3–13
Fees: Day £10,170–£14,070

Eagle House School
Sandhurst, Berkshire GU47 8PH
Tel: 01344 772134
Headmaster: Mr A P N Barnard
BA(Hons), PGCE
Age range: 3–13
No. of pupils: 380
Fees: Day £11,580–£18,105
FB £24,330

Elstree School
Woolhampton, Reading,
Berkshire RG7 5TD
Tel: 0118 971 3302
Headmaster: Mr S Inglis
Age range: B3–13 G3–8
No. of pupils: 248
Fees: Day £11,550–£21,000
WB £26,250–£26,850 FB
£26,700–£27,300

Eton College
Windsor, Berkshire SL4 6DW
Tel: 01753 671249
Head Master: Simon Henderson MA
Age range: B13–18
No. of pupils: 1300 VIth520
Fees: FB £40,668

Eton End PNEU School
35 Eton Road, Datchet,
Slough, Berkshire SL3 9AX
Tel: 01753 541075
Headmistress: Sarah Stokes
BA(Hons), PGCE
Age range: B3–7 G3–11
No. of pupils: 245
Fees: Day £9,375–£11,985

Heathfield School
London Road, Ascot,
Berkshire SL5 8BQ
Tel: 01344 898342
Head of School: Mrs Marina
Gardiner Legge
Age range: G11–18
No. of pupils: 200

Hemdean House School
Hemdean Road, Caversham,
Reading, Berkshire RG4 7SD
Tel: 0118 947 2590
Head Teacher: Mrs H Chalmers BSc
Age range: B4–11 G4–11
Fees: Day £8,490–£9,300

Herries Preparatory School
Dean Lane, Cookham
Dean, Berkshire SL6 9BD
Tel: 01628 483350
Headmistress: Fiona Long
Age range: 3–11
Fees: Day £9,210–£10,800

Highfield Preparatory
School
2 West Road, Maidenhead,
Berkshire SL6 1PD
Tel: 01628 624918
Headteacher: Mrs Joanna Leach
Age range: B3–5 G3–11
Fees: Day £9,225–£12,180

Holme Grange School
Heathlands Road, Wokingham,
Berkshire RG40 3AL
Tel: 0118 978 1566
Headteacher: Mrs Claire Robinson
Age range: 3–16 years
No. of pupils: 509
Fees: Day £10,185–£14,985

Impact International
College
81 London Street, Reading,
Berkshire RG1 4QA
Tel: 0118 956 0610
Head: Mr Alan Loveridge
16+

Kids Inc Day Nursery
– Crowthorne
59-61 Dukes Ride, Crowthorne,
Berkshire RG45 6NS
Tel: 01344 780670

Lambrook School
Winkfield Row, Nr Ascot,
Berkshire RG42 6LU
Tel: 01344 882717
Headmaster: Mr Jonathan Perry
Age range: 3–13
No. of pupils: 540
Fees: Day £11,250–£19,737
WB £22,008–£23,664

LEIGHTON PARK SCHOOL
For further details see p. 102
Shinfield Road, Reading,
Berkshire RG2 7ED
Tel: 0118 987 9600
Email: admissions@
leightonpark.com
Website:
www.leightonpark.com
Head: Mr Matthew L S Judd BA,
PGCE
Age range: 11–18
No. of pupils: 460

Long Close School
Upton Court Road, Upton,
Slough, Berkshire SL3 7LU
Tel: 01753 520095
Headteacher (Interim): Kam Nijjar
Age range: 2–16
No. of pupils: 329

Luckley House School
Luckley Road, Wokingham,
Berkshire RG40 3EU
Tel: 0118 978 4175
Head: Mrs Jane Tudor
Age range: G11–18
No. of pupils: 230
Fees: Day £16,620 WB
£26,955 FB £29,082

Ludgrove
Wokingham, Berkshire RG40 3AB
Tel: 0118 978 9881
Head of School: Mr Simon Barber
Age range: B8–13
No. of pupils: 190

LVS ASCOT
For further details see p. 104
London Road, Ascot,
Berkshire SL5 8DR
Tel: 01344 882770
Email: enquiries@lvs.
ascot.sch.uk
Website: www.lvs.ascot.sch.uk
Headmistress: Mrs Christine
Cunniffe BA (Hons), MMus, MBA
Age range: 4–18
No. of pupils: 830
Fees: Day £10,380–£19,896
FB £26,562–£34,953

Meadowbrook
Montessori School
Malt Hill Road, Warfield,
Bracknell, Berkshire RG42 6JQ
Tel: 01344 890869
Director of Education: Mrs S Gunn
Age range: 3–11
No. of pupils: 78
Fees: Day £10,044–£11,385

Newbold School
Popeswood Road, Binfield,
Bracknell, Berkshire RG42 4AH
Tel: 01344 421088
Headteacher: Mrs Jaki Crissey MA,
BA, PGCE Primary
Age range: 3–11
Fees: Day £4,500

Our Lady's Preparatory School
The Avenue, Crowthorne,
Wokingham, Berkshire RG45 6PB
Tel: 01344 773394
Headmistress: Mrs Helene Robinson
Age range: 3 months–11 years
No. of pupils: 100
Fees: Day £7,080

Padworth College
Padworth, Reading,
Berkshire RG7 4NR
Tel: 0118 983 2644
Acting Principal: Mr Chris Randell
Age range: 13–19
No. of pupils: 116 VIth50
Fees: Day £14,400 FB £29,400

PANGBOURNE COLLEGE
For further details see p. 105
Pangbourne, Reading,
Berkshire RG8 8LA
Tel: 0118 984 2101
Email: admissions@
pangbourne.com
Website:
www.pangbourne.com
Headmaster: Thomas J C
Garnier
Age range: 11–18
No. of pupils: 429 VIth62
Fees: Day £17,655–£24,885
FB £24,870–£35,190

Papplewick School
Windsor Road, Ascot,
Berkshire SL5 7LH
Tel: 01344 621488
Head: Mr T W Bunbury BA, PGCE
Age range: B6–13
No. of pupils: 195

Queen Anne's School
6 Henley Road, Caversham,
Reading, Berkshire RG4 6DX
Tel: 0118 918 7300
Headmistress: Mrs Julia Harrington
BA(Hons), PGCE, NPQH
Age range: G11–18
No. of pupils: 336 VIth100
Fees: Day £24,135 WB
£32,070–£33,810 FB £35,580

Queensmead School
King's Road, Windsor,
Berkshire SL4 2AX
Tel: 01753 863779
Head: Mr Simon Larter
Age range: 2–18
No. of pupils: 300
Fees: Day £7,128–£15,318

Reading Blue Coat School
Holme Park, Sonning Lane, Sonning,
Reading, Berkshire RG4 6SU
Tel: 0118 944 1005
Headmaster: Mr Jesse Elzinga
Age range: B11–18 G16–18
No. of pupils: 710 VIth230
Fees: Day £16,695

Reddam House Berkshire
Bearwood Road, Sindlesham,
Wokingham, Berkshire RG41 5BG
Tel: 0118 974 8300
Principal: Mrs Tammy Howard
Age range: 3 months–18 years
No. of pupils: 570
Fees: Day £10,200–£17,280 WB
£27,075–£31,215 FB £28,665–£32,805

Redroofs School for the Performing Arts (Redroofs Theatre School)
26 Bath Road, Maidenhead,
Berkshire SL6 4JT
Tel: 01628 674092
Principal: June Rose
Age range: 8–18
No. of pupils: 100
Fees: Day £4,882–£5,527

St Andrew's School
Buckhold, Pangbourne,
Reading, Berkshire RG8 8QA
Tel: 0118 974 4276
Headmaster: Mr Jonathan Bartlett
BSc QTS
Age range: 3–13
Fees: Day £5,430–£18,150 WB £3,360

St Bernard's Preparatory School
Hawtrey Close, Slough,
Berkshire SL1 1TB
Tel: 01753 521821
Head Teacher: Mr N Cheesman
Age range: 2–11
Fees: Day £8,850–£10,545

St Edward's Prep
64 Tilehurst Road, Reading,
Berkshire RG30 2JH
Tel: 0118 957 4342
Headmaster: Derek Suttie
Age range: B4–11
No. of pupils: 170
Fees: Day £6,585–£11,025

St George's Ascot
Wells Lane, Ascot, Berkshire SL5 7DZ
Tel: 01344 629920
Headmistress: Mrs Liz Hewer MA
(Hons) (Cantab) PGCE
Age range: G11–18
No. of pupils: 270 VIth70
Fees: Day £22,800 WB
£34,050–£34,680 FB £35,460

St George's School Windsor Castle
Windsor, Berkshire SL4 1QF
Tel: 01753 865553
Head Master: Mr J R Jones
Age range: 3–13
Fees: Day £10,044–£16,674
WB £20,700 FB £21,438

ST JOHN'S BEAUMONT PREPARATORY SCHOOL
For further details see p. 107
Priest Hill, Old Windsor,
Berkshire SL4 2JN
Tel: 01784 432428
Email: abarker@sjb.email
Website: www.sjbwindsor.uk
Headmaster: Mr G E F Delaney
BA(Hons), PGCE, MSc (Oxon)
Age range: B3–13
No. of pupils: 290
Fees: Day £3,264–£6,244
FB £7,580–£9,573

St Joseph's College
Upper Redlands Road,
Reading, Berkshire RG1 5JT
Tel: 0118 966 1000
Headmaster: Mr Andrew Colpus
Age range: 3–18
No. of pupils: VIth65
Fees: Day £6,672–£11,406

St Mary's School Ascot
St Mary's Road, Ascot,
Berkshire SL5 9JF
Tel: 01344 296614
Headmistress: Mrs Mary Breen
BSc, MSc
Age range: G11–18
No. of pupils: 390 VIth120
Fees: Day £26,190 FB £36,780

St Piran's Preparatory School
Gringer Hill, Maidenhead,
Berkshire SL6 7LZ
Tel: 01628 594302
Headmaster: Mr J A Carroll
BA(Hons), BPhilEd, PGCE, NPQH
Age range: 3–11
Fees: Day £10,857–£16,566

Sunningdale School
Dry Arch Road, Sunningdale,
Berkshire SL5 9PY
Tel: 01344 620159
Headmaster: Tom Dawson MA,
PGCE
Age range: B7–13
No. of pupils: 90

Teikyo School UK
Framewood Road, Wexham,
Slough, Berkshire SL2 4QS
Tel: 01753 663711
Headmaster: Tadashi Nakayama
Age range: 16–18

The Abbey School
Kendrick Road, Reading,
Berkshire RG1 5DZ
Tel: 0118 987 2256
Head: Mrs Rachel S E Dent
Age range: G3–18
No. of pupils: 1100
Fees: Day £17,040

The Marist Preparatory School
King's Road, Sunninghill,
Ascot, Berkshire SL5 7PS
Tel: 01344 626137
Vice Principal: Jane Gow
Age range: G2–11
No. of pupils: 225
Fees: Day £9,780–£11,940

The Marist Schools
King's Road, Sunninghill,
Ascot, Berkshire SL5 7PS
Tel: 01344 624291
Head of Secondary School: Mr K
McCloskey
Age range: G2–18
No. of pupils: 550 VIth60
Fees: Day £9,780–£14,610

The Oratory Preparatory School
Great Oaks, Goring Heath,
Reading, Berkshire RG8 7SF
Tel: 0118 984 4511
Headmaster: Mr Rob Stewart
Age range: 2–13
No. of pupils: 400
Fees: Day £10,266–£16,443
WB £21,153 FB £24,522

The Oratory School
Woodcote, Reading,
Berkshire RG8 0PJ
Tel: 01491 683500
Head Master: Mr J J Smith BA(Hons),
MEd, PGCE
Age range: B11–18
No. of pupils: 380 VIth120
Fees: Day £24,966 FB £34,299

The Vine Christian School
SORCF Christian Centre,
Basingstoke Road, Three Mile
Cross, Reading, Berkshire RG7 1AT
Tel: 0118 988 6464
Head of School: Mrs Eve Strike
Age range: 5–13
No. of pupils: 9

Upton House School
115 St Leonard's Road,
Windsor, Berkshire SL4 3DF
Tel: 01753 862610
Headmistress: Rhian Thornton
Age range: 2–11
No. of pupils: 280

Waverley School
Waverley Way, Finchampstead,
Wokingham, Berkshire RG40 4YD
Tel: 0118 973 1121
Principal: Mr Guy Shore
Age range: 3–11
Fees: Day £8,589–£11,982

Wellington College
Duke's Ride, Crowthorne,
Berkshire RG45 7PU
Tel: +44 (0)1344 444000
Master: Mr Julian Thomas
Age range: 13–18
No. of pupils: 1040 VIth455
Fees: Day £29,040–
£33,360 FB £39,750

Buckinghamshire

Akeley Wood School
Akeley Wood, Buckingham,
Buckinghamshire MK18 5AE
Tel: 01280 814110
Headmaster: Dr Jerry Grundy BA,
PhD
Age range: 12 months–18 years
No. of pupils: 833 VIth119
Fees: Day £7,185–£10,575

Ashfold School
Dorton House, Dorton, Aylesbury,
Buckinghamshire HP18 9NG
Tel: 01844 238237
Headmaster: Mr Michael Chitty BSc
Age range: 3–13
No. of pupils: 280 VIth28
Fees: Day £9,525–£16,845
WB £20,190

**Broughton Manor
Preparatory School**
Newport Road, Broughton, Milton
Keynes, Buckinghamshire MK10 9AA
Tel: 01908 665234
Headmaster: Mr James Canwell
Age range: 2 months–11 years
No. of pupils: 250
Fees: Day £13,980

Caldicott
Crown Lane, Farnham Royal,
Buckinghamshire SL2 3SL
Tel: 01753 649301
Headmaster: Mr Jeremy Banks BA
(Hons) QTS, MEd
Age range: B7–13
No. of pupils: 250
Fees: Day £16,833–£18,780 WB
£24,918–£27,687 FB £24,918–£27,687

**Chesham Preparatory
School**
Two Dells Lane, Chesham,
Buckinghamshire HP5 3QF
Tel: 01494 782619
Headmaster: Mr Beale
Age range: 3–13
No. of pupils: 392
Fees: Day £9,270–£14,400

**Childfirst Day Nursery
Aylesbury**
Green End, off Rickford's Hill,
Aylesbury, Buckinghamshire
HP20 2SA
Tel: 01296 392516
Registrar: Mrs Carole Angood
Age range: 2 months–7 years
No. of pupils: 80
Fees: Day £6,276

**Childfirst Pre School
Aylesbury**
35 Rickfords Hill, Aylesbury,
Buckinghamshire HP20 2RT
Tel: 01296 433224

Crown House School
19 London Road, High Wycombe,
Buckinghamshire HP11 1BJ
Tel: 01494 529927
Headmaster: Ben Kenyon
Age range: 3–11
No. of pupils: 120
Fees: Day £9,005–£10,185

Dair House School
Bishops Blake, Beaconsfield
Road, Farnham Royal,
Buckinghamshire SL2 3BY
Tel: 01753 643964
Headmaster: Mr Terry Wintle
BEd(Hons)
Age range: 3–11
No. of pupils: 125
Fees: Day £3,425–£4,345

DAVENIES SCHOOL
For further details see p. 101
Station Road, Beaconsfield,
Buckinghamshire HP9 1AA
Tel: 01494 685400
Email: office@davenies.co.uk
Website: www.davenies.co.uk
Headmaster: Mr Carl Rycroft
BEd (Hons)
Age range: B4–13
No. of pupils: 337
Fees: Day £11,985–£17,400

Filgrave School
Filgrave Village, Newport
Pagnell, Milton Keynes,
Buckinghamshire MK16 9ET
Tel: 01234 711534
Headteacher: Mrs H Schofield
BA(Hons), MA, PGCE
Age range: 2–7
No. of pupils: 27
Fees: Day £5,160

**Focus School – Stoke
Poges Campus**
School Lane, Stoke Poges,
Buckinghamshire SL2 4QA
Tel: 01753 662167
Headteacher: Mr Connery Wiltshire
Age range: 11–16
No. of pupils: 120

Gateway School
1 High Street, Great Missenden,
Buckinghamshire HP16 9AA
Tel: 01494 862407
Headteacher: Mrs Sue LaFarge
BA(Hons), PGCE
Age range: 2–11
No. of pupils: 355
Fees: Day £2,235–£11,175

**Godstowe Preparatory
School**
Shrubbery Road, High Wycombe,
Buckinghamshire HP13 6PR
Tel: 01494 529273
Headmistress: Sophie Green
Age range: B3–7 G3–13
No. of pupils: 409
Fees: Day £10,800–
£16,620 FB £24,645

Griffin House School
Little Kimble, Aylesbury,
Buckinghamshire HP17 0XP
Tel: 01844 346154
Headmaster: Mr Tim Walford
Age range: 3–11
No. of pupils: 100
Fees: Day £8,238–£8,580

Heatherton House School
Copperkins Lane,
Chesham Bois, Amersham,
Buckinghamshire HP6 5QB
Tel: 01494 726433
Headteacher: Mrs Debbie
Isaachsen
Age range: B3–4 G3–11
Fees: Day £1,140–£13,335

High March School
23 Ledborough Lane, Beaconsfield,
Buckinghamshire HP9 2PZ
Tel: 01494 675186
Headmistress: Mrs S J Clifford BEd
(Oxon), MA (London)
Age range: B3–4 G3–11
No. of pupils: 307
Fees: Day £5,730–£14,805

**Milton Keynes
Preparatory School**
Tattenhoe Lane, Milton Keynes,
Buckinghamshire MK3 7EG
Tel: 01908 642111
Heads of School: Mr C Bates & Mr
S Driver
Age range: 2 months–11 years
No. of pupils: 500
Fees: Day £4,560–£15,120

Pipers Corner School
Pipers Lane, Great
Kingshill, High Wycombe,
Buckinghamshire HP15 6LP
Tel: 01494 718 255
Headmistress: Mrs H J Ness-Gifford
BA(Hons), PGCE
Age range: G4–18
No. of pupils: VIth72
Fees: Day £8,880–£18,390

**St Teresa's Catholic
School & Nursery**
Aylesbury Road, Princes
Risborough, Buckinghamshire
HP27 0JW
Tel: 01844 345005
Joint Heads: Mrs Jane Draper & Mrs
Yasmin Roberts
Age range: 3–11
No. of pupils: 130
Fees: Day £8,985–£9,165

Stowe School
Buckingham, Buckinghamshire
MK18 5EH
Tel: 01280 818000
Headmaster: Dr Anthony
Wallersteiner
Age range: 13–18
No. of pupils: 769 VIth318
Fees: Day £26,355 FB £36,660

Swanbourne House School
Swanbourne, Milton Keynes,
Buckinghamshire MK17 0HZ
Tel: 01296 720264
Head of School: Mrs Jane Thorpe
Age range: 3–13
No. of pupils: 323
Fees: Day £1,410–£18,360 FB £23,520

The Beacon School
Chesham Bois, Amersham,
Buckinghamshire HP6 5PF
Tel: 01494 433654
Headmaster: William Phelps
Age range: B3–13
No. of pupils: 470
Fees: Day £11,850–£17,250

The Grove Independent School
Redland Drive, Loughton, Milton
Keynes, Buckinghamshire MK5 8HD
Tel: 01908 690590
Principal: Mrs Deborah Berkin
Age range: 3 months–13 years
No. of pupils: 210

The Webber Independent School
Soskin Drive, Stantonbury
Fields, Milton Keynes,
Buckinghamshire MK14 6DP
Tel: 01908 574740
Principal: Mrs Hilary Marsden
Age range: 3–18
No. of pupils: 300 VIth15
Fees: Day £9,030–£12,705

Thornton College
Thornton, Milton Keynes,
Buckinghamshire MK17 0HJ
Tel: 01280 812610
Headmistress: Mrs Jo Storey
Age range: B2–4 G2–16
No. of pupils: 370
Fees: Day £9,555–£15,240 WB
£16,320–£20,655 FB £20,295–£25,185

Walton Pre-Preparatory School & Nursery
The Old Rectory, Walton
Drive, Milton Keynes,
Buckinghamshire MK7 6BB
Tel: 01908 678403
Headmistress: Mrs Chantelle
McLaughlan
Age range: 2 months–5 years
No. of pupils: 120
Fees: Day £7,200–£14,280

Wycombe Abbey
High Wycombe,
Buckinghamshire HP11 1PE
Tel: +44 (0)1494 897008
Headmistress: Mrs Rhiannon J
Wilkinson MA (Oxon) MEd
Age range: G11–18
No. of pupils: 631
Fees: Day £29,205 FB £38,940

Gayhurst School
Bull Lane, Gerrards Cross,
Buckinghamshire SL9 8RJ
Tel: 01753 882690
Headmaster: Gareth R A Davies
Age range: 3–11
Fees: Day £12,159–£15,438

Maltman's Green School
Maltman's Lane, Gerrards Cross,
Buckinghamshire SL9 8RR
Tel: 01753 883022
Headmistress: Mrs J Pardon MA,
BSc(Hons), PGCE
Age range: G2–11
No. of pupils: 394
Fees: Day £1,860–£5,090

St Mary's School
94 Packhorse Road, Gerrards
Cross, Buckinghamshire SL9 8JQ
Tel: 01753 883370
Head of School: Mrs P Adams
Age range: G3–18
No. of pupils: 350 VIth50
Fees: Day £5,670–£16,980

Thorpe House School
Oval Way, Gerrards Cross,
Buckinghamshire SL9 8QA
Tel: 01753 882474
Headmaster: Mr Terence Ayres
Age range: B3–16
Fees: Day £10,950–£16,962

East Sussex

Ashdown House School
Forest Row, East Sussex RH18 5JY
Tel: 01342 822574
Headmaster: Mike Davies
Age range: 4–13
No. of pupils: 141
Fees: Day £8,970–£20,100 FB £27,450

Bartholomews Tutorial College
22-23 Prince Albert Street,
Brighton, East Sussex BN1 1HF
Tel: 01273 205965/205141
Director of Studies: Mike Balmer BEd
Age range: 16+
No. of pupils: 40 VIth25
Fees: Day £25,000 WB
£30,000 FB £30,000

Battle Abbey School
Battle, East Sussex TN33 0AD
Tel: 01424 772385
Headmaster: Mr D Clark BA(Hons)
Age range: 2–18
No. of pupils: 286 VIth48
Fees: Day £6,939–£16,914
FB £26,649–£31,932

Bede's School
The Dicker, Upper Dicker,
Hailsham, East Sussex BN27 3QH
Tel: +44 (0)1323843252
Head: Mr Peter Goodyer
Age range: 3 months–18
No. of pupils: 800 VIth295
Fees: Day £10,230–£17,400
FB £22,290–£25,650

Bellerbys College Brighton
1 Billinton Way, Brighton,
East Sussex BN1 4LF
Tel: +44 (0)1273 339333
Principal: Mr Simon Mower
Age range: 13–18

Bricklehurst Manor Preparatory
Bardown Road, Stonegate,
Wadhurst, East Sussex TN5 7EL
Tel: 01580 200448
Principal: Mrs C Flowers
Age range: 3–11
No. of pupils: 117

Brighton & Hove High School GDST
Montpelier Road, Brighton,
East Sussex BN1 3AT
Tel: 01273 280280
Head: Jennifer Smith
Age range: G3–18
No. of pupils: 680 VIth70
Fees: Day £7,191–£14,421

Brighton & Hove Montessori School
67 Stanford Avenue, Brighton,
East Sussex BN1 6FB
Tel: 01273 702485
Headteacher: Mrs Daisy Cockburn
AMI, MontDip
Age range: 2–11

Brighton College
Eastern Road, Brighton,
East Sussex BN2 0AL
Tel: 01273 704200
Head Master: Richard Cairns MA
Age range: 3–18
No. of pupils: 950
Fees: Day £10,050–£24,540 WB
£33,390–£34,410 FB £37,470–£45,210

Brighton Steiner School
John Howard House, Roedean
Road, Brighton, East Sussex BN2 5RA
Tel: 01273 386300
Chair of the College of Teachers:
Carrie Rawle
Age range: 3–16
Fees: Day £7,800–£8,100

Buckswood School
Broomham Hall, Rye
Road, Guestling, Hastings,
East Sussex TN35 4LT
Tel: 01424 813 813
School Director: Mr Giles Sutton
Age range: 10–19
No. of pupils: 420

Buckswood St George's
Westwood House, 7-9
Holmesdale Gardens, Hastings,
East Sussex TN34 1LY
Tel: 01424 813696
College Director: Ian Godfrey
Age range: B16–19 G16–20
No. of pupils: VIth50

Charters Ancaster
Woodsgate Place, Gunters Lane,
Bexhill-on-Sea, East Sussex TN39 4EB
Tel: 01424 216670
Nursery Manager: Susannah
Crump
Age range: 6 months–5
No. of pupils: 125

Claremont Preparatory & Nursery School
Ebdens Hill, Baldslow, St Leonards-
on-Sea, East Sussex TN37 7PW
Tel: 01424 751555
Headmistress: Abra Stoakley
Age range: 1–13
Fees: Day £6,900–£12,600

Claremont Senior & Sixth Form School
Bodiam, Nr Robertsbridge,
East Sussex TN32 5UJ
Tel: 01580 830396
Headmaster: Mr. Giles Perrin
Age range: 14–18
Fees: Day £17,400

Darvell School
Darvell Bruderhof, Robertsbridge,
East Sussex TN32 5DR
Tel: 01580 883300
Headteacher: Mr Arnold Meier
Age range: 4–16
No. of pupils: 121

Deepdene School
195 New Church Road, Hove,
East Sussex BN3 4ED
Tel: 01273 418984
Heads: Mrs Nicola Gane & Miss
Elizabeth Brown
Age range: 6 months–11 years
Fees: Day £8,349
£

Dharma School
The White House, Ladies Mile
Road, Patcham, Brighton,
East Sussex BN1 8TB
Tel: 01273 502055
Headteacher: Clare Eddison
Age range: 3–11
Fees: Day £8,208
£

Eastbourne College
Old Wish Road, Eastbourne,
East Sussex BN21 4JX
Tel: 01323 452323 (Admissions)
Headmaster: Mr Tom Lawson
MA(Oxon)
Age range: 13–18
No. of pupils: 614 VIth284
Fees: Day £23,130–£23,505
FB £35,250–£35,655

European School of Animal Osteopathy
25 Old Steine, Brighton,
East Sussex BN1 1EL
Tel: 01273 673332
Head: Jean-Yves Girard

Greenfields Independent Day & Boarding School
Priory Road, Forest Row,
East Sussex RH18 5JD
Tel: +44 (0)1342 822189
Executive Head: Mr. Jeff Smith
Age range: 2–19

Hove College
48 Cromwell Road, Hove,
East Sussex BN3 3ER
Tel: 01273 772577
Director: Mr John Veale

Lancing College Preparatory School at Hove
The Droveway, Hove,
East Sussex BN3 6LU
Tel: 01273 503452
Headmistress: Mrs Kirsty Keep BEd
Age range: 3–13
No. of pupils: 181
Fees: Day £3,960–£15,975
£

Lewes Old Grammar School
High Street, Lewes, East
Sussex BN7 1XS
Tel: 01273 472634
Headmaster: Mr Robert Blewitt
Age range: 3–18
No. of pupils: 463 VIth50
Fees: Day £8,760–£14,625

Mayfield School
The Old Palace, Mayfield,
East Sussex TN20 6PH
Tel: +44 (0)1435 874600
Head: Ms Antonia Beary MA, Mphil
(Cantab), PGCE
Age range: G11–18
No. of pupils: 365 VIth100
Fees: Day £21,000 FB £33,900

Michael Hall School
Kidbrooke Park, Priory Road,
Forest Row, East Sussex RH18 5BG
Tel: 01342 822275
Age range: 0–18
Fees: Day £9,245–£12,670 FB £8,065

Roedean Moira House
Upper Carlisle Road, Eastbourne,
East Sussex BN20 7TE
Tel: 01323 644144
Headmaster: Mr Andrew Wood
Age range: G0–18
No. of pupils: 289

ROEDEAN SCHOOL
For further details see p. 106
Roedean Way, Brighton,
East Sussex BN2 5RQ
Tel: 01273 667500
Email: info@roedean.co.uk
Website: www.roedean.co.uk
Headmaster: Mr. Oliver Bond
BA(Essex), PGCE, NPQH
Age range: G11–18
No. of pupils: 607 VIth167
Fees: Day £5,480–£7,165 WB
£9,690–£10,805
FB £10,620–£12,855

Sacred Heart School
Mayfield Lane, Durgates,
Wadhurst, East Sussex TN5 6DQ
Tel: 01892 783414
Headteacher: Mrs H Blake
BA(Hons), PGCE
Age range: 2–11
No. of pupils: 121
Fees: Day £8,355
£

Skippers Hill Manor Prep School
Five Ashes, Mayfield,
East Sussex TN20 6HR
Tel: 01825 830234
Headmaster: Mr M Hammond MA,
BA, PGCE
Age range: 2–13
No. of pupils: 174
Fees: Day £8,400–£13,440
£

St Andrew's Prep
Meads Street, Eastbourne,
East Sussex BN20 7RP
Tel: 01323 733203
Headmaster: Gareth Jones MEd,
BA(Hons), PGCE
Age range: 9 months–13 years
No. of pupils: 380

St Bede's Preparatory School
Duke's Drive, Eastbourne,
East Sussex BN20 7XL
Tel: 01323 734222
Head: Mr Giles Entwisle
Age range: 3 months–13 years
No. of pupils: 395
Fees: Day £10,230–£17,400
FB £22,290–£25,650

St Christopher's School
33 New Church Road, Hove,
East Sussex BN3 4AD
Tel: 01273 735404
Headmaster: Mr Julian Withers
Age range: 4–13
Fees: Day £8,370–£12,720
£

The Academy of Creative Training
8-10 Rock Place, Brighton,
East Sussex BN2 1PF
Tel: 01273 818266

The Drive Prep School
101 The Drive, Hove, East
Sussex BN3 3JE
Tel: 01273 738444
Head Teacher: Mrs S Parkinson
CertEd, CertPerfArts
Age range: 7–16

Torah Montessori Nursery
29 New Church Road, Hove,
East Sussex BN3 4AD
Tel: 01273 328675
Principal: P Efune
Age range: 1–4

Vinehall School
Robertsbridge, East Sussex TN32 5JL
Tel: 01580 880413
Headmaster: Joff Powis
Age range: 2–13
No. of pupils: 260
Fees: Day £9,555–£17,817 WB
£20,916–£21,360 FB £22,641–£23,208

Windlesham School
190 Dyke Road, Brighton,
East Sussex BN1 5AA
Tel: 01273 553645
Headmaster: Mr John Ingrassia
Age range: 3–11
No. of pupils: 195
Fees: Day £6,015–£8,955
£

Essex

Alleyn Court Preparatory School
Wakering Road, Southend-
on-Sea, Essex SS3 0PW
Tel: 01702 582553
Headmaster: Mr Rupert Snow
Age range: 2–11
Fees: Day £3,258–£12,729
£

Brentwood Preparatory School
Middleton Hall, Brentwood,
Essex CM15 8EQ
Tel: +44 (0)1277 243333
Headmaster: Mr Jason Whiskerd
Age range: 3–11
No. of pupils: 411

Brentwood School
Middleton Hall Lane,
Brentwood, Essex CM15 8EE
Tel: 01277 243243
Headmaster: Mr Ian Davies
Age range: 3–18
No. of pupils: 1600
Fees: Day £18,945 FB £37,128

Colchester High School
Wellesley Road, Colchester,
Essex CO3 3HD
Tel: 01206 573389
Principal: David Young BA(Hons),
PGCE
Age range: 2–16
No. of pupils: 486
Fees: Day £3,300–£10,000
£

Coopersale Hall School
Flux's Lane, off Stewards Green Road, Epping, Essex CM16 7PE
Tel: 01992 577133
Headmistress: Miss Kaye Lovejoy
Age range: 2–11
No. of pupils: 275
Fees: Day £10,350–£10,575

Dame Bradbury's School
Ashdon Road, Saffron Walden, Essex CB10 2AL
Tel: 01799 522348
Headmistress: Ms Tracy Handford
Age range: 3–11
No. of pupils: 254
Fees: Day £4,350–£13,800
£ ✐

Elm Green Preparatory School
Parsonage Lane, Little Baddow, Chelmsford, Essex CM3 4SU
Tel: 01245 225230
Principal: Ms Ann Milner
Age range: 4–11
No. of pupils: 220
Fees: Day £8,844
✐

Empire College London
Forest House, 16-20 Clements Road, Ilford, Essex IG1 1BA
Tel: 020 8553 2683
Head: Ms Aaiesha Tak
16+

Felsted Preparatory School
Felsted, Great Dunmow, Essex CM6 3JL
Tel: 01371 822610
Headmaster: Mr Simon James
Age range: 4–13
No. of pupils: 460
Fees: Day £9,285–£17,820
FB £23,250–£24,465
⚑ £ ✐

Felsted School
Felsted, Great Dunmow, Essex CM6 3LL
Tel: 01371 822605
Headmaster: Mr Chris Townsend
Age range: 13–18
No. of pupils: 550
Fees: Day £7,850 FB £11,995
⚑ Ⓐ ⚑ £ IB ✐ 16+

Gosfield School
Cut Hedge Park, Halstead Road, Gosfield, Halstead, Essex CO9 1PF
Tel: 01787 474040
Headteacher: Mr Guy Martyn
Age range: 4–18
No. of pupils: VIth21
Fees: Day £6,690–£15,525
⚑ Ⓐ ⚑ £ ✐ 16+

Great Warley School
Warley Street, Great Warley, Brentwood, Essex CM13 3LA
Tel: 01277 233288
Head: Mr David Bell
Age range: 3–11

Heathcote School
Eves Corner, Danbury, Chelmsford, Essex CM3 4QB
Tel: 01245 223131
Headmistress: Caroline Forgeron
Age range: 2–11
Fees: Day £4,830–£7,245
£ ✐

Herington House School
1 Mount Avenue, Hutton, Brentwood, Essex CM13 2NS
Tel: 01277 211595
Principal: Mr R. Dudley-Cooke
Age range: 3–11
No. of pupils: 130
Fees: Day £1,955–£3,865
£ ✐

Holmwood House Preparatory School
Chitts Hill, Lexden, Colchester, Essex CO3 9ST
Tel: 01206 574305
Headmaster: Alexander Mitchell
Age range: 4–13
No. of pupils: 302
Fees: Day £10,140–£17,895 FB £35
⚑ ✐

Hutton Manor School
428 Rayleigh Road, Hutton, Brentwood, Essex CM13 1SD
Tel: 01277 245585
Head: Paula Hobbs
Age range: 3–11

Kids Inc Day Nursery – Beehive Lane Ilford
229-231 Beehive Lane, Ilford, Essex IG4 5EB
Tel: 020 8550 7400

Kids Inc Day Nursery – Loughton
29 Old Station Road, Loughton, Essex IG10 4PE
Tel: 020 8502 4488

Kids Inc Day Nursery – York Road Ilford
81-85 York Road, Ilford, Essex IG1 3AF
Tel: 020 8478 6510

Littlegarth School
Horkesley Park, Nayland, Colchester, Essex CO6 4JR
Tel: 01206 262332
Headmaster: Mr Peter H Jones
Age range: 2–11 years
No. of pupils: 318
Fees: Day £3,205–£3,723
£ ✐

Maldon Court Preparatory School
Silver Street, Maldon, Essex CM9 4QE
Tel: 01621 853529
Headteacher: Elaine Mason
Age range: 3–11
Fees: Day £8,236.80
✐

New Hall School
The Avenue, Boreham, Chelmsford, Essex CM3 3HS
Tel: 01245 467588
Principal: Mrs Katherine Jeffrey MA, BA, PGCE, MA(Ed Mg), NPQH
Age range: Coed 3-11, Single 11-16, Coed 16–18
No. of pupils: 1180 VIth217
Fees: Day £9,801–£19,878 WB £19,761–£28,569 FB £21,531–£30,681
⚑ Ⓐ ⚑ £ ✐ 16+

Oxford House School
2-4 Lexden Road, Colchester, Essex CO3 3NE
Tel: 01206 576686
Head Teacher: Mrs Sarah Leyshon
Age range: 2–11
No. of pupils: 158

Saint Nicholas School
Hillingdon House, Hobbs Cross Road, Harlow, Essex CM17 0NJ
Tel: 01279 429910
Headmaster: Mr D Bown
Age range: 4–16
No. of pupils: 400
Fees: Day £9,960–£12,660
£

Saint Pierre School
16 Leigh Road, Leigh-on-Sea, Southend-on-Sea, Essex SS9 1LE
Tel: 01702 474164
Headmaster: Mr Chris Perkins
Age range: 2–11+
Fees: Day £7,218–£8,181
£

St Anne's Preparatory School
New London Road, Chelmsford, Essex CM2 0AW
Tel: 01245 353488
Head: Mrs Fiona Pirrie
Age range: 3–11
No. of pupils: 160
Fees: Day £3,450–£8,100

St Cedd's School
178a New London Road, Chelmsford, Essex CM2 0AR
Tel: 01245 392810
Head: Mr Matthew Clarke
Age range: 3–11
No. of pupils: 400
Fees: Day £8,550–£10,515
✐

St John's School
Stock Road, Billericay, Essex CM12 0AR
Tel: 01277 623070
Head Teacher: Mrs F Armour BEd(Hons)
Age range: 2–16 years
No. of pupils: 392
Fees: Day £5,328–£13,500
✐

St Margaret's Preparatory School
Hall Drive, Gosfield, Halstead, Essex CO9 1SE
Tel: 01787 472134
Headmaster: Mr. Callum Douglas
Age range: 2–11
Fees: Day £3,150–£3,946
£ ✐

St Mary's School
Lexden Road, Colchester, Essex CO3 3RB
Tel: 01206 572544   Admissions: 01206 216420
Principal: Mrs H K Vipond MEd, BSc(Hons), NPQH
Age range: B3–4 G3–16
No. of pupils: 430
Fees: Day £6,855–£14,985
⚑ £ ✐

St Michael's Church Of England Preparatory School
198 Hadleigh Road, Leigh-on-Sea, Southend-on-Sea, Essex SS9 2LP
Tel: 01702 478719
Head: Steve Tompkins BSc(Hons), PGCE, MA, NPQH
Age range: 3–11
No. of pupils: 271
Fees: Day £4,104–£9,600
£ ✐

St Philomena's Catholic School
Hadleigh Road, Frinton-on-Sea, Essex CO13 9HQ
Tel: 01255 674492
Headmistress: Mrs B McKeown DipEd
Age range: 4–11
Fees: Day £6,240–£7,500
£ ✐

Thorpe Hall School
Wakering Road, Southend-on-Sea, Essex SS1 3RD
Tel: 01702 582340
Headmaster: Mr Andrew Hampton
Age range: 2–16 years
No. of pupils: 359
Fees: Day £9,000–£12,600
£ ✐

Ursuline Preparatory School
Old Great Ropers, Great Ropers Lane, Warley, Brentwood, Essex CM13 3HR
Tel: 01277 227152
Headmistress: Mrs Pauline Wilson MSc
Age range: 3–11
Fees: Day £6,450–£12,015
✐

Widford Lodge School
Widford Road, Chelmsford, Essex CM2 9AN
Tel: 01245 352581
Headteacher: Miss Michelle Cole
Age range: 2–11
No. of pupils: 230
Fees: Day £7,800–£9,657
✐

Hampshire

Alton School
Anstey Lane, Alton, Hampshire GU34 2NG
Tel: 01420 82070
Head: Graham Maher
Age range: 0–18
No. of pupils: 502 VIth53
Ⓐ £ ⑯

Ballard School
Fernhill Lane, New Milton, Hampshire BH25 5SU
Tel: 01425 626900
Headmaster: Mr Andrew McCleave
Age range: 2–16 years
No. of pupils: 400
Fees: Day £8,340–£15,315
£ ✐

Bedales Prep School, Dunhurst
Petersfield, Hampshire GU32 2DP
Tel: 01730 300200
Head of School: Colin Baty
Age range: 8–13
No. of pupils: 200
Fees: Day £16,920–£18,765
FB £22,215–£24,930
Ⓐ ⛨ £ ✐

Bedales School
Church Road, Steep, Petersfield, Hampshire GU32 2DG
Tel: 01730 711733
Head of School: Magnus Bashaarat
Age range: 13–18
No. of pupils: 463
Fees: Day £28,515 FB £36,285
🌐 Ⓐ ⛨ £ ✐ ⑯

Boundary Oak School
Roche Court, Fareham, Hampshire PO17 5BL
Tel: 01329 280955/820373
Head: Mr James Polansky
Age range: 2–16
No. of pupils: 120
Fees: Day £8,949–£14,487 WB £15,723–£20,514 FB £17,658–£22,449
⛨ £ ✐

Brockwood Park & Inwoods School
Brockwood Park, Bramdean, Hampshire SO24 0LQ
Tel: +44 (0)1962 771744
Principal: Mr Antonio Autor
Age range: 14–19
No. of pupils: 112 VIth39
Fees: Day £5,630–£6,400 FB £21,400
🌐 Ⓐ ⛨ £ ✐ ⑯

Brookham School
Highfield Lane, Liphook, Hampshire GU30 7LQ
Tel: 01428 722005
Headteacher: Mrs Sophie Baber
Age range: 3–8
No. of pupils: 162
Fees: Day £11,100–£15,000
✐

Churcher's College
Petersfield, Hampshire GU31 4AS
Tel: 01730 263033
Headmaster: Mr Simon Williams MA, BSc
Age range: 3–18 years
Fees: Day £9,915–£15,420
Ⓐ £ ✐ ⑯

Clay Hill School
Clay Hill, Lyndhurst, Hampshire SO43 7DE
Tel: 023 8028 3633
Head of School: Mrs. Helen Sharpe
Age range: 5–19

Daneshill School
Stratfield Turgis, Basingstoke, Hampshire RG27 0AR
Tel: 01256 882707
Headmaster: Mr David Griffiths
Age range: 3–13
Fees: Day £10,650–£14,000
✐

Ditcham Park School
Ditcham Park, Petersfield, Hampshire GU31 5RN
Tel: 01730 825659
Headmaster: Mr Graham Spawforth MA, MEd
Age range: 2.5–16
No. of pupils: 379
Fees: Day £2,835–£4,753
£ ✐

Durlston Court
Becton Lane, Barton-on-Sea, New Milton, Hampshire BH25 7AQ
Tel: 01425 610010
Head of School: Mr Richard May
Age range: 2–13
No. of pupils: 296
Fees: Day £3,540–£15,390
£ ✐

Farleigh School
Red Rice, Andover, Hampshire SP11 7PW
Tel: 01264 710766
Headmaster: Father Simon Everson
Age range: 3–13
Fees: Day £5,385–£19,590 FB £21,675–£25,485
⛨ £ ✐

Farnborough Hill
Farnborough Road, Farnborough, Hampshire GU14 8AT
Tel: 01252 545197
Head: Mrs A Neil BA, MEd, PGCE
Age range: G11–18
No. of pupils: 550 VIth90
Fees: Day £14,796
⛨ Ⓐ £ ✐ ⑯

Forres Sandle Manor
Fordingbridge, Hampshire SP6 1NS
Tel: 01425 653181
Headmaster: Mr M N Hartley BSc(Hons)
Age range: 3–13
No. of pupils: 264
⛨ £ ✐

Glenhurst School
16 Beechworth Road, Havant, Hampshire PO9 1AX
Tel: 023 9248 4054
Principal: Mrs E M Haines
Age range: 3 months–5 years
✐

Hampshire Collegiate School
Embley Park, Romsey, Hampshire SO51 6ZE
Tel: 01794 512206
Headteacher: Mr Cliff Canning
Age range: 2–18
No. of pupils: 500
Fees: Day £8,499–£29,988
🌐 Ⓐ ⛨ £ ✐ ⑯

Highfield School
Highfield Lane, Liphook, Hampshire GU30 7LQ
Tel: 01428 728000
Headmaster: Mr Phillip Evitt MA(Cantab), PGCE
Age range: 8–13
No. of pupils: 292
Fees: Day £3,700–£8,750 FB £23,850–£26,250
⛨ £ ✐

King Edward VI School
Wilton Road, Southampton, Hampshire SO15 5UQ
Tel: 023 8070 4561
Head Master: Mr A J Thould MA(Oxon)
Age range: 11–18
No. of pupils: 960
Fees: Day £16,050
Ⓐ £ ✐ ⑯

Kingscourt School
182 Five Heads Road, Catherington, Hampshire PO8 9NJ
Tel: 023 9259 3251
Head of School: Mr Jamie Lewis
Age range: 3–11
No. of pupils: 210
Fees: Day £2,856

Lord Wandsworth College
Long Sutton, Hook, Hampshire RG29 1TB
Tel: 01256 862201
Head of School: Mr Adam Williams
Age range: 11–18 years
No. of pupils: 615
Fees: Day £20,430–£23,460 WB £28,290–£31,800 FB £29,250–£33,300
🌐 Ⓐ ⛨ £ ✐ ⑯

Mayville High School
35/37 St Simon's Road, Southsea, Portsmouth, Hampshire PO5 2PE
Tel: 023 9273 4847
Headteacher: Mrs Rebecca Parkyn
Age range: 6 months–16 years
No. of pupils: 479
Fees: Day £7,635–£11,235
£ ✐

Meoncross School
Burnt House Lane, Stubbington, Fareham, Hampshire PO14 2EF
Tel: 01329 662182
Headmaster: Mr Mark Cripps
Age range: 2–16
No. of pupils: 405
Fees: Day £8,736–£12,576
£ ✐

Moyles Court School
Moyles Court, Ringwood, Hampshire BH24 3NF
Tel: 01425 472856
Headmaster: Mr R Milner-Smith
Age range: 3–16
Fees: Day £2,112–£4,766 FB £6,876–£8,675
🌐 ⛨

New Forest Small School
1 Southampton Road, Lyndhurst, Hampshire SO43 7BU
Tel: 02380 284 415
Headteacher: Mr Nicholas Alp
Age range: 3–16

Portsmouth High School GDST
Kent Road, Southsea, Portsmouth, Hampshire PO5 3EQ
Tel: 023 9282 6714
Headmistress: Mrs Jane Prescott BSc NPQH
Age range: G3–18
No. of pupils: 500
Fees: Day £2,500–£4,663

Prince's Mead School
Worthy Park House, Kings Worthy, Winchester, Hampshire SO21 1AN
Tel: 01962 888000
Headmaster: Peter Thacker
Age range: 4–11

Ringwood Waldorf School
Folly Farm Lane, Ashley, Ringwood, Hampshire BH24 2NN
Tel: 01425 472664
Age range: 3–18
No. of pupils: 235
Fees: Day £6,240–£9,000

Rookwood School
Weyhill Road, Andover, Hampshire SP10 3AL
Tel: 01264 325900
Headmaster: Mr A Kirk-Burgess BSc, PGCE, MSc (Oxon)
Age range: 2–16
Fees: Day £9,360–£15,600 FB £23,250–£27,465

Salesian College
Reading Road, Farnborough, Hampshire GU14 6PA
Tel: 01252 893000
Headmaster: Mr Gerard Owens
Age range: B11–18 G16–18
No. of pupils: 650 VIth140
Fees: Day £11,961

Sherborne House School
Lakewood Road, Chandlers Ford, Eastleigh, Hampshire SO53 1EU
Tel: 023 8025 2440
Head Teacher: Mrs Heather Hopson-Hill
Age range: 3–11
No. of pupils: 293
Fees: Day £8,295–£9,675

Sherfield School
Sherfield-on-Loddon, Hook, Hampshire RG27 0HU
Tel: +44 (0)1256 884 800
Acting Head Master: Mr Christopher James-Roll BSc (Hons), PGCE
Age range: 3 months–18 years
No. of pupils: 445 VIth16
Fees: Day £9,930–£16,594 WB £18,408–£25,375 FB £21,474–£29,601

St John's College
Grove Road South, Southsea, Portsmouth, Hampshire PO5 3QW
Tel: 023 9281 5118
Headmaster: Mr Timothy Bayley BSc (Hons), MA, PGCE
Age range: 2–18
No. of pupils: 560 VIth86
Fees: Day £9,225–£12,090 FB £25,200–£28,740

ST NEOT'S SCHOOL
For further details see p. 108
St Neot's Road, Eversley, Hampshire RG27 0PN
Tel: 0118 9739650
Email: admissions@stneotsprep.co.uk
Website: www.stneotsprep.co.uk
Head of School: Deborah Henderson
Age range: 2–13 years
No. of pupils: 335
Fees: Day £3,635–£5,200

St Nicholas' School
Redfields House, Redfields Lane, Church Crookham, Fleet, Hampshire GU52 0RF
Tel: 01252 850121
Headmistress: Dr O Wright PhD, MA, BA Hons, PGCE
Age range: B3–7 G3–16
No. of pupils: 325

St Swithun's Prep
Alresford Road, Winchester, Hampshire SO21 1HA
Tel: 01962 835750
Headmistress: Mrs R Lyons-Smith BSc, PGCE, MBA
Age range: B3–7 G3–11
No. of pupils: 191
Fees: Day £5,424–£13,971

ST SWITHUN'S SCHOOL
For further details see p. 109
Alresford Road, Winchester, Hampshire SO21 1HA
Tel: 01962 835700
Email: office@stswithuns.com
Website: www.stswithuns.com
Head of School: Jane Gandee MA(Cantab)
Age range: G11–18
No. of pupils: 510

St. Mary's Independent School
57 Midanbury Lane, Bitterne Park, Southampton, Hampshire SO18 4DJ
Tel: 023 8067 1267
Executive Head: Mrs C Charlemagne
Age range: 3–16
No. of pupils: 470
Fees: Day £7,620–£9,900

Stockton House School
Stockton Avenue, Fleet, Hampshire GU51 4NS
Tel: 01252 616323
Early Years Manager: Mrs Jenny Bounds BA EYPS
Age range: 2–5

The Gregg Prep School
17-19 Winn Road, Southampton, Hampshire SO17 1EJ
Tel: 023 8055 7352
Head Teacher: Mrs J Caddy
Age range: 3–11
Fees: Day £8,295

The Gregg School
Townhill Park House, Cutbush Lane, Southampton, Hampshire SO18 2GF
Tel: 023 8047 2133
Headteacher: Mrs S Sellers PGDip, MSc, BSc(Hons), NPQH, PGCE
Age range: 11–16
No. of pupils: 300
Fees: Day £12,825

The King's School
Lakesmere House, Allington Lane, Fair Oak, Eastleigh, Southampton, Hampshire SO50 7DB
Tel: 023 8060 0986
Head of School: Mrs H Bowden BA (Hons), PGCE
Age range: 3–16
No. of pupils: 256
Fees: Day £4,560–£7,680

The Pilgrims' School
3 The Close, Winchester, Hampshire SO23 9LT
Tel: 01962 854189
Headmaster: Mr Tom Burden
Age range: B4–13
No. of pupils: 250
Fees: Day £18,150–£19,245 FB £24,330

The Portsmouth Grammar School
High Street, Portsmouth, Hampshire PO1 2LN
Tel: +44 (0)23 9236 0036
Headmistress: Dr Anne Cotton
Age range: 2–18
No. of pupils: 1556 VIth336
Fees: Day £10,233–£15,951

The Stroud School
Highwood House, Highwood Lane, Romsey, Hampshire SO51 9ZH
Tel: 01794 513231
Headmaster: Mr Joel Worrall
Age range: 3–13

Twyford School
Twyford, Winchester, Hampshire SO21 1NW
Tel: 01962 712269
Headmaster: Dr S J Bailey BEd, PhD, FRSA
Age range: 3–13
Fees: Day £10,953–£19,509 WB £24,552

Walhampton
Walhampton, Lymington, Hampshire SO41 5ZG
Tel: 01590 613 300
Headmaster: Mr Titus Mills
Age range: 2–13
No. of pupils: 353
Fees: Day £9,000–£17,625 FB £20,250–£24,750

West Hill Park Preparatory School
Titchfield, Fareham, Hampshire PO14 4BS
Tel: 01329 842356
Headmaster: A P Ramsay BEd(Hons), MSc
Age range: 2–13
No. of pupils: 288
Fees: Day £10,800–£18,300 FB £19,500–£22,650

Winchester College
College Street, Winchester, Hampshire SO23 9NA
Tel: 01962 621247
Headmaster: Dr. T R Hands
Age range: B13–18
No. of pupils: 690 VIth280
Fees: FB £39,912

Woodhill School, Botley
Brook Lane, Botley, Southampton, Hampshire SO30 2ER
Tel: 01489 781112
Head Teacher: Mrs M Dacombe
Age range: 3–11
No. of pupils: 100
Fees: Day £7,050

Yateley Manor School
51 Reading Road, Yateley, Hampshire GU46 7UQ
Tel: 01252 405500
Headmaster: Mr Robert Upton
Age range: 3–13
No. of pupils: 453
Fees: Day £11,160–£15,300

Hertfordshire

Abbot's Hill School
Bunkers Lane, Hemel Hempstead,
Hertfordshire HP3 8RP
Tel: 01442 240333
Headmistress: Mrs E Thomas BA
(Hons), PGCE, NPQH
Age range: G4–16
No. of pupils: 530
(symbols)

Aldenham School
Elstree, Hertfordshire WD6 3AJ
Tel: 01923 858122
Headmaster: Mr James C Fowler
MA
Age range: 3–18
No. of pupils: 700
Fees: Day £16,491–£22,614
FB £22,791–£33,234
(symbols)

Aldwickbury School
Wheathampstead Road,
Harpenden, Hertfordshire AL5 1AD
Tel: 01582 713022
Headmaster: Mr V W Hales
Age range: B4–13
No. of pupils: 330
Fees: Day £13,110–£16,215
(symbols)

Beechwood Park School
Markyate, St Albans,
Hertfordshire AL3 8AW
Tel: 01582 840333
Headmaster: Mr E Balfour BA
(Hons), PGCE
Age range: 3–13
No. of pupils: 532
Fees: Day £11,025–£16,530
WB £20,460
(symbols)

BERKHAMSTED SCHOOL
For further details see p. 99
Overton House, 131 High
Street, Berkhamsted,
Hertfordshire HP4 2DJ
Tel: 01442 358001
Email: admissions@
berkhamsted.com
Website:
www.berkhamsted.com
Principal: Mr Richard Backhouse
MA(Cantab)
Age range: 3–18
No. of pupils: 1792 VIth395
Fees: Day £10,365–£20,640
WB £27,635 FB £32,880
(symbols)

Bhaktivedanta Manor School
Hilfield Lane, Aldenham, Watford,
Hertfordshire WD25 8EZ
Tel: 01923 851000 Ext:241
Headteacher: Guru Carana
Padma dasi
Age range: 4–12
No. of pupils: 45
Fees: Day £1,860

Bishop's Stortford College
10 Maze Green Road, Bishop's
Stortford, Hertfordshire CM23 2PJ
Tel: 01279 838575
Headmaster: Mr Jeremy Gladwin
Age range: 13–18
No. of pupils: VIth249
Fees: Day £19,662–£19,839 WB
£30,228–£30,411 FB £30,528–£30,711
(symbols)

Bishop's Stortford College Prep School
Maze Green Road, Bishop's
Stortford, Hertfordshire CM23 2PH
Tel: 01279 838607
Head of the Prep School: Mr Bill
Toleman
Age range: 4–13
No. of pupils: 590
Fees: Day £9,090–£15,729 WB
£21,102–£22,911 FB £21,327–£23,142
(symbols)

Champneys International College of Health & Beauty
Chesham Road, Wigginton,
Tring, Hertfordshire HP23 6HY
Tel: 01442 291333
College Principal: Ms Pam Clegg
Age range: 16+
No. of pupils: 61
Fees: Day £3,000–£9,050
(symbols)

Charlotte House Preparatory School
88 The Drive, Rickmansworth,
Hertfordshire WD3 4DU
Tel: 01923 772101
Head: Miss P Woodcock
Age range: G3–11
No. of pupils: 140
Fees: Day £3,432–£12,102
(symbols)

Duncombe School
4 Warren Park Road, Bengeo,
Hertford, Hertfordshire SG14 3JA
Tel: 01992 414100
Headmaster: Mr Jeremy Phelan
M.A. (Ed)
Age range: 2–11
No. of pupils: 301
Fees: Day £10,380–£14,565
(symbols)

Edge Grove School
Aldenham Village,
Hertfordshire WD25 8NL
Tel: 01923 855724
Headmaster: Mr Ben Evans BA
(Hons), PGCE
Age range: 3–13
No. of pupils: 494
Fees: Day £6,930–£16,935
WB £20,756–£23,150
(symbols)

Egerton Rothesay School
Durrants Lane, Berkhamsted,
Hertfordshire HP4 3UJ
Tel: 01442 865275
Headteacher: Mr Colin Parker
BSc(Hons), Dip.Ed (Oxon), PGCE,
C.Math MIMA
Age range: 5–19
No. of pupils: 179
Fees: Day £16,020–£22,800
(symbols)

Haberdashers' Aske's School
Butterfly Lane, Elstree,
Borehamwood,
Hertfordshire WD6 3AF
Tel: 020 8266 1700
Headmaster: Mr P B Hamilton MA
Age range: B5–18
No. of pupils: 1402 VIth310
Fees: Day £15,339–£20,346
(symbols)

Haberdashers' Aske's School for Girls
Aldenham Road,
Elstree, Borehamwood,
Hertfordshire WD6 3BT
Tel: 020 8266 2300
Headmistress: Miss Biddie A
O'Connor MA (Oxon)
Age range: G4–18
No. of pupils: 1190
Fees: Day £16,980–£18,393
(symbols)

Haileybury
Haileybury, Hertford,
Hertfordshire SG13 7NU
Tel: +44 (0)1992 706200
The Master: Mr Martin Collier MA
BA PGCE
Age range: 11–18
No. of pupils: 833 VIth317
Fees: Day £17,031–£25,620
FB £21,837–£34,422
(symbols)

Haresfoot School
Chesham Road, Berkhamsted,
Hertfordshire HP4 2SZ
Tel: 01442 872742
Principal: Karen O'Connor BA
PGCE NPQH
Age range: 3–7
Fees: Day £1,845–£7,770
(symbols)

Heath Mount School
Woodhall Park, Watton-at-Stone,
Hertford, Hertfordshire SG14 3NG
Tel: 01920 830230
Headmaster: Mr Chris Gillam
BEd(Hons)
Age range: 3–13
No. of pupils: 480
Fees: Day £11,550–£17,805
(symbols)

High Elms Manor School
High Elms Lane, Watford,
Hertfordshire WD25 0JX
Tel: 01923 681 103
Headmistress: Ms Liadain O'Neill BA
(Hons), AMI 0-3, AMI 3-6, Early Years
FdA Dist.+
Age range: 2–12
No. of pupils: 100
Fees: Day £10,500–£12,675
(symbols)

Howe Green House School
Great Hallingbury, Bishop's
Stortford, Hertfordshire CM22 7UF
Tel: 01279 657706
Head of School: Mrs Deborah Mills
Age range: 2–11
Fees: Day £8,235–£11,793
(symbols)

Immanuel College
87/91 Elstree Road, Bushey,
Hertfordshire WD23 4EB
Tel: 020 8950 0604
Headmaster: Mr Gary Griffin
Age range: 4–18
No. of pupils: 520 VIth127
Fees: Day £10,995
(symbols)

Kingshott
Stevenage Road, St Ippolyts,
Hitchin, Hertfordshire SG4 7JX
Tel: 01462 432009
Headmaster: Mr Mark Seymour
Age range: 3–13 years
No. of pupils: 403
Fees: Day £6,090–£13,125
(symbols)

Little Acorns Montessori School
Lincolnsfield Centre,
Bushey Hall Drive, Bushey,
Hertfordshire WD23 2ER
Tel: 01923 230705
Head of School: Lola Davies BPA,
AMIDip
Age range: 12 months–6
No. of pupils: 28
Fees: Day £2,120
(symbols)

Lochinver House School
Heath Road, Little Heath, Potters
Bar, Hertfordshire EN6 1LW
Tel: 01707 653064
Headmaster: Ben Walker BA(Hons),
PGCE, CELTA
Age range: B4–13
No. of pupils: 349
Fees: Day £11,175–£14,685
(symbols)

Lockers Park
Lockers Park Lane, Hemel Hempstead, Hertfordshire HP1 1TL
Tel: 01442 251712
Headmaster: Mr C R Wilson
Age range: B4–13 G4–7
No. of pupils: 170
Fees: Day £10,050–£16,530 FB £23,160

Longwood School
Bushey Hall Drive, Bushey, Hertfordshire WD23 2QG
Tel: 01923 253715
Head Teacher: Claire May
Age range: 3 months–11
Fees: Day £3,705–£7,800

Manor Lodge School
Rectory Lane, Ridge Hill, Shenley, Hertfordshire WD7 9BG
Tel: 01707 642424
Head of School: Mrs A Lobo
Age range: 3–11
No. of pupils: 427
Fees: Day £11,100–£12,300

Merchant Taylors' Prep
Moor Farm, Sandy Lodge Road, Rickmansworth, Hertfordshire WD3 1LW
Tel: 01923 825648
Headmaster: Dr Karen McNerney BSc (Hons), PGCE, MSc, EdD
Age range: B4–13
No. of pupils: 300
Fees: Day £5,148–£16,000

Princess Helena College
Preston, Hitchin, Hertfordshire SG4 7RT
Tel: 01462 443888
Headmistress: Mrs Sue Wallace-Woodroffe
Age range: G11–18
No. of pupils: 194 VIth35
Fees: Day £16,125–£19,635 FB £22,965–£28,545

Queenswood
Shepherd's Way, Brookmans Park, Hatfield, Hertfordshire AL9 6NS
Tel: 01707 602500
Principal: Mrs Jo Cameron
Age range: G11–18
No. of pupils: 400 VIth120
Fees: Day £20,925–£24,825 WB 23,355–31,035 FB £23,985–£33,750

Radlett Preparatory School
Kendal Hall, Watling Street, Radlett, Hertfordshire WD7 7LY
Tel: 01923 856812
Principal: Mr G White BEd (Hons)
Age range: 4–11
Fees: Day £9,735

Sherrardswood School
Lockleys, Welwyn, Hertfordshire AL6 0BJ
Tel: 01438 714282
Headmistress: Mrs Anna Wright
Age range: 2–18
No. of pupils: 357
Fees: Day £10,383–£16,113

St Albans High School for Girls
Townsend Avenue, St Albans, Hertfordshire AL1 3SJ
Tel: 01727 853800
Headmistress: Mrs Jenny Brown MA (Oxon)
Age range: G4–18
No. of pupils: 940 VIth170

St Albans School
Abbey Gateway, St Albans, Hertfordshire AL3 4HB
Tel: 01727 855521
Headmaster: Mr JWJ Gillespie MA(Cantab), FRSA
Age range: B11–18 G16–18
No. of pupils: 870
Fees: Day £18,600

St Albans Tutors
69 London Road, St Albans, Hertfordshire AL1 1LN
Tel: 01727 842348
Principals: Mr. A N Jemal & Mr Elvis Cotena
Age range: 15+
Fees: Day £2,700–£5,900

St Christopher School
Barrington Road, Letchworth, Hertfordshire SG6 3JZ
Tel: 01462 650 850
Head: Richard Palmer
Age range: 3–18
No. of pupils: 511 VIth78
Fees: Day £4,590–£18,075 WB £19,950–£24,675 FB £31,650

St Columba's College
King Harry Lane, St Albans, Hertfordshire AL3 4AW
Tel: 01727 855185
Headmaster: David R Buxton
Age range: B4–18
No. of pupils: 860 VIth150
Fees: Day £10,482–£15,699

St Columba's College Prep School
King Harry Lane, St Albans, Hertfordshire AL3 4AW
Tel: 01727 862616
Head of Prep: Mrs Ruth Loveman
Age range: B4–11
No. of pupils: 250
Fees: Day £10,482–£13,557

St Edmund's College & Prep School
Old Hall Green, Nr Ware, Hertfordshire SG11 1DS
Tel: 01920 824247
Head: Paulo Durán BA MA
Age range: 3–18
No. of pupils: 799 VIth135
Fees: Day £10,650–£17,205 WB £22,665–£25,905 FB £26,040–£29,865

St Edmund's Prep
Old Hall Green, Ware, Hertfordshire SG11 1DS
Tel: 01920 824239
Head: Mr Steven Cartwright BSc (Surrey)
Age range: 3–11
No. of pupils: 185
Fees: Day £10,650–£13,365

St Francis' College
Broadway, Letchworth Garden City, Hertfordshire SG6 3PJ
Tel: 01462 670511
Headmistress: Mrs B Goulding
Age range: G3–18
No. of pupils: 460 VIth75
Fees: Day £9,990–£16,980 WB £22,350–£26,475 FB £27,990–£31,995

St Hilda's
High Street, Bushey, Hertfordshire WD23 3DA
Tel: 020 8950 1751
Headmistress: Miss Sarah-Jane Styles MA
Age range: B2–4 G2–11
Fees: Day £12,012–£12,843

St Hilda's School
28 Douglas Road, Harpenden, Hertfordshire AL5 2ES
Tel: 01582 712307
Headmaster: Mr Dan Sayers
Age range: G3–11 years
No. of pupils: 144
Fees: Day £6,615–£11,535

St John's Preparatory School
The Ridgeway, Potters Bar, Hertfordshire EN6 5QT
Tel: 01707 657294
Headmistress: Mrs C Tardios BA(Hons)
Age range: 4–11
No. of pupils: 184
Fees: Day £10,350–£10,980

St Joseph's In The Park
St Mary's Lane, Hertingfordbury, Hertford, Hertfordshire SG14 2LX
Tel: 01992 513810
Head of School: Mr Douglas Brown
Age range: 3–11
No. of pupils: 150
Fees: Day £5,718–£16,899

St Margaret's School, Bushey
Merry Hill Road, Bushey, Hertfordshire WD23 1DT
Tel: 020 8416 4400
Head: Mrs Rose Hardy MA(Oxon), MEd, FRSA
Age range: G4–18 years
No. of pupils: 450 VIth100
Fees: Day £11,286–£16,902 WB £23,220–£27,279 FB £31,770

Stanborough School
Stanborough Park, Garston, Watford, Hertfordshire WD25 9JT
Tel: 01923 673268
Acting Head Teacher: Ms Eileen Hussey
Age range: 3–17
No. of pupils: 300
Fees: Day £6,630–£10,224 WB £10,350–£13,995

Stormont
The Causeway, Potters Bar, Hertfordshire EN6 5HA
Tel: 01707 654037
Head of School: Mrs Sharon Martin
Age range: G4–11
Fees: Day £12,300–£13,050

The Christian School (Takeley)
Dunmow Road, Brewers End, Takeley, Bishop's Stortford, Hertfordshire CM22 6QH
Tel: 01279 871182
Headmaster: M E Humphries
Age range: 3–16
Fees: Day £6,012–£8,436

The King's School
Elmfield, Ambrose Lane, Harpenden, Hertfordshire AL5 4DU
Tel: 01582 767566
Principal: Mr Clive John Case BA, HDE
Age range: 4–16
Fees: Day £7,680

The Purcell School, London
Aldenham Road, Bushey, Hertfordshire WD23 2TS
Tel: 01923 331100
Headteacher: Dr Bernard Trafford
Age range: 10–18
No. of pupils: 180
Fees: Day £25,707 FB £32,826

Tring Park School for the Performing Arts
Tring Park, Tring, Hertfordshire HP23 5LX
Tel: 01442 824255
Principal: Mr Stefan Anderson MA, ARCM, ARCT
Age range: 8–19
No. of pupils: 374 VIth266
Fees: Day £14,865–£23,655 FB £25,275–£35,760

Westbrook Hay Prep School
London Road, Hemel Hempstead, Hertfordshire HP1 2RF
Tel: 01442 256143
Headmaster: Keith D Young BEd(Hons)
Age range: 3–13
No. of pupils: 300
Fees: Day £10,125–£14,580
£ ✎

York House School
Redheath, Sarratt Road, Croxley Green, Rickmansworth, Hertfordshire WD3 4LW
Tel: 01923 772395
Headmaster: Jon Gray BA(Ed)
Age range: 3–13
No. of pupils: 240
Fees: Day £10,440–£13,905
£ ✎

Kent

Ashford School
East Hill, Ashford, Kent TN24 8PB
Tel: 01233 739030
Head: Mr Michael Hall
Age range: 3 months–18 years
No. of pupils: 835 VIth170
Fees: Day £10,500–£16,800 WB £24,000 FB £36,000
🌐 A 🏛 £ ✎ 16

Beech Grove School
Beech Grove Bruderhof, Sandwich Road, Nonington, Dover, Kent CT15 4HH
Tel: 01304 842980
Head: Mr Timothy Maas
Age range: 4–14
No. of pupils: 63

Beechwood Sacred Heart
12 Pembury Road, Tunbridge Wells, Kent TN2 3QD
Tel: 01892 532747
Acting Head: Mrs Helen Rowe
Age range: 3–18
No. of pupils: 400 VIth70
Fees: Day £8,685–£17,385 WB £26,850 FB £29,850
A 🏛 £ ✎ 16

Benenden School
Cranbrook, Kent TN17 4AA
Tel: 01580 240592
Headmistress: Mrs S Price
Age range: G11–18
No. of pupils: 550
Fees: FB £12,650
♀ 🌐 A 🏛 £ ✎ 16

Bethany School
Curtisden Green, Goudhurst, Cranbrook, Kent TN17 1LB
Tel: 01580 211273
Headmaster: Mr Francie Healy BSc, HDipEd, NPQH
Age range: 11–18 years
No. of pupils: 313 VIth98
Fees: Day £16,725–£18,465 WB £25,950–£28,655 FB £27,990–£31,500
🌐 A 🏛 £ ✎ 16

Bronte School
Mayfield, 7 Pelham Road, Gravesend, Kent DA11 0HN
Tel: 01474 533805
Headmistress: Ms Emma Wood
Age range: 3–11
No. of pupils: 120
Fees: Day £9,330
✎

Bryony School
Marshall Road, Rainham, Gillingham, Kent ME8 0AJ
Tel: 01634 231511
Joint Head: Mr D Edmunds
Age range: 2–11
No. of pupils: 168
Fees: Day £5,978–£6,511
✎

CATS Canterbury
68 New Dover Road, Canterbury, Kent CT1 3LQ
Tel: +44 (0)1227866540
Principal: Dr Sarah Lockyer
Age range: 14–18
No. of pupils: 400
🌐 16 A 🏛 IB 16

Chartfield School
45 Minster Road, Westgate on Sea, Kent CT8 8DA
Tel: 01843 831716
Head & Proprietor: Miss L P Shipley
Age range: 4–11
No. of pupils: 50
Fees: Day £2,700–£3,450
✎

Cobham Hall School
Cobham, Kent DA12 3BL
Tel: 01474 823371
Headmistress: Ms Maggie Roberts
Age range: G11–18
No. of pupils: 180
♀ 🌐 🏛 £ IB ✎ 16

Derwent Lodge School for Girls
Somerhill, Tonbridge, Kent TN11 0NJ
Tel: 01732 352124
Head of School: Mrs Helen Hoffmann
Age range: G7–11
No. of pupils: 134
Fees: Day £15,465
♀ £ ✎

Dover College
Effingham Crescent, Dover, Kent CT17 9RH
Tel: 01304 205969
Headmaster: Mr Gareth Doodes MA (Hons)
Age range: 3–18
No. of pupils: 301
Fees: Day £7,725–£16,050 WB £21,000–£25,500 FB £24,750–£31,500
🌐 A 🏛 £ ✎ 16

Dulwich Prep Cranbrook
Coursehorn, Cranbrook, Kent TN17 3NP
Tel: 01580 712179
Headmaster: Mr Paul David BEd(Hons)
Age range: 3–13
No. of pupils: 535
Fees: Day £5,970–£18,390
£ ✎

Elliott Park School
18-20 Marina Drive, Minster, Sheerness, Kent ME12 2DP
Tel: 01795 873372
Head: Ms Colleen Hiller
Age range: 3–11
No. of pupils: 65
Fees: Day £5,431
✎

European School of Osteopathy
Boxley House, The Street, Boxley, Maidstone, Kent ME14 3DZ
Tel: 01622 671 558
Principal: Mr Renzo Molinari DO
16

Fosse Bank School
Mountains, Noble Tree Road, Hildenborough, Tonbridge, Kent TN11 8ND
Tel: 01732 834212
Headmistress: Miss Alison Cordingley
Age range: 3–11
No. of pupils: 124
Fees: Day £10,083–£12,543
£

Gad's Hill School
Higham, Rochester, Medway, Kent ME3 7PA
Tel: 01474 822366
Headmaster: Mr Paul Savage
Age range: 3–16
No. of pupils: 370
Fees: Day £8,988–£12,504
£

Haddon Dene School
57 Gladstone Road, Broadstairs, Kent CT10 2HY
Tel: 01843 861176
Head: Miss Alison Hatch
Age range: 3–11
No. of pupils: 200
Fees: Day £5,700–£7,230
✎

Hilden Grange School
62 Dry Hill Park Road, Tonbridge, Kent TN10 3BX
Tel: 01732 352706
Headmaster: Mr J Withers BA(Hons)
Age range: 3–13
No. of pupils: 311
✎

Hilden Oaks School & Nursery
38 Dry Hill Park Road, Tonbridge, Kent TN10 3BU
Tel: 01732 353941
Head of School: Mrs. K J M Joiner
Age range: 3 months–11
Fees: Day £8,985–£12,450
£ ✎

Holmewood House School
Barrow Lane, Langton Green, Tunbridge Wells, Kent TN3 0EB
Tel: 01892 860000
Headmaster: Mr Scott Carnochan
Age range: 3–13
No. of pupils: 450
🏛 £ ✎

Kent College
Whitstable Road, Canterbury, Kent CT2 9DT
Tel: 01227 763231
Executive Head Master: Dr D J Lamper
Age range: 0–18 years
No. of pupils: 756
Fees: Day £16,464–£18,315 FB £25,236–£34,491
🌐 A 🏛 £ IB ✎ 16

Kent College Junior School
Harbledown, Canterbury, Kent CT2 9AQ
Tel: 01227 762436
Headmaster: Mr Andrew Carter
Age range: 0–11
No. of pupils: 202
Fees: Day £9,990–£16,011 FB £25,236
🏛 ✎

Kent College Pembury
Old Church Road, Pembury, Tunbridge Wells, Kent TN2 4AX
Tel: +44 (0)1892 822006
Headmistress: Ms J Lodrick
Age range: G3–18
No. of pupils: 650 VIth102
Fees: Day £9,459–£20,571 WB £25,710 FB £25,710–£32,778
♀ 🌐 A 🏛 £ ✎ 16

**Kids Inc Day Nursery
– Bluewater**
West Village, Bluewater,
Greenhithe, Kent DA9 9SE
Tel: 01322 386624

**King's Preparatory
School, Rochester**
King Edward Road, Rochester,
Medway, Kent ME1 1UB
Tel: 01634 888577
Headmaster: Mr Tom Morgan
Age range: 8–13
No. of pupils: 220
Fees: Day £13,185–£14,955

King's Rochester
Satis House, Boley Hill,
Rochester, Kent ME1 1TE
Tel: 01634 888555
Principal: Mr J Walker
Age range: 13–18
No. of pupils: 625 VIth92
Fees: Day £7,125–£19,320
FB £21,960–£31,590

Linton Park School
3 Eccleston Road, Tovil,
Maidstone, Kent ME17 4HT
Tel: 01622 740820
Headteacher: Kate Edwards
Age range: 7–18
No. of pupils: 134

**Lorenden Preparatory
School**
Painter's Forstal, Faversham,
Kent ME13 0EN
Tel: 01795 590030
Headmistress: Mrs K Uttley
Age range: 3–11
No. of pupils: 120
Fees: Day £8,640–£12,540

Marlborough House School
High Street, Hawkhurst,
Kent TN18 4PY
Tel: 01580 753555
Headmaster: Mr Martyn Ward BEd
(Hons)
Age range: 2–13
No. of pupils: 334
Fees: Day £8,730–£18,060

**Meredale Independent
Primary School**
Solomon Road, Rainham,
Gillingham, Kent ME8 8EB
Tel: 01634 231405
Headteacher: Mrs Michelle Homer
Age range: 3–11
No. of pupils: 53
Fees: Day £6,945–£7,815

Northbourne Park School
Betteshanger, Deal, Kent CT14 0NW
Tel: 01304 611215/218
Headmaster: Mr Sebastian Rees
BA(Hons), PGCE, NPQH
Age range: 3–13
No. of pupils: 175
Fees: Day £7,632–£16,755
WB £20,985 FB £24,300

Radnor House, Sevenoaks
Combe Bank Drive,
Sevenoaks, Kent TN14 6AE
Tel: 01959 563720
Head: Mr David Paton BComm
(Hons) PGCE MA
Age range: 2.5–18
No. of pupils: 250

**Rochester Independent
College**
Star Hill, Rochester,
Medway, Kent ME1 1XF
Tel: 01634 828115
Principals: Alistair Brownlow, Brian
Pain, Pauline Bailey
Age range: 11–19
No. of pupils: 306 VIth233
Fees: Day £12,600–£18,000
WB £12,000 FB £13,500

Rose Hill School
Coniston Avenue, Tunbridge
Wells, Kent TN4 9SY
Tel: 01892 525591
Head: Emma Neville
Age range: 3–13
Fees: Day £11,325–£15,225

Russell House School
Station Road, Otford,
Sevenoaks, Kent TN14 5QU
Tel: 01959 522352
Headmaster: Mr Craig McCarthy
Age range: 2–11
No. of pupils: 193

Sackville School
Tonbridge Rd, Hildenborough,
Tonbridge, Kent TN11 9HN
Tel: 01732 838888
Headmaster: Mr Justin Foster-
Gandey BSc (hons)
Age range: 11–18
No. of pupils: 160 VIth29
Fees: Day £15,297

Saint Ronan's School
Water Lane, Hawkhurst,
Kent TN18 5DJ
Tel: 01580 752271
Headmaster: William Trelawny-
Vernon BSc(Hons)
Age range: 3–13
No. of pupils: 300
Fees: Day £10,476–£17,952 FB £21,681

**Sevenoaks
Preparatory School**
Godden Green, Sevenoaks,
Kent TN15 0JU
Tel: 01732 762336
Headmaster: Mr Luke Harrison
Age range: 2–13
No. of pupils: 388
Fees: Day £10,350–£14,295

Sevenoaks School
High Street, Sevenoaks,
Kent TN13 1HU
Tel: +44 (0)1732 455133
Head: Dr Katy Ricks MA, DPhil
Age range: 11–18
No. of pupils: 1093
Fees: Day £23,355–£26,523
FB £37,296–£40,464

Shernold School
Hill Place, Queens Avenue,
Maidstone, Kent ME16 0ER
Tel: 01622 752868
Head Teacher: Ms. Sandra
Dinsmore
Age range: 3–11
No. of pupils: 142
Fees: Day £6,900–£7,800

Solefield School
Solefield Road, Sevenoaks,
Kent TN13 1PH
Tel: 01732 452142
Headmaster: Mr D A Philps
BSc(Hons)
Age range: B4–13
No. of pupils: 180
Fees: Day £11,970–£14,580

Somerhill Pre-Prep
Somerhill, Five Oak Green Road,
Tonbridge, Kent TN11 0NJ
Tel: 01732 352124
Headmistress: Miss Zoe Humm
Age range: 3–7
No. of pupils: 245
Fees: Day £10,050–£11,685

Spring Grove School
Harville Road, Wye,
Ashford, Kent TN25 5EZ
Tel: 01233 812337
Headmaster: Mr Bill Jones
Age range: 2–11
No. of pupils: 194
Fees: Day £8,700–£12,600

St Andrew's School
24-28 Watts Avenue, Rochester,
Medway, Kent ME1 1SA
Tel: 01634 843479
Principal: Mrs E Steinmann-Gilbert
Age range: 2–11
No. of pupils: 367
Fees: Day £7,464–£7,902

St Edmund's Junior School
St Thomas Hill, Canterbury,
Kent CT2 8HU
Tel: 01227 475600
Head: Edward O'Connor
Age range: 3–13
No. of pupils: 230
Fees: Day £7,647–£15,594
WB £24,267 FB £26,628

St Edmund's School
St Thomas' Hill, Canterbury,
Kent CT2 8HH
Tel: 01227 475601
Head: Mr Edward O'Connor
Age range: 3–18
No. of pupils: 535
Fees: Day £7,647–£20,466 WB
£24,267–£32,595 FB £26,628–£34,968

St Faith's at Ash School
5 The Street, Ash, Canterbury,
Kent CT3 2HH
Tel: 01304 813409
Headmaster: Mr Lawrence Groves
Age range: 2–11
No. of pupils: 225
Fees: Day £5,220–£9,525

**St Joseph's Convent
Prep School**
46 Old Road East, Gravesend,
Kent DA12 1NR
Tel: 01474 533012
Head Teacher: Miss D Buckley
Age range: 3–11
No. of pupils: 146
Fees: Day £8,310

St Lawrence College
Ramsgate, Kent CT11 7AE
Tel: 01843 572931
Principal: Mr Antony Spencer
Age range: 3–18
No. of pupils: 640 VIth115
Fees: Day £7,470–£18,495
FB £26,055–£34,635

**St Michael's
Preparatory School**
Otford Court, Otford,
Sevenoaks, Kent TN14 5SA
Tel: 01959 522137
Headteacher: Mrs Jill Aisher
Age range: 2–13
No. of pupils: 472
Fees: Day £11,850–£14,400

Steephill School
Off Castle Hill, Fawkham,
Longfield, Kent DA3 7BG
Tel: 01474 702107
Head: Mrs C Birtwell BSc, MBA,
PGCE
Age range: 3–11
No. of pupils: 131
Fees: Day £9,420

Sutton Valence Preparatory School
Chart Sutton, Maidstone,
Kent ME17 3RF
Tel: 01622 842117
Head: Miss C Corkran
Age range: 3–11
No. of pupils: 320
Fees: Day £3,000–£4,610

Sutton Valence School
North Street, Sutton
Valence, Kent ME17 3HL
Tel: 01622 845200
Headmaster: Bruce Grindlay MA
Cantab, MusB, FRCO, CHM
Age range: 11–18
No. of pupils: 570

The Granville School
2 Bradbourne Park Road,
Sevenoaks, Kent TN13 3LJ
Tel: 01732 453039
Headmistress: Mrs J Scott
BEd(Cantab)
Age range: B3–4 G3–11
No. of pupils: 195
Fees: Day £5,862–£15,111

The Junior King's School, Canterbury
Milner Court, Sturry,
Canterbury, Kent CT2 0AY
Tel: 01227 714000
Head: Emma Károlyi
Age range: 3–13
Fees: Day £11,145–£18,735
FB £25,710

The King's School, Canterbury
The Precincts, Canterbury,
Kent CT1 2ES
Tel: 01227 595501
Head: Mr P Roberts
Age range: 13–18
No. of pupils: 858 VIth385
Fees: Day £27,495 FB £37,455

The Mead School
16 Frant Road, Tunbridge
Wells, Kent TN2 5SN
Tel: 01892 525837
Headmaster: Mr Andrew Webster
Age range: 3–11
No. of pupils: 188
Fees: Day £4,236–£10,785

The New Beacon School
Brittains Lane, Sevenoaks,
Kent TN13 2PB
Tel: 01732 452131
Headmaster: Mr M Piercy BA(Hons)
Age range: B4–13
No. of pupils: 400
Fees: Day £11,100–£15,885

Tonbridge School
Tonbridge, Kent TN9 1JP
Tel: 01732 365555
Headmaster: Mr James Priory
Age range: B13–18
No. of pupils: 788

Walthamstow Hall Pre-Prep and Junior School
Sevenoaks, Kent TN13 3LD
Tel: 01732 451334
Headmistress: Miss S Ferro
Age range: G2–11
No. of pupils: 218
Fees: Day £11,775–£14,850

Walthamstow Hall School
Sevenoaks, Kent TN13 3UL
Tel: 01732 451334
Headmistress: Miss S Ferro
Age range: G2–18
No. of pupils: 500 VIth80
Fees: Day £11,775–£20,070

Wellesley House
114 Ramsgate Road,
Broadstairs, Kent CT10 2DG
Tel: 01843 862991
Headmaster: Mr G D Franklin
Age range: 7–13
No. of pupils: 133
Fees: Day £11,961–£19,479 FB £25,752

Yardley Court
Somerhill, Five Oak Green Road,
Tonbridge, Kent TN11 0NJ
Tel: 01732 352124
Headmaster: Duncan Sinclair
Age range: B7–13
No. of pupils: 260
Fees: Day £15,465

Surrey

Aberdour School
Brighton Road, Burgh Heath,
Tadworth, Surrey KT20 6AJ
Tel: 01737 354119
Headmaster: Mr S. D. Collins
Age range: 2–13 years
No. of pupils: 357
Fees: Day £1,350–£4,650

ACS Cobham International School
Heywood, Portsmouth Road,
Cobham, Surrey KT11 1BL
Tel: +44 (0) 1932 867251
Head of School: Mr Simon Leyshon
Age range: 2–18
No. of pupils: 1460
Fees: Day £11,250–£27,110 WB
£38,810–£41,570 FB £44,170–£46,930

ACS Egham International School
Woodlee, London Road,
Egham, Surrey TW20 0HS
Tel: +44 (0) 1784 430 800
Head of School: Jeremy Lewis
Age range: 4–18
Fees: Day £10,870–£25,360

Aldro School
Shackleford, Godalming,
Surrey GU8 6AS
Tel: 01483 810266
Head: James & Jenny Hanson
Age range: B7–13
No. of pupils: 220
Fees: Day £16,869–£18,729
FB £22,446–£24,309

Amesbury
Hazel Grove, Hindhead,
Surrey GU26 6BL
Tel: 01428 604322
Headmaster: Mr Nigel Taylor MA
Age range: 2–13
No. of pupils: 360

Banstead Preparatory School
Sutton Lane, Banstead,
Surrey SM7 3RA
Tel: 01737 363601
Headteacher: Miss Vicky Ellis
Age range: 2–11
No. of pupils: 225

Barfield School
Guildford Road, Runfold,
Farnham, Surrey GU10 1PB
Tel: 01252 782271
Head of School: James Reid
Age range: 2–13 years
No. of pupils: 170
Fees: Day £3,258–£13,980

Barrow Hills School
Roke Lane, Witley, Godalming,
Surrey GU8 5NY
Tel: +44 (0)1428 683639
Headmaster: Mr Sean Skehan
Age range: 2–13
No. of pupils: 223
Fees: Day £15,360

Belmont Preparatory School
Feldemore, Holmbury St Mary,
Dorking, Surrey RH5 6LQ
Tel: 01306 730852
Headmistress: Mrs Helen Skrine BA,
PGCE, NPQH, FRSA
Age range: 2–13
No. of pupils: 227
Fees: Day £9,390–£15,930
WB £22,215–£22,695

Bishopsgate School
Bishopsgate Road, Englefield
Green, Egham, Surrey TW20 0YJ
Tel: 01784 432109
Headmaster: Mr R Williams
Age range: 3–13
Fees: Day £5,415–£15,378

Box Hill School
Old London Road, Mickleham,
Dorking, Surrey RH5 6EA
Tel: 01372 373382
Headmaster: Mr Corydon Lowde
Age range: 11–18
No. of pupils: 425 VIth96
Fees: Day £17,850–£19,710 WB
£27,510–£28,800 FB £33,690–£35,100

Cambridge Management College
4-8 Castle Street, Oakington,
Kingston upon Thames,
Surrey KT11SS
Tel: 08003166282
Principal: Dr Peter Holmes

Caterham School
Harestone Valley, Caterham,
Surrey CR3 6YA
Tel: 01883 343028
Head: Mr C. W. Jones MA(Cantab)
Age range: 11–18
No. of pupils: VIth321
Fees: Day £18,045 WB
£30,936 FB £34,710

Charterhouse
Godalming, Surrey GU7 2DX
Tel: +44 (0)1483 291501
Headmaster: Dr Alex Peterken
Age range: B13–18 G16–18
No. of pupils: 810

Chinthurst School
Tadworth Street, Tadworth,
Surrey KT20 5QZ
Tel: 01737 812011
Head: Miss Catherine Trundle
Age range: B3–11
No. of pupils: 170
Fees: Day £11,010–£14,850
(£) (✎)

City of London Freemen's School
Ashtead Park, Ashtead,
Surrey KT21 1ET
Tel: 01372 277933
Headmaster: Mr R Martin
Age range: 7–18
No. of pupils: 877 VIth213
Fees: Day £13,398–£18,279 WB
£27,906–£27,957 FB £30,780–£30,816
(♿)(A)(♟)(£)(✎)(16+)

Claremont Fan Court School
Claremont Drive, Esher,
Surrey KT10 9LY
Tel: 01372 467841
Head: Mr William Brierly
Age range: 2–18
No. of pupils: 780
Fees: Day £10,680–£17,670
(A)(£)(✎)(16+)

Coworth Flexlands School
Valley End, Chobham,
Surrey GU24 8TE
Tel: 01276 855707
Head of School: Nicola Cowell
Age range: B3–7 G3–11
No. of pupils: 135
(✎)

Cranleigh Preparatory School
Horseshoe Lane, Cranleigh,
Surrey GU6 8QH
Tel: 01483 274199
Headmaster: Mr M T Wilson BSc
Age range: 7–13
No. of pupils: 290
Fees: Day £14,955–£19,395
FB £23,430
(♟)

Cranleigh School
Horseshoe Lane, Cranleigh,
Surrey GU6 8QQ
Tel: +44 (0) 1483 273666
Headmaster: Mr Martin Reader
MA, MPhil, MBA
Age range: 7–18 (including
Prep School)
No. of pupils: 654 VIth240
Fees: Day £31,170 FB £37,905
(♿)(A)(♟)(£)(✎)(16+)

CRANMORE SCHOOL
For further details see p. 100
Epsom Road, West Horsley,
Surrey KT24 6AT
Tel: 01483 280340
Email: office@
cranmoreprep.co.uk
Website:
www.cranmoreprep.co.uk
Headmaster: Mr Michael
Connolly BSc, BA, MA, MEd
Age range: 2–13
No. of pupils: 420
Fees: Day £11,850
(£)(✎)

Danes Hill School
Leatherhead Road, Oxshott,
Surrey KT22 0JG
Tel: 01372 842509
Headmaster: Mr W Murdock BA
Age range: 3–13
No. of pupils: 872
Fees: Day £10,650–£14,400
(£)(✎)

Danesfield Manor School
Rydens Avenue, Walton-on-
Thames, Surrey KT12 3JB
Tel: 01932 220930
Principal: Mrs Jo Smith
Age range: 2–11
No. of pupils: 170
Fees: Day £9,135–£9,756
(✎)

Downsend School
1 Leatherhead Road,
Leatherhead, Surrey KT22 8TJ
Tel: 01372 372197
Headmaster: Mr Ian Thorpe
Age range: 2–13
No. of pupils: 675
Fees: Day £13,455–£15,435

Downsend School (Ashtead Pre-Prep)
Ashtead Lodge, 22 Oakfield
Road, Ashtead, Surrey KT21 2RE
Tel: 01372 385439
Head Teacher: Tessa Roberts
Age range: 2–6
No. of pupils: 66
Fees: Day £11,535

Downsend School (Epsom Pre-Prep)
Epsom Lodge, 6 Norman Avenue,
Epsom, Surrey KT17 3AB
Tel: 01372 385438
Head Teacher: Vanessa Conlan
Age range: 2–6
No. of pupils: 110
Fees: Day £11,535

Downsend School (Leatherhead Pre-Prep)
Leatherhead Lodge, Epsom Road,
Leatherhead, Surrey KT22 8ST
Tel: 01372 372123
Headteacher: Mrs Gill Brooks
Age range: 2–6
No. of pupils: 106
Fees: Day £11,535

Drayton House Pre-School and Nursery
35 Austen Road, Guildford,
Surrey GU1 3NP
Tel: 01483 504707
Headmistress: Mrs J Tyson-Jones
Froebel Cert.Ed. London University
Age range: 6 months–5 years
No. of pupils: 65
Fees: Day £4,420–£12,500
(✎)

Duke of Kent School
Peaslake Road, Ewhurst,
Surrey GU6 7NS
Tel: 01483 277313
Head: Mrs Sue Knox
Age range: 3–16
No. of pupils: 234
Fees: Day £6,960–£18,090
(♿)(♟)(£)(✎)

Dunottar School
High Trees Road, Reigate,
Surrey RH2 7EL
Tel: 01737 761945
Head of School: Mr Mark Tottman
Age range: 11–18
No. of pupils: 365
Fees: Day £16,035
(A)(£)(16+)

Edgeborough
Frensham, Farnham,
Surrey GU10 3AH
Tel: 01252 792495
Headmaster: Mr Dan Thornburn
Age range: 2–13
No. of pupils: 285
Fees: Day £10,740–£17,535
(♟)(£)(✎)

Emberhurst School
94 Ember Lane, Esher,
Surrey KT10 8EN
Tel: 020 8398 2933
Headmistress: Mrs P Chadwick BEd
Age range: 2–7
No. of pupils: 70

Epsom College
Epsom, Surrey KT17 4JQ
Tel: 01372 821000
Headmaster: Mr Jay A Piggot MA
Age range: 11–18
No. of pupils: 884
Fees: Day £18,765–£25,266
WB £33,849 FB £37,263
(♿)(A)(♟)(£)(✎)(16+)

Essendene Lodge School
Essendene Road, Caterham,
Surrey CR3 5PB
Tel: 01883 348349
Head Teacher: Mrs K Ali
Age range: 2–11
No. of pupils: 153
Fees: Day £3,315–£7,305
(£)(✎)

Ewell Castle School
Church Street, Ewell, Epsom,
Surrey KT17 2AW
Tel: 020 8393 1413
Principal: Mr Peter Harris
Age range: 3–18
No. of pupils: 557
Fees: Day £4,953–£16,692
(A)(£)(✎)(16+)

Feltonfleet School
Cobham, Surrey KT11 1DR
Tel: 01932 862264
Head of School: Mrs S Lance
Age range: 3–13
No. of pupils: 398
Fees: Day £11,799–£17,325
WB £21,051
(♟)(£)(✎)

Focus School – Hindhead Campus
Tilford Road, Hindhead,
Surrey GU26 6SJ
Tel: 01428 601800
Head: Mr Kristian Still
Age range: 8–18
No. of pupils: 90

Frensham Heights
Rowledge, Farnham,
Surrey GU10 4EA
Tel: 01252 792561
Headmaster: Mr Andrew Fisher BA,
MEd, FRSA
Age range: 3–18
No. of pupils: 497 VIth105
Fees: Day £6,900–£20,430
FB £26,370–£30,810
(♿)(A)(♟)(£)(✎)(16+)

Glenesk School
Ockham Road North, East
Horsley, Surrey KT24 6NS
Tel: 01483 282329
Headmistress: Mrs Sarah Bradley
Age range: 2–7
No. of pupils: 100
Fees: Day £2,457–£12,579
(£)(✎)

Greenfield School
Brooklyn Road, Woking,
Surrey GU22 7TP
Tel: 01483 772525
Headmistress: Mrs Tania Botting BEd
Age range: 3–11
No. of pupils: 179
Fees: Day £5,763–£13,485
(£)(✎)

Guildford High School
London Road, Guildford,
Surrey GU1 1SJ
Tel: 01483 561440
Headmistress: Mrs F J Boulton BSc,
MA
Age range: G4–18
No. of pupils: 980 VIth160
Fees: Day £10,728–£17,214
(♟)(A)(£)(16+)

Hall Grove School
London Road, Bagshot,
Surrey GU19 5HZ
Tel: 01276 473059
Headmaster: Mr Alastair Graham
Age range: 3–13
No. of pupils: 430
Fees: Day £10,800–£14,700

Halstead Preparatory School
Woodham Rise, Woking,
Surrey GU21 4EE
Tel: 01483 772682
Headmistress: Mrs P Austin
Age range: G3–11
No. of pupils: 220
Fees: Day £10,800–£14,400

Hampton Court House
Hampton Court Road, East
Molesey, Surrey KT8 9BS
Tel: 020 8943 0889
Headmaster: Mr Guy Holloway
Age range: 3–18
No. of pupils: 248 VIth30
Fees: Day £13,665–£19,506

HawleyHurst School
Fernhill Road, Blackwater,
Camberley, Surrey GU17 9HU
Tel: 01276 587190
Principal: Miss V S Smit
Age range: 2–19

Hazelwood School
Wolf's Hill, Limpsfield,
Oxted, Surrey RH8 0QU
Tel: 01883 712194
Head: Mrs Lindie Louw
Age range: 2–13
No. of pupils: 399
Fees: Day £9,975–£15,900

Hoe Bridge School
Hoe Place, Old Woking Road,
Woking, Surrey GU22 8JE
Tel: 01483 760018 &
01483 772194
Head: Mr C Webster MA BSc (Hons)
PGCE
Age range: 3–13
No. of pupils: 460
Fees: Day £5,940–£15,345

Hurtwood House
Holmbury St Mary, Dorking,
Surrey RH5 6NU
Tel: 01483 279000
Principal: Mr Cosmo Jackson
Age range: 16–18
No. of pupils: 300
Fees: Day £28,950 FB £43,428

ISL Surrey Primary School
Old Woking Road, Woking,
Surrey GU22 8HY
Tel: +44 (0)1483 750409
Principal: Richard Parker
Age range: 2–11 years
No. of pupils: 100
Fees: Day £10,450–£15,500

Kids Inc Day Nursery – Guildford
Railton Road, Queen Elizabeth
Park, Guildford, Surrey GU2 9LX
Tel: 01483 237999

King Edward's Witley
Godalming, Surrey GU8 5SG
Tel: +44 (0)1428 686700
Headmaster: Mr John Attwater MA
Age range: 11–18
No. of pupils: 400
Fees: Day £20,460 FB £31,995

Kingswood House School
56 West Hill, Epsom, Surrey KT19 8LG
Tel: 01372 723590
Headmaster: Mr Duncan Murphy
BA (Hons), MEd, FRSA
Age range: B3–16
No. of pupils: 210
Fees: Day £10,740–£14,850

Lanesborough
Maori Road, Guildford,
Surrey GU1 2EL
Tel: 01483 880489
Head: Mrs Clare Turnbull BA(Hons)
MEd
Age range: B3–13
No. of pupils: 350
Fees: Day £10,890–£15,270

Lingfield College
Racecourse Road, Lingfield,
Surrey RH7 6PH
Tel: 01342 833176
Headmaster: Mr R Bool
Age range: 2–18
No. of pupils: 935
Fees: Day £11,250–£19,473

Longacre School
Hullbrook Lane, Shamley Green,
Guildford, Surrey GU5 0NQ
Tel: 01483 893225
Head of School: Mr Matthew Bryan
Age range: 2–11
No. of pupils: 260

Lyndhurst School
36 The Avenue, Camberley,
Surrey GU15 3NE
Tel: 01276 22895
Head: Mr A Rudkin BEd(Hons)
Age range: 2–11
Fees: Day £9,300–£12,675

Manor House School, Bookham
Manor House Lane, Little Bookham,
Leatherhead, Surrey KT23 4EN
Tel: 01372 457077
Headteacher: Ms Tracey Fantham
Age range: B2–4 G2–16
No. of pupils: 300
Fees: Day £9,255–£17,403

Micklefield School
10/12 Somers Road, Reigate,
Surrey RH2 9DU
Tel: 01737 242615
Headmistress: Mrs L Rose BEd(Hons),
CertEd, Dip PC
Age range: 3–11
No. of pupils: 272
Fees: Day £3,360–£11,925

Milbourne Lodge School
Arbrook Lane, Esher,
Surrey KT10 9EG
Tel: 01372 462737
Head: Mrs Judy Waite
Age range: 4–13
No. of pupils: 283
Fees: Day £12,240–£15,390

New Life Christian Primary School
Cairo New Road, Croydon,
Surrey CR0 1XP
Tel: 020 8680 7671 Ext:327

Notre Dame School
Cobham, Surrey KT11 1HA
Tel: 01932 869990
Head of Seniors: Mrs Anna King
MEd, MA (Cantab), PGCE
Age range: 2–18
No. of pupils: 600

Oakhyrst Grange School
160 Stanstead Road,
Caterham, Surrey CR3 6AF
Tel: 01883 343344
Headmaster: Mr Alex Gear
Age range: 4–11 years
No. of pupils: 155

Parkside School
The Manor, Stoke d'Abernon,
Cobham, Surrey KT11 3PX
Tel: 01932 862749
Headmaster: Mr Mark Beach
Age range: B2–13 G2–4
No. of pupils: 382
Fees: Day £12,165–£16,692

Prior's Field
Priorsfield Road, Godalming,
Surrey GU7 2RH
Tel: 01483 810551
Head of School: Mrs T Kirnig
Age range: G11–18
No. of pupils: 450
Fees: Day £17,300 FB £29,925

Reed's School
Sandy Lane, Cobham,
Surrey KT11 2ES
Tel: 01932 869001
Headmaster: Mr Mark Hoskins BA
MA MSc
Age range: B11–18 G16–18
No. of pupils: 650 VIth230
Fees: Day £19,740–£24,675
FB £26,310–£31,800

Reigate Grammar School
Reigate Road, Reigate,
Surrey RH2 0QS
Tel: 01737 222231
Headmaster: Mr Shaun Fenton MA
(Oxon) MEd (Oxon)
Age range: 11–18
No. of pupils: 969 VIth262
Fees: Day £18,600–£18,720

Reigate St Mary's Prep & Choir School
Chart Lane, Reigate,
Surrey RH2 7RN
Tel: 01737 244880
Headmaster: Mr Marcus Culverwell
MA
Age range: 3–11
No. of pupils: 350

Ripley Court School
Rose Lane, Ripley, Surrey GU23 6NE
Tel: 01483 225217
Headmaster: Mr A J Gough
Age range: 3–13
No. of pupils: 281
Fees: Day £9,300–£14,160

Rowan Preparatory School
6 Fitzalan Road, Claygate,
Surrey KT10 0LX
Tel: 01372 462627
Headmistress: Mrs Susan Clarke
BEd, NPQH
Age range: G2–11
No. of pupils: 317
Fees: Day £11,190–£14,850

Royal Grammar School, Guildford
High Street, Guildford,
Surrey GU1 3BB
Tel: 01483 880600
Headmaster: Dr J M Cox BSc, PhD
Age range: B11–18
No. of pupils: 940
Fees: Day £18,285

Royal School of Needlework
Apartment 12A, Hampton
Court Palace, East Molesey,
Surrey KT8 9AU
Tel: 020 8943 1432
Principal: Mrs E Elvin
Age range: 17–30
No. of pupils: 24

Rydes Hill Preparatory School
Rydes Hill House, Aldershot Road, Guildford, Surrey GU2 8BP
Tel: 01483 563160
Headmistress: Mrs Sarah Norville
Age range: B3–7 G3–11
No. of pupils: 180
£ 🖊

Shrewsbury Lodge School
22 Milbourne Lane, Esher, Surrey KT10 9EA
Tel: 01372 462781
Head: Mr James Tilly BA (Hons), QTS
Age range: 3–7
Fees: Day £8,199–£13,080

Sir William Perkins's School
Guildford Road, Chertsey, Surrey KT16 9BN
Tel: 01932 574900
Head: Mr C Muller
Age range: G11–18 years
No. of pupils: 605 Vlth140
Fees: Day £15,915
🧍 A £ IB 16

St Catherine's, Bramley
Bramley, Guildford, Surrey GU5 0DF
Tel: 01483 899609
Headmistress: Mrs A M Phillips MA(Cantab)
Age range: G4–18
No. of pupils: 900
Fees: Day £8,985–£18,375
FB £30,285
🧍 👥 A £ £ 🖊 16

St Christopher's School
6 Downs Road, Epsom, Surrey KT18 5HE
Tel: 01372 721807
Headteacher: Mrs A C Thackray MA, BA(Hons)
Age range: 3–7
No. of pupils: 137
Fees: Day £10,065
£ 🖊

St Edmund's School
Portsmouth Road, Hindhead, Surrey GU26 6BH
Tel: 01428 604808
Headmaster: Mr A J Walliker MA(Cantab), MBA, PGCE
Age range: 2–16
No. of pupils: 410
Fees: Day £9,585–£15,945
👥 £ 🖊

St George's College
Weybridge Road, Addlestone, Weybridge, Surrey KT15 2QS
Tel: 01932 839300
Headmistress: Mrs Rachel Owens
Age range: 11–18
No. of pupils: 909 Vlth250
Fees: Day £16,845–£19,185
A 🖊 16

St George's Junior School
Thames Street, Weybridge, Surrey KT13 8NL
Tel: 01932 839400
Head Master: Mr Antony Hudson MA (CANTAB), PGCE, NPQH
Age range: 3–11 years
No. of pupils: 644
Fees: Day £5,385–£13,965
£ 🖊

St Hilary's School
Holloway Hill, Godalming, Surrey GU7 1RZ
Tel: 01483 416551
Headmistress: Mrs Jane Whittingham BEdCert, ProfPracSpLD
Age range: B2–11 G2–11
No. of pupils: 250
Fees: Day £10,092–£14,850
£ 🖊

St Ives School
Three Gates Lane, Haslemere, Surrey GU27 2ES
Tel: 01428 643734
Headteacher: Kay Goldsworthy
Age range: 2–11
No. of pupils: 149
Fees: Day £8,850–£13,650
£ 🖊

St John's School
Epsom Road, Leatherhead, Surrey KT22 8SP
Tel: 01372 373000
Head of School: Mrs Rowena Cole
Age range: 11–18
No. of pupils: 761
Fees: Day £19,200–£24,300
WB £24,330–£30,705
👥 A £ £ 16

St Teresa's Effingham (Preparatory School)
Effingham, Surrey RH5 6ST
Tel: 01372 453456
Headmaster: Mr. Mike Farmer
Age range: B2–4 G2–11
No. of pupils: 100
Fees: Day £1,185–£13,890
WB £24,300 FB £27,300
🧍 £ 🖊

St Teresa's Effingham (Senior School)
Beech Avenue, Effingham, Surrey RH5 6ST
Tel: 01372 452037
Head: Mr Mike Farmer
Age range: G11–18
No. of pupils: 640 Vlth90
Fees: Day £16,980–£17,595 WB £27,489–£27,795 FB £29,340–£29,955
🧍 👥 A £ £ 🖊 16

St. Andrew's School
Church Hill House, Horsell, Woking, Surrey GU21 4QW
Tel: 01483 760943
Headmaster: Mr A Perks
Age range: 3–13
No. of pupils: 300
Fees: Day £3,789–£14,925
£ 🖊

Surbiton Preparatory School
3 Avenue Elmers, Surbiton, Surrey KT6 4SP
Tel: 020 8390 6640
Principal: Mrs Rebecca Glover
Age range: B4–11 G4–11
No. of pupils: 135
Fees: Day £10,857–£13,974
🧍 👥 🖊

Tante Marie Culinary Academy
Woodham House, Carlton Road, Woking, Surrey GU21 4HF
Tel: 01483 726957
Principal: Mr Andrew Maxwell
Age range: 16–60
No. of pupils: 72
Fees: Day £20,750
16 🖊 16

TASIS The American School in England
Coldharbour Lane, Thorpe, Surrey TW20 8TE
Tel: +44 (0)1932 582316
Head of School: Mr Bryan Nixon
Age range: 3–18
No. of pupils: 662
Fees: Day £11,230–£23,890
FB £43,550
👥 🧍 IB 16

The Hawthorns School
Pendell Court, Bletchingley, Redhill, Surrey RH1 4QJ
Tel: 01883 743048
Head of School: Mr Adrian Floyd
Age range: 2–13
No. of pupils: 520
Fees: Day £10,320–£14,880
£ 🖊

The Royal Junior School
Portsmouth Road, Hindhead, Surrey GU26 6BW
Tel: 01428 607977
Head of School: Mrs Kerrie Daunter B.Ed (Hons)
Age range: 6 weeks–11 years
Fees: Day £10,200–£11,955
👥

The Royal School
Farnham Lane, Haslemere, Surrey GU27 1HQ
Tel: 01428 605805
Principal: Mrs Anne Lynch BA (Hons), PGCE, FRSA
Age range: 11–18 years
Fees: Day £17,925–£18,144 WB £26,895–£27,114 FB £30,600–£30,819
👥 A £ £ 🖊 16

Tormead School
27 Cranley Road, Guildford, Surrey GU1 2JD
Tel: 01483 575101
Headmistress: Mrs Christina Foord
Age range: G4–18
No. of pupils: 760 Vlth120
Fees: Day £8,100–£15,450
🧍 A £ 🖊 16

Warlingham Park School
Chelsham Common, Warlingham, Surrey CR6 9PB
Tel: 01883 626844
Headmaster: Mr M R Donald BSc
Age range: 2–11
No. of pupils: 96
Fees: Day £4,110–£8,310
🖊

Weston Green School
Weston Green Road, Thames Ditton, Surrey KT7 0JN
Tel: 020 8398 2778
Head: Mrs Sarah Evans
Age range: 4–11
Fees: Day £9,867–£11,094
🖊

Westward School
47 Hersham Road, Walton-on-Thames, Surrey KT12 1LE
Tel: 01932 220911
Headmistress: Mrs Shelley Stevenson
Age range: 3–12
No. of pupils: 140
Fees: Day £7,230–£8,070
£ 🖊

Woldingham School
Marden Park, Woldingham, Surrey CR3 7YA
Tel: 01883 349431
Headmistress: Mrs Alex Hutchinson
Age range: G11–18
No. of pupils: 530 Vlth150
Fees: Day £20,580–£22,440
FB £33,570–£36,540
🧍 👥 A £ £ 🖊 16

Woodcote House School
Snows Ride, Windlesham, Surrey GU20 6PF
Tel: 01276 472115
Headmaster: Mr D.M.K. Paterson
Age range: B7–13
No. of pupils: 100
Fees: Day £17,850 FB £23,850
🧍 👥 £ 🖊

World Federation of Hairdressing & Beauty Schools
PO Box 367, Coulsdon, Surrey CR5 2TP
Tel: 01737 551355
16

Yehudi Menuhin School
Stoke Road, Stoke d'Abernon, Cobham, Surrey KT11 3QQ
Tel: 01932 864739
Head of School: Kate Clanchy
Age range: 7–19
No. of pupils: 80 Vlth36
Fees: FB £34,299
👥 A £ £ 🖊 16

West Berkshire

Brockhurst & Marlston House Schools
Hermitage, Newbury, West Berkshire RG18 9UL
Tel: 01635 200293
Joint Heads: Mr David Fleming & Mrs Caroline Riley
Age range: 3–13
No. of pupils: 275
Fees: Day £10,650–£17,850 FB £23,925

Cheam School
Headley, Newbury, West Berkshire RG19 8LD
Tel: +44 (0)1635 268242
Headmaster: Mr Martin Harris
Age range: 3–13
No. of pupils: 407
Fees: Day £11,940–£21,285 FB £26,055–£27,630

Downe House School
Hermitage Road, Cold Ash, Thatcham, West Berkshire RG18 9JJ
Tel: 01635 200286
Headmistress: Mrs E McKendrick BA(Liverpool)
Age range: G11–18
No. of pupils: VIth174
Fees: Day £27,495 FB £37,530

Horris Hill
Newtown, Newbury, West Berkshire RG20 9DJ
Tel: 01635 40594
Headmaster: Mr G F Tollit B.A.(Hons)
Age range: B4–13
No. of pupils: 120
Fees: Day £5,600 FB £8,900

Marlston House Preparatory School
Hermitage, Newbury, West Berkshire RG18 9UL
Tel: 01635 200293
Headmistress: Mrs Caroline Riley MA, BEd
Age range: G3–13
No. of pupils: 110
Fees: Day £10,650–£17,850 FB £23,925

Newbury Hall
Enborne Road, (corner of Rockingham Road), Newbury, West Berkshire RG14 6AD
Tel: +44 (0)1635 36879

St Gabriel's
Sandleford Priory, Newbury, West Berkshire RG20 9BD
Tel: 01635 555680
Principal: Mr Richard Smith MA (Hons), MEd, PGCE
Age range: B6 months–11 G6 months–18
No. of pupils: 469 VIth40
Fees: Day £10,668–£17,418

St Michael's School
Harts Lane, Burghclere, Newbury, West Berkshire RG20 9JW
Tel: 01635 278137
Headmaster: Rev. Fr. Patrick Summers
Age range: 5–18
No. of pupils: VIth5

The Cedars School
Church Road, Aldermaston, West Berkshire RG7 4LR
Tel: 0118 971 4251
Headteacher: Mrs Jane O'Halloran
Age range: 4–11
No. of pupils: 50
Fees: Day £8,910

Thorngrove School
The Mount, Highclere, Newbury, West Berkshire RG20 9PS
Tel: 01635 253172
Headmaster: Mr Adam King
Age range: 2–13
Fees: Day £14,070–£17,595

West Sussex

Ardingly College
College Road, Ardingly, Haywards Heath, West Sussex RH17 6SQ
Tel: +44 (0)1444 893320
Headmaster: Mr Ben Figgis
Age range: 13–18
No. of pupils: 559
Fees: Day £22,995–£23,610 FB £33,405–£35,910

Ardingly College Preparatory School
Haywards Heath, West Sussex RH17 6SQ
Tel: 01444 893200
Headmaster: Mr Harry Hastings
Age range: 2–13
Fees: Day £9,195–£15,750

Ashton Park School
Brinsbury Campus East, Stane Street, North Heath, Pulborough, West Sussex RH20 1DJ
Tel: 01798 875836
Head: Mr G Holding
Age range: 11–16
No. of pupils: 66

Brambletye
Brambletye, East Grinstead, West Sussex RH19 3PD
Tel: 01342 321004
Headmaster: Will Brooks
Age range: 2–13
No. of pupils: 280
Fees: Day £9,615–£20,730 FB £24,705–£25,275

Burgess Hill Girls
Keymer Road, Burgess Hill, West Sussex RH15 0EG
Tel: 01444 241050
Head of School: Liz Laybourn
Age range: B2.5–4 G2.5–18
No. of pupils: 505 VIth70
Fees: Day £7,800–£19,200 FB £28,050–£34,200

Chichester High Schools Sixth Form
Kingsham Road, Chichester, West Sussex PO19 8AE
Tel: +44 1243 832 546

Christ's Hospital
Horsham, West Sussex RH13 0LJ
Tel: 01403 211293
Headmaster: Mr Simon Reid
Age range: 11–18
No. of pupils: 900
Fees: Day £16,950–£21,330 FB £32,790

Conifers School
Egmont Road, Midhurst, West Sussex GU29 9BG
Tel: 01730 813243
Headmistress: Mrs Emma Smyth
Age range: 2–13
No. of pupils: 104
Fees: Day £7,110–£9,450

Copthorne Prep School
Effingham Lane, Copthorne, West Sussex RH10 3HR
Tel: 01342 712311
Headmaster: Mr Chris Jones
Age range: 2–13
No. of pupils: 340
Fees: Day £9,240–£16,095 WB £17,565 FB £23,985

Cottesmore School
Buchan Hill, Pease Pottage, West Sussex RH11 9AU
Tel: 01293 520648
Head: T F Rogerson
Age range: 4–13
No. of pupils: 170
Fees: Day £3,199–£4,267 FB £9,095

Cumnor House Sussex
London Road, Danehill, Haywards Heath, West Sussex RH17 7HT
Tel: 01825 792 006
Headmaster: Christian Heinrich
Age range: 2–13
No. of pupils: 385
Fees: Day £8,985–£19,530 WB £22,635 FB £23,250

Dorset House School
The Manor, Church Lane, Bury, Pulborough, West Sussex RH20 1PB
Tel: 01798 831456
Headmaster: Matt Thomas
Age range: 3–13
No. of pupils: 135
Fees: Day £8,550–£17,850

Farlington School
Strood Park, Horsham, West Sussex RH12 3PN
Tel: 01403 282573
Headmistress: Ms Louise Higson BSc, PGCE
Age range: B4–6 G3–18
No. of pupils: 300
Fees: Day £5,400–£17,670 WB £23,205–£28,515 FB £24,540–£29,850

Great Ballard School
Eartham House, Eartham, Nr Chichester, West Sussex PO18 0LR
Tel: 01243 814236
Head: Mr Richard Evans
Age range: 2–13
No. of pupils: 136
Fees: Day £8,580–£15,930 WB £17,010

Great Walstead School
East Mascalls Lane, Lindfield, Haywards Heath, West Sussex RH16 2QL
Tel: 01444 483528
Headmaster: Mr Chris Calvey
Age range: 2.5–13
No. of pupils: 465
Fees: Day £11,055–£15,510

Handcross Park School
Handcross, Haywards Heath, West Sussex RH17 6HF
Tel: 01444 400526
Headmaster: Mr Richard Brown
Age range: 2–13
No. of pupils: 339
Fees: Day £3,230–£6,360 WB £5,370–£7,480 FB £6,030–£8,130

Hurstpierpoint College
College Lane, Hurstpierpoint, West Sussex BN6 9JS
Tel: 01273 833636
Headmaster: Mr. T J Manly BA, MSc
Age range: 4–18
No. of pupils: 1156
Fees: Day £8,790–£22,860 WB £28,800

Hurstpierpoint College Prep School
Hurstpierpoint, West Sussex BN6 9JS
Tel: 01273 834975
Head: Mr I D Pattison BSc
Age range: 4–13
No. of pupils: 360

Lancing College
Lancing, West Sussex BN15 0RW
Tel: 01273 465805
Head Master: Mr Dominic T Oliver MPhil
Age range: 13–18
No. of pupils: 550 VIth255
Fees: Day £8,190 FB £11,995

Lancing College Preparatory School at Worthing
Broadwater Road, Worthing, West Sussex BN14 8HU
Tel: 01903 201123
Head: Mrs Heather Beeby
Age range: 2–13
No. of pupils: 165
Fees: Day £8,115–£11,460

Oakwood Preparatory School
Chichester, West Sussex PO18 9AN
Tel: 01243 575209
Headteacher: Mrs Clare Bradbury
Age range: 2.5–11
No. of pupils: 260
Fees: Day £1,715–£5,010

Our Lady of Sion School
Gratwicke Road, Worthing, West Sussex BN11 4BL
Tel: 01903 204063
Headmaster: Dr Simon Orchard
Age range: 2–18
No. of pupils: 528 VIth55
Fees: Day £8,310–£13,050

Pennthorpe School
Church Street, Horsham, West Sussex RH12 3HJ
Tel: 01403 822391
Headmistress: Alexia Bolton
Age range: 2–13
No. of pupils: 362
Fees: Day £2,070–£16,605

Rikkyo School in England
Guildford Road, Rudgwick, Horsham, West Sussex RH12 3BE
Tel: 01403 822107
Headmaster: Mr Roger Munechika
Age range: 10–18
No. of pupils: 116
Fees: FB £15,000–£21,600

Seaford College
Lavington Park, Petworth, West Sussex GU28 0NB
Tel: 01798 867392
Headmaster: J P Green MA BA
Age range: 7–18
No. of pupils: 732 VIth194
Fees: Day £10,320–£21,390 WB £21,510–£28,980 FB £33,090

Shoreham College
St Julians Lane, Shoreham-by-Sea, West Sussex BN43 6YW
Tel: 01273 592681
Headmaster: Mr R Taylor-West
Age range: 3–16 years
No. of pupils: 375
Fees: Day £9,750–£15,150

Slindon College
Slindon House, Slindon, Arundel, West Sussex BN18 0RH
Tel: 01243 814320
Head Teacher: Mr Mark Birkbeck
Age range: B8–18 years
No. of pupils: 80 VIth17
Fees: Day £21,795 FB £32,280

Sompting Abbotts Preparatory School for Boys and Girls
Church Lane, Sompting, West Sussex BN15 0AZ
Tel: 01903 235960
Principal: Mrs P M Sinclair
Age range: 2–13
No. of pupils: 185
Fees: Day £9,195–£11,805

The Prebendal School
52-55 West Street, Chichester, West Sussex PO19 1RT
Tel: 01243 772220
Headteacher: Mrs L Salmond Smith
Age range: 3–13
No. of pupils: 181
Fees: Day £8,160–£15,495 WB £18,975–£20,100 FB £22,290

The Towers Convent School
Convent of the Blessed Sacrement, Henfield Road, Upper Beeding, Steyning, West Sussex BN44 3TF
Tel: 01903 812185
Headmistress: Mrs Clare Trelfa
Age range: B4–11 G4–16
No. of pupils: 320
Fees: Day £8,190–£11,550

Westbourne House School
Shopwyke, Chichester, West Sussex PO20 2BH
Tel: 01243 782739
Headmaster: Mr Martin Barker
Age range: 2.5–13 years
No. of pupils: 420
Fees: Day £10,440–£17,985 FB £21,465–£24,105

Windlesham House School
London Road, Washington, Pulborough, West Sussex RH20 4AY
Tel: 01903 874701
Headmaster: Mr Richard Foster BEd(Hons)
Age range: 4–13
No. of pupils: 340

Worth School
Paddockhurst Road, Turners Hill, Crawley, West Sussex RH10 4SD
Tel: +44 (0)1342 710200
Head Master: Stuart McPherson
Age range: 11–18
No. of pupils: 580 VIth222
Fees: Day £15,960–£23,730 FB £21,210–£33,690

International Schools in London and the South-East

KEY TO SYMBOLS

- (†) Boys' school
- (♀) Girls' school
- (🌐) International school
- (16) Tutorial or sixth form college
- (A) A levels
- (🏛) Boarding accommodation
- (£) Bursaries
- (IB) International Baccalaureate
- (✐) Learning support
- (16) Entrance at 16+
- (✿) Vocational qualifications
- (IAPS) Independent Association of Prep Schools
- (HMC) The Headmasters' & Headmistresses' Conference
- (ISA) Independent Schools Association
- (GSA) Girls' School Association
- (BSA) Boarding Schools' Association
- (S) Society of Heads

Unless otherwise indicated, all schools are coeducational day schools. Single-sex and boarding schools will be indicated by the relevant icon.

London

Central London

CATS London
43-45 Bloomsbury Square,
London WC1A 2RA
Tel: 02078 411580
Principal: Mario Di Clemente
Age range: 15–24
(⚙)(A)(♿)(£)(16+)

ÉCOLE JEANNINE MANUEL - LONDON
For further details see p. 56
43-45 Bedford Square,
London WC1B 3DN
Tel: 020 3829 5970
Email: admissions@
jmanuel.uk.net
Website: www.ecolejeannine
manuel.org.uk
Head of School: Pauline Prévot
Age range: 3–18 years
No. of pupils: 442
Fees: Day £17,460.00
(⚙)(£)(IB)

North London

Dwight School London
6 Friern Barnet Lane,
London N11 3LX
Tel: +44 (0)20 8920 0637
Head: Mrs Alison Cobbin BA, Dip
Ed, MBA
Age range: 3–18
(⚙)(£)(IB)(✏)(16+)

North-West London

College Francais Bilingue De Londres
87 Holmes Road, Kentish
Town, , London NW5 3AX
Tel: +44 (0) 20 7993 7400
Principal: Mr François-Xavier Gabet
Age range: 5–15
No. of pupils: 210
(⚙)

International Community School
7B Wyndham Place,
London NW1 4PT
Tel: +44 (0) 20 7298 8817
Head of School: Ms Rose Threlfall
Age range: 3–18
No. of pupils: 190
Fees: Day £19,400.00–£26,000.00
(⚙)(IB)(✏)(16+)

Mill Hill School
The Ridgeway, Mill Hill
Village, London NW7 1QS
Tel: 020 8959 1176
Head: Mrs Jane Sanchez
Age range: 13–18
No. of pupils: 689 VIth259
Fees: Day £21,141.00 WB
£28,524.00 FB £33,717.00
(⚙)(A)(♿)(£)(16+)

Southbank International School - Hampstead
16 Netherhall Gardens,
London NW3 5TH
Tel: 020 7243 3803
Principal: Shirley Harwood
Age range: 3–11
No. of pupils: 210
Fees: Day £16,530.00–£25,740.00
(⚙)(IB)

The American School in London
One Waverley Place,
London NW8 0NP
Tel: 020 7449 1221
Head: Robin Appleby
Age range: 4–18
No. of pupils: 1350
Fees: Day £27,050.00–£31,200.00
(⚙)(16+)

The Mount, Mill Hill International
Milespit Hill, London NW7 2RX
Tel: +44 (0)20 3826 33
Head of School: Ms Sarah Bellotti
Age range: 13–17
No. of pupils: 68
Fees: Day £24,990.00 WB
£34,461.00 FB £40,539.00
(⚙)(♿)

South-East London

Bellerbys College London
Bounty House, Greenwich,
London SE8 3DE
Tel: +44 (0)208 694 7000
Principal: Ms Alison Baines
Age range: 15–19
(⚙)(16+)(A)(♿)

DLD COLLEGE LONDON
For further details see p. 55
199 Westminster Bridge
Road, London SE1 7FX
Tel: +44 (0)20 7935 8411
Email: dld@dld.org
Website: www.dldcollege.co.uk
Principal: Irfan H Latif BSc (Hons)
PGCE FRSA FRSC
No. of pupils: 426
Fees: Day £23,500.00–£29,950.00
FB £18,000.00–£28,000.00
(⚙)(16+)(A)(♿)(£)(✏)

Dulwich College
London SE21 7LD
Tel: 020 8693 3601
Master: Dr J A F Spence
Age range: B0–18
No. of pupils: 1589 VIth470
Fees: Day £20,448.00 WB
£40,017.00 FB £42,681.00
(♂)(⚙)(A)(♿)(£)(✏)(16+)

St Dunstan's College
Stanstead Road, London SE6 4TY
Tel: 020 8516 7200
Headmaster: Mr Nicholas Hewlett
Age range: 3–18
No. of pupils: 870
(⚙)(A)(£)(16+)

South-West London

Centre Academy London
92 St John's Hill, Battersea,
London SW11 1SH
Tel: 020 7738 2344
Headteacher: Rachel Maddison
Age range: 9–19
Fees: Day £27,600.00–£40,100.00
(⚙)(£)(✏)(16+)

Eaton Square School
79 Eccleston Square,
London SW1V 1PP
Tel: 020 7931 9469
Headmaster: Mr Sebastian Hepher
BEd(Hons)
Age range: 2–13
No. of pupils: 529
Fees: Day £20,850.00–£21,900.00
(⚙)(£)(✏)

Ecole Charles De Gaulle - Wix
Clapham Common North
Side, London SW4 0AJ
Tel: +44 20 7738 0287
Headteacher: Mr Blanchard
Age range: 5–11
No. of pupils: 100
(⚙)

Ecole Marie D'Orliac
60 Clancarty Road,
London SW6 3AA
Tel: +44 7736 020 58 63
Principal: Mr Olivier Rauch
Age range: 4–11
No. of pupils: 50
(⚙)

HILL HOUSE INTERNATIONAL JUNIOR SCHOOL
For further details see p. 62
17 Hans Place, Chelsea,
London SW1X 0EP
Tel: 020 7584 1331
Email: info@
hillhouseschool.co.uk
Website:
www.hillhouseschool.co.uk
Principals: Richard, Janet,
William & Edmund Townend
Age range: 4–13
No. of pupils: 740
Fees: Day £13,200.00–£17,400.00
(⚙)(£)(✏)

King's College School
Southside, Wimbledon
Common, London SW19 4TT
Tel: 020 8255 5300
Head Master: A D Halls MA
Age range: B11–18 G16–18
No. of pupils: 967
Fees: Day £19,530.00–£21,600.00
(♂)(⚙)(A)(£)(IB)(16+)

Lycée Français Charles de Gaulle
35 Cromwell Road,
London SW7 2DG
Tel: 020 7584 6322
Head of School: Mr Olivier Rauch
Age range: 5–19
No. of pupils: 4000
(⚙)(A)(£)(✏)(16+)

St Paul's School
Lonsdale Road, Barnes,
London SW13 9JT
Tel: 020 8748 9162
High Master: Prof Mark Bailey
Age range: B13–18
No. of pupils: 897
Fees: Day £25,032.00 FB £37,611.00
(♂)(⚙)(A)(♿)(£)(✏)(16+)

Wandsworth Preparatory School
The Old Library, 2 Allfarthing
Lane, London SW18 2PQ
Tel: 0208 870 4133
Head of School: Miss Bridget Saul
BA (Hons), PGCE, MA
Age range: 4–11
No. of pupils: 115
Fees: Day £4,570.00
(⚙)(£)

Westminster School
Little Dean's Yard, Westminster,
London SW1P 3PF
Tel: 020 7963 1003
Headmaster: Mr Patrick Derham
Age range: B13–18 G16–18
No. of pupils: 744
Fees: Day £26,130.00–
£28,566.00 FB £37,740.00
(♂)(⚙)(A)(♿)(£)(✏)(16+)

West London

Bales College
742 Harrow Road, Kensal
Town, London W10 4AA
Tel: 020 8960 5899
Principal: William Moore
Age range: 11–19
No. of pupils: 90
Fees: Day £11,550.00–£12,750.00

Ecole Francaise Jacques Prevert
59 Brook Green, London W6 7BE
Tel: 020 7602 6871
Headteacher: Delphine Gentil
Age range: 4–11

Fulham Prep School
200 Greyhound Road,
London W14 9SD
Tel: 020 7386 2444
Head of School: Mr Neill Lunnon
Age range: 4–18
No. of pupils: 647
Fees: Day £16,869.00–£19,749.00

Halcyon London International School
33 Seymour Place, ,
London W1H 5AU
Tel: +44 (0)20 7258 1169
Headteacher: Mr Barry Mansfield
Age range: 11–18
No. of pupils: 172

Instituto Español Vicente Cañada Blanch
317 Portobello Road,
London W10 5SZ
Tel: +44 (0) 20 8969 2664
Principal: Carmen Pinilla Padilla
Age range: 4–19
No. of pupils: 405

International School of London (ISL)
139 Gunnersbury Avenue,
London W3 8LG
Tel: +44 (0)20 8992 5823
Principal: Mr Richard Parker
Age range: 3–18 years
No. of pupils: 450
Fees: Day £19,000.00–£26,300.00

King Fahad Academy
Bromyard Avenue, Acton,
London W3 7HD
Tel: 020 8743 0131
Director General: Dr Abdulghani Alharbi
Age range: 3–19
No. of pupils: 500
Fees: Day £3,300.00–£4,300.00

Southbank International School - Kensington
36-38 Kensington Park
Road, London W11 3BU
Tel: +44 (0)20 7243 3803
Principal: Siobhan McGrath
Age range: 3–11
No. of pupils: 210
Fees: Day £16,530.00–£25,740.00

Southbank International School - Westminster
63-65 Portland Place,
London W1B 1QR
Tel: 020 7243 3803
Principal: Dr Paul Wood
Age range: 11–19

The Godolphin and Latymer School
Iffley Road, Hammersmith,
London W6 0PG
Tel: +44 (0)20 8741 1936
Head Mistress: Dr Frances Ramsey
Age range: G11–18
No. of pupils: 800
Fees: Day £21,615.00

Berkshire

Bradfield College
Bradfield, Berkshire RG7 6AU
Tel: 0118 964 4516
Headmaster: Dr Christopher Stevens
Age range: 13–18
No. of pupils: 800
Fees: Day £29,925.00 FB £37,404.00

Eton College
Windsor, Berkshire SL4 6DW
Tel: 01753 671249
Head Master: Simon Henderson MA
Age range: B13–18
No. of pupils: 1300 VIth520
Fees: FB £40,668.00

Heathfield School
London Road, Ascot,
Berkshire SL5 8BQ
Tel: 01344 898342
Head of School: Mrs Marina Gardiner Legge
Age range: G11–18
No. of pupils: 200

LEIGHTON PARK SCHOOL
For further details see p. 102
Shinfield Road, Reading,
Berkshire RG2 7ED
Tel: 0118 987 9600
Email: admissions@leightonpark.com
Website: www.leightonpark.com
Head: Mr Matthew L S Judd BA, PGCE
Age range: 11–18
No. of pupils: 460

Luckley House School
Luckley Road, Wokingham,
Berkshire RG40 3EU
Tel: 0118 978 4175
Head: Mrs Jane Tudor
Age range: G11–18
No. of pupils: 230
Fees: Day £16,620.00 WB £26,955.00 FB £29,082.00

LVS ASCOT
For further details see p. 104
London Road, Ascot,
Berkshire SL5 8DR
Tel: 01344 882770
Email: enquiries@lvs.ascot.sch.uk
Website: www.lvs.ascot.sch.uk
Headmistress: Mrs Christine Cunniffe BA (Hons), MMus, MBA
Age range: 4–18
No. of pupils: 830
Fees: Day £10,380.00–£19,896.00 FB £26,562.00–£34,953.00

Padworth College
Padworth, Reading,
Berkshire RG7 4NR
Tel: 0118 983 2644
Acting Principal: Mr Chris Randell
Age range: 13–19
No. of pupils: 116 VIth50
Fees: Day £14,400.00 FB £29,400.00

PANGBOURNE COLLEGE
For further details see p. 105
Pangbourne, Reading,
Berkshire RG8 8LA
Tel: 0118 984 2101
Email: admissions@pangbourne.com
Website: www.pangbourne.com
Headmaster: Thomas J C Garnier
Age range: 11–18
No. of pupils: 429 VIth62
Fees: Day £17,655.00–£24,885.00 FB £24,870.00–£35,190.00

Queen Anne's School
6 Henley Road, Caversham,
Reading, Berkshire RG4 6DX
Tel: 0118 918 7300
Headmistress: Mrs Julia Harrington BA(Hons), PGCE, NPQH
Age range: G11–18
No. of pupils: 336 VIth100
Fees: Day £24,135.00 WB £32,070.00–£33,810.00 FB £35,580.00

Reddam House Berkshire
Bearwood Road, Sindlesham,
Wokingham, Berkshire RG41 5BG
Tel: 0118 974 8300
Principal: Mrs Tammy Howard
Age range: 3 months–18 years
No. of pupils: 800
Fees: Day £10,200.00–£17,280.00 WB £27,075.00–£31,215.00 FB £28,665.00–£32,805.00

St George's Ascot
Wells Lane, Ascot, Berkshire SL5 7DZ
Tel: 01344 629920
Headmistress: Mrs Liz Hewer MA (Hons) (Cantab) PGCE
Age range: G11–18
No. of pupils: 270 VIth70
Fees: Day £22,800.00 WB £34,050.00–£34,680.00 FB £35,460.00

St Mary's School Ascot
St Mary's Road, Ascot,
Berkshire SL5 9JF
Tel: 01344 296614
Headmistress: Mrs Mary Breen BSc, MSc
Age range: G11–18
No. of pupils: 390 VIth120
Fees: Day £26,190.00 FB £36,780.00

The Abbey School
Kendrick Road, Reading,
Berkshire RG1 5DZ
Tel: 0118 987 2256
Head: Mrs Rachel S E Dent
Age range: G3–18
No. of pupils: 1100
Fees: Day £17,040.00

The Oratory School
Woodcote, Reading,
Berkshire RG8 0PJ
Tel: 01491 683500
Head Master: Mr J J Smith BA(Hons),
MEd, PGCE
Age range: B11–18
No. of pupils: 380 VIth120
Fees: Day £24,966.00 FB £34,299.00

Wellington College
Duke's Ride, Crowthorne,
Berkshire RG45 7PU
Tel: +44 (0)1344 444000
Master: Mr Julian Thomas
Age range: 13–18
No. of pupils: 1040 VIth455
Fees: Day £29,040.00–
£33,360.00 FB £39,750.00

Buckinghamshire

Thornton College
Thornton, Milton Keynes,
Buckinghamshire MK17 0HJ
Tel: 01280 812610
Headmistress: Mrs Jo Storey
Age range: B2–4 G2–16
No. of pupils: 370
Fees: Day £9,555.00–£15,240.00
WB £16,320.00–£20,655.00
FB £20,295.00–£25,185.00

Wycombe Abbey
High Wycombe,
Buckinghamshire HP11 1PE
Tel: +44 (0)1494 897008
Headmistress: Mrs Rhiannon J
Wilkinson MA (Oxon) MEd
Age range: G11–18
No. of pupils: 631
Fees: Day £29,205.00 FB £38,940.00

East Sussex

Battle Abbey School
Battle, East Sussex TN33 0AD
Tel: 01424 772385
Headmaster: Mr D Clark BA(Hons)
Age range: 2–18
No. of pupils: 286 VIth48
Fees: Day £6,939.00–£16,914.00
FB £26,649.00–£31,932.00

Bede's School
The Dicker, Upper Dicker,
Hailsham, East Sussex BN27 3QH
Tel: +44 (0)1323843252
Head: Mr Peter Goodyer
Age range: 3 months–18
No. of pupils: 800 VIth295
Fees: Day £10,230.00–£17,400.00
FB £22,290.00–£25,650.00

Bellerbys College Brighton
1 Billinton Way, Brighton,
East Sussex BN1 4LF
Tel: +44 (0)1273 339333
Principal: Mr Simon Mower
Age range: 13–18

Brighton College
Eastern Road, Brighton,
East Sussex BN2 0AL
Tel: 01273 704200
Head Master: Richard Cairns MA
Age range: 3–18
No. of pupils: 950
Fees: Day £10,050.00–£24,540.00
WB £33,390.00–£34,410.00
FB £37,470.00–£45,210.00

Buckswood School
Broomham Hall, Rye
Road, Guestling, Hastings,
East Sussex TN35 4LT
Tel: 01424 813 813
School Director: Mr Giles Sutton
Age range: 10–19
No. of pupils: 420

Eastbourne College
Old Wish Road, Eastbourne,
East Sussex BN21 4JX
Tel: 01323 452323 (Admissions)
Headmaster: Mr Tom Lawson
MA(Oxon)
Age range: 13–18
No. of pupils: 614 VIth284
Fees: Day £23,130.00–£23,505.00
FB £35,250.00–£35,655.00

Greenfields Independent Day & Boarding School
Priory Road, Forest Row,
East Sussex RH18 5JD
Tel: +44 (0)1342 822189
Executive Head: Mr. Jeff Smith
Age range: 2–19

Mayfield School
The Old Palace, Mayfield,
East Sussex TN20 6PH
Tel: +44 (0)1435 874600
Head: Ms Antonia Beary MA, Mphil
(Cantab), PGCE
Age range: G11–18
No. of pupils: 365 VIth100
Fees: Day £21,000.00 FB £33,900.00

Michael Hall School
Kidbrooke Park, Priory Road,
Forest Row, East Sussex RH18 5BG
Tel: 01342 822275
Age range: 0–18
Fees: Day £9,245.00–
£12,670.00 FB £8,065.00

Roedean Moira House
Upper Carlisle Road, Eastbourne,
East Sussex BN20 7TE
Tel: 01323 644144
Headmaster: Mr Andrew Wood
Age range: G0–18
No. of pupils: 289

ROEDEAN SCHOOL
For further details see p. 106
Roedean Way, Brighton,
East Sussex BN2 5RQ
Tel: 01273 667500
Email: info@roedean.co.uk
Website: www.roedean.co.uk
Headmaster: Mr. Oliver Bond
BA(Essex), PGCE, NPQH
Age range: G11–18
No. of pupils: 568 VIth171
Fees: Day £15,960.00–£20,865.00
WB £28,230.00–£31,470.00
FB £30,930.00–£37,440.00

Essex

Brentwood School
Middleton Hall Lane,
Brentwood, Essex CM15 8EE
Tel: 01277 243243
Headmaster: Mr Ian Davies
Age range: 3–18
No. of pupils: 1600
Fees: Day £18,945.00 FB £37,128.00
ⓐ Ⓐ ⓔ Ⓔ ⒾⒷ ✎ ⑯

Chigwell School
High Road, Chigwell, Essex IG7 6QF
Tel: 020 8501 5700
Headmaster: Mr M E Punt MA, MSc
Age range: 4–18
No. of pupils: 915 VIth185
Fees: Day £11,985.00–
£17,985.00 FB £30,885.00
ⓐ Ⓐ ⓔ Ⓔ ✎ ⑯

Felsted School
Felsted, Great Dunmow,
Essex CM6 3LL
Tel: 01371 822605
Headmaster: Mr Chris Townsend
Age range: 13–18
No. of pupils: 550
Fees: Day £7,850.00 FB £11,995.00
ⓐ Ⓐ ⓔ Ⓔ ⒾⒷ ✎ ⑯

Gosfield School
Cut Hedge Park, Halstead Road,
Gosfield, Halstead, Essex CO9 1PF
Tel: 01787 474040
Headteacher: Mr Guy Martyn
Age range: 4–18
No. of pupils: VIth21
Fees: Day £6,690.00–£15,525.00
ⓐ Ⓐ ⓔ Ⓔ ✎ ⑯

New Hall School
The Avenue, Boreham,
Chelmsford, Essex CM3 3HS
Tel: 01245 467588
Principal: Mrs Katherine Jeffrey MA,
BA, PGCE, MA(Ed Mg), NPQH
Age range: Coed 3-11,
Single 11-16, Coed 16–18
No. of pupils: 1180 VIth217
Fees: Day £9,801.00–£19,878.00
WB £19,761.00–£28,569.00 FB
£21,531.00–£30,681.00
ⓐ Ⓐ ⓔ Ⓔ ✎ ⑯

Hampshire

Bedales School
Church Road, Steep, Petersfield,
Hampshire GU32 2DG
Tel: 01730 711733
Head of School: Magnus Bashaarat
Age range: 13–18
No. of pupils: 463
Fees: Day £28,515.00 FB £36,285.00
ⓐ Ⓐ ⓔ Ⓔ ✎ ⑯

Brockwood Park & Inwoods School
Brockwood Park, Bramdean,
Hampshire SO24 0LQ
Tel: +44 (0)1962 771744
Principal: Mr Antonio Autor
Age range: 14–19
No. of pupils: 112 VIth39
Fees: Day £5,630.00–
£6,400.00 FB £21,400.00
ⓐ Ⓐ ⓔ Ⓔ ✎ ⑯

Hampshire Collegiate School
Embley Park, Romsey,
Hampshire SO51 6ZE
Tel: 01794 512206
Headteacher: Mr Cliff Canning
Age range: 2–18
No. of pupils: 500
Fees: Day £8,499.00–£29,988.00
ⓐ Ⓐ ⓔ Ⓔ ✎ ⑯

Lord Wandsworth College
Long Sutton, Hook,
Hampshire RG29 1TB
Tel: 01256 862201
Head of School: Mr Adam Williams
Age range: 11–18 years
No. of pupils: 615
Fees: Day £20,430.00–£23,460.00
WB £28,290.00–£31,800.00
FB £29,250.00–£33,300.00
ⓐ Ⓐ ⓔ Ⓔ ✎ ⑯

Moyles Court School
Moyles Court, Ringwood,
Hampshire BH24 3NF
Tel: 01425 472856
Headmaster: Mr R Milner-Smith
Age range: 3–16
Fees: Day £2,112.00–£4,766.00
FB £6,876.00–£8,675.00
ⓐ ⓔ

Rookwood School
Weyhill Road, Andover,
Hampshire SP10 3AL
Tel: 01264 325900
Headmaster: Mr A Kirk-Burgess BSc,
PGCE, MSc (Oxon)
Age range: 2–16
Fees: Day £9,360.00–£15,600.00
FB £23,250.00–£27,465.00
ⓐ ⓔ Ⓔ ✎

Sherfield School
Sherfield-on-Loddon, Hook,
Hampshire RG27 0HU
Tel: +44 (0)1256 884 800
Acting Head Master: Mr
Christopher James-Roll BSc (Hons),
PGCE
Age range: 3 months–18 years
No. of pupils: 445 VIth16
Fees: Day £9,930.00–£16,594.00
WB £18,408.00–£25,375.00
FB £21,474.00–£29,601.00
ⓐ ⓔ Ⓔ ✎ ⑯ 🌐

St John's College
Grove Road South, Southsea,
Portsmouth, Hampshire PO5 3QW
Tel: 023 9281 5118
Headmaster: Mr Timothy Bayley BSc
(Hons), MA, PGCE
Age range: 2–18
No. of pupils: 560 VIth86
Fees: Day £9,225.00–£12,090.00
FB £25,200.00–£28,740.00
ⓐ Ⓐ ⓔ Ⓔ ✎ ⑯ 🌐

ST SWITHUN'S SCHOOL
For further details see p. 109
Alresford Road, Winchester,
Hampshire SO21 1HA
Tel: 01962 835700
Email: office@stswithuns.com
Website: www.stswithuns.com
Head of School: Jane Gandee
MA(Cantab)
Age range: G11–18
No. of pupils: 510
🚶 ⓐ Ⓐ ⓔ Ⓔ ✎ ⑯

The Portsmouth Grammar School
High Street, Portsmouth,
Hampshire PO1 2LN
Tel: +44 (0)23 9236 0036
Headmistress: Dr Anne Cotton
Age range: 2–18
No. of pupils: 1556 VIth336
Fees: Day £10,233.00–£15,951.00
ⓐ Ⓐ Ⓔ ⒾⒷ ✎ ⑯

Winchester College
College Street, Winchester,
Hampshire SO23 9NA
Tel: 01962 621247
Headmaster: Dr. T R Hands
Age range: B13–18
No. of pupils: 690 VIth280
Fees: FB £39,912.00
🚶 ⓐ ⓔ Ⓔ ✎ ⑯

Hertfordshire

Aldenham School
Elstree, Hertfordshire WD6 3AJ
Tel: 01923 858122
Headmaster: Mr James C Fowler MA
Age range: 3–18
No. of pupils: 700
Fees: Day £16,491.00–£22,614.00
FB £22,791.00–£33,234.00

BERKHAMSTED SCHOOL
For further details see p. 99
Overton House, 131 High Street, Berkhamsted, Hertfordshire HP4 2DJ
Tel: 01442 358001
Email: admissions@berkhamsted.com
Website: www.berkhamsted.com
Principal: Mr Richard Backhouse MA(Cantab)
Age range: 3–18
No. of pupils: 1792 VIth395
Fees: Day £10,365.00–£20,640.00
WB £27,635.00 FB £32,880.00

Bishop's Stortford College
10 Maze Green Road, Bishop's Stortford, Hertfordshire CM23 2PJ
Tel: 01279 838575
Headmaster: Mr Jeremy Gladwin
Age range: 13–18
No. of pupils: VIth249
Fees: Day £19,662.00–£19,839.00
WB £30,228.00–£30,411.00
FB £30,528.00–£30,711.00

Bishop's Stortford College Prep School
Maze Green Road, Bishop's Stortford, Hertfordshire CM23 2PH
Tel: 01279 838607
Head of the Prep School: Mr Bill Toleman
Age range: 4–13
No. of pupils: 590
Fees: Day £9,090.00–£15,729.00
WB £21,102.00–£22,911.00 FB £21,327.00–£23,142.00

Haileybury
Haileybury, Hertford, Hertfordshire SG13 7NU
Tel: +44 (0)1992 706200
The Master: Mr Martin Collier MA BA PGCE
Age range: 11–18
No. of pupils: 833 VIth317
Fees: Day £17,031.00–£25,620.00
FB £21,837.00–£34,422.00

Princess Helena College
Preston, Hitchin, Hertfordshire SG4 7RT
Tel: 01462 443888
Headmistress: Mrs Sue Wallace-Woodroffe
Age range: G11–18
No. of pupils: 194 VIth35
Fees: Day £16,125.00–£19,635.00
FB £22,965.00–£28,545.00

St Christopher School
Barrington Road, Letchworth, Hertfordshire SG6 3JZ
Tel: 01462 650 850
Head: Richard Palmer
Age range: 3–18
No. of pupils: 511 VIth78
Fees: Day £4,590.00–£18,075.00 WB £19,950.00–£24,675.00 FB £31,650.00

St Edmund's College & Prep School
Old Hall Green, Nr Ware, Hertfordshire SG11 1DS
Tel: 01920 824247
Head: Paulo Durán BA MA
Age range: 3–18
No. of pupils: 799 VIth135
Fees: Day £10,650.00–£17,205.00
WB £22,665.00–£25,905.00
FB £26,040.00–£29,865.00

St Francis' College
Broadway, Letchworth Garden City, Hertfordshire SG6 3PJ
Tel: 01462 670511
Headmistress: Mrs B Goulding
Age range: G3–18
No. of pupils: 460 VIth75
Fees: Day £9,990.00–£16,980.00
WB £22,350.00–£26,475.00
FB £27,990.00–£31,995.00

St Margaret's School, Bushey
Merry Hill Road, Bushey, Hertfordshire WD23 1DT
Tel: 020 8416 4400
Head: Mrs Rose Hardy MA(Oxon), MEd, FRSA
Age range: G4–18 years
No. of pupils: 450 VIth100
Fees: Day £11,286.00–£16,902.00 WB £23,220.00–£27,279.00 FB £31,770.00

Stanborough School
Stanborough Park, Garston, Watford, Hertfordshire WD25 9JT
Tel: 01923 673268
Acting Head Teacher: Ms Eileen Hussey
Age range: 3–17
No. of pupils: 300
Fees: Day £6,630.00–£10,224.00
WB £10,350.00–£13,995.00

The Purcell School, London
Aldenham Road, Bushey, Hertfordshire WD23 2TS
Tel: 01923 331100
Headteacher: Dr Bernard Trafford
Age range: 10–18
No. of pupils: 180
Fees: Day £25,707.00 FB £32,826.00

The Royal Masonic School for Girls
Rickmansworth Park, Rickmansworth, Hertfordshire WD3 4HF
Tel: 01923 773168
Headmaster: Mr Kevin Carson M.Phil (Cambridge)
Age range: G4–18
No. of pupils: 930 VIth165
Fees: Day £11,475.00–£17,475.00
WB £20,115.00–£27,495.00 FB £21,225.00–£29,835.00

Tring Park School for the Performing Arts
Tring Park, Tring, Hertfordshire HP23 5LX
Tel: 01442 824255
Principal: Mr Stefan Anderson MA, ARCM, ARCT
Age range: 8–19
No. of pupils: 374 VIth266
Fees: Day £14,865.00–£23,655.00
FB £25,275.00–£35,760.00

Kent

Ashford School
East Hill, Ashford, Kent TN24 8PB
Tel: 01233 739030
Head: Mr Michael Hall
Age range: 3 months–18 years
No. of pupils: 835 VIth170
Fees: Day £10,500.00–£16,800.00
WB £24,000.00 FB £36,000.00

Ashgrove School
116 Widmore Road, Bromley, Kent BR1 3BE
Tel: 020 8460 4143
Principal: Patricia Ash CertEd, BSc(Hons), PhD, CMath, FIMA
Age range: 4–11
No. of pupils: 106
Fees: Day £8,730.00

Benenden School
Cranbrook, Kent TN17 4AA
Tel: 01580 240592
Headmistress: Mrs S Price
Age range: G11–18
No. of pupils: 550
Fees: FB £12,650.00

Bethany School
Curtisden Green, Goudhurst, Cranbrook, Kent TN17 1LB
Tel: 01580 211273
Headmaster: Mr Francie Healy BSc, HDipEd, NPQH
Age range: 11–18 years
No. of pupils: 313 VIth98
Fees: Day £16,725.00–£18,465.00
WB £25,950.00–£28,655.00
FB £27,990.00–£31,500.00

CATS Canterbury
68 New Dover Road, Canterbury, Kent CT1 3LQ
Tel: +44 (0)1227866540
Principal: Dr Sarah Lockyer
Age range: 14–18
No. of pupils: 400

Cobham Hall School
Cobham, Kent DA12 3BL
Tel: 01474 823371
Headmistress: Ms Maggie Roberts
Age range: G11–18
No. of pupils: 180

Dover College
Effingham Crescent,
Dover, Kent CT17 9RH
Tel: 01304 205969
Headmaster: Mr Gareth Doodes
MA (Hons)
Age range: 3–18
No. of pupils: 301
Fees: Day £7,725.00–£16,050.00
WB £21,000.00–£25,500.00
FB £24,750.00–£31,500.00

Farringtons School
Perry Street, Chislehurst,
Kent BR7 6LR
Tel: 020 8467 0256
Head: Mrs Dorothy Nancekievill
Age range: 3–18
No. of pupils: 700 VIth100
Fees: Day £15,120.00 WB
£29,850.00 FB £31,680.00

Kent College
Whitstable Road, Canterbury,
Kent CT2 9DT
Tel: 01227 763231
Executive Head Master: Dr D J
Lamper
Age range: 0–18 years
No. of pupils: 756
Fees: Day £16,464.00–£18,315.00
FB £25,236.00–£34,491.00

Kent College Pembury
Old Church Road, Pembury,
Tunbridge Wells, Kent TN2 4AX
Tel: +44 (0)1892 822006
Headmistress: Ms J Lodrick
Age range: G3–18
No. of pupils: 650 VIth102
Fees: Day £9,459.00–£20,571.00 WB
£25,710.00 FB £25,710.00–£32,778.00

King's Rochester
Satis House, Boley Hill,
Rochester, Kent ME1 1TE
Tel: 01634 888555
Principal: Mr J Walker
Age range: 13–18
No. of pupils: 625 VIth92
Fees: Day £7,125.00–£19,320.00
FB £21,960.00–£31,590.00

Rochester Independent College
Star Hill, Rochester,
Medway, Kent ME1 1XF
Tel: 01634 828115
Principals: Alistair Brownlow, Brian
Pain, Pauline Bailey
Age range: 11–19
No. of pupils: 306 VIth233
Fees: Day £12,600.00–£18,000.00
WB £12,000.00 FB £13,500.00

Sevenoaks School
High Street, Sevenoaks,
Kent TN13 1HU
Tel: +44 (0)1732 455133
Head: Dr Katy Ricks MA, DPhil
Age range: 11–18
No. of pupils: 1093
Fees: Day £23,355.00–£26,523.00
FB £37,296.00–£40,464.00

St Edmund's School
St Thomas' Hill, Canterbury,
Kent CT2 8HU
Tel: 01227 475601
Head: Mr Edward O'Connor
Age range: 3–18
No. of pupils: 535
Fees: Day £7,647.00–£20,466.00
WB £24,267.00–£32,595.00 FB
£26,628.00–£34,968.00

St Lawrence College
Ramsgate, Kent CT11 7AE
Tel: 01843 572931
Principal: Mr Antony Spencer
Age range: 3–18
No. of pupils: 640 VIth115
Fees: Day £7,470.00–£18,495.00
FB £26,055.00–£34,635.00

Sutton Valence School
North Street, Sutton
Valence, Kent ME17 3HL
Tel: 01622 845200
Headmaster: Bruce Grindlay MA
Cantab, MusB, FRCO, CHM
Age range: 11–18
No. of pupils: 570

The King's School, Canterbury
The Precincts, Canterbury,
Kent CT1 2ES
Tel: 01227 595501
Head: Mr P Roberts
Age range: 13–18
No. of pupils: 858 VIth385
Fees: Day £27,495.00 FB £37,455.00

Tonbridge School
Tonbridge, Kent TN9 1JP
Tel: 01732 365555
Headmaster: Mr James Priory
Age range: B13–18
No. of pupils: 788

Middlesex

ACS Hillingdon International School
Hillingdon Court, 108 Vine
Lane, Hillingdon, Uxbridge,
Middlesex UB10 0BE
Tel: +44 (0) 1895 259 771
Head: Martin Hall
Age range: 4–18
No. of pupils: 520
Fees: Day £10,640.00–£24,400.00

North London Collegiate School
Canons, Canons Drive,
Edgware, Middlesex HA8 7RJ
Tel: +44 (0)20 8952 0912
Headmistress: Mrs Sarah Clark
Age range: G4–18
No. of pupils: 1080
Fees: Day £5,641.00–£6,676.00

RADNOR HOUSE
For further details see p. 96
Pope's Villa, Cross
Deep, Twickenham,
Middlesex TW1 4QG
Tel: 020 8891 6264
Email: admissions@
radnorhouse.org
Website:
www.radnor-twickenham.org/
Head of School: Darryl Wideman
MA (Oxon.)
Age range: 9–18
No. of pupils: 417

St Helen's School
Eastbury Road, Northwood,
Middlesex HA6 3AS
Tel: +44 (0)1923 843210
Headmistress: Dr Mary Short BA,
PhD
Age range: G3–18
No. of pupils: VIth165

Surrey

ACS Cobham International School
Heywood, Portsmouth Road,
Cobham, Surrey KT11 1BL
Tel: +44 (0) 1932 867251
Head of School: Mr Simon Leyshon
Age range: 2–18
No. of pupils: 1460
Fees: Day £11,250.00–£27,110.00
WB £38,810.00–£41,570.00
FB £44,170.00–£46,930.00

ACS Egham International School
Woodlee, London Road,
Egham, Surrey TW20 0HS
Tel: +44 (0) 1784 430 800
Head of School: Jeremy Lewis
Age range: 4–18
Fees: Day £10,870.00–£25,360.00

Box Hill School
Old London Road, Mickleham,
Dorking, Surrey RH5 6EA
Tel: 01372 373382
Headmaster: Mr Corydon Lowde
Age range: 11–18
No. of pupils: 425 VIth96
Fees: Day £17,850.00–£19,710.00
WB £27,510.00–£28,800.00
FB £33,690.00–£35,100.00

Caterham School
Harestone Valley, Caterham,
Surrey CR3 6YA
Tel: 01883 343028
Head: Mr C. W. Jones MA(Cantab)
Age range: 11–18
No. of pupils: VIth321
Fees: Day £18,045.00 WB
£30,936.00 FB £34,710.00

Charterhouse
Godalming, Surrey GU7 2DX
Tel: +44 (0)1483 291501
Headmaster: Dr Alex Peterken
Age range: B13–18 G16–18
No. of pupils: 810

City of London Freemen's School
Ashtead Park, Ashtead,
Surrey KT21 1ET
Tel: 01372 277933
Headmaster: Mr R Martin
Age range: 7–18
No. of pupils: 877 VIth213
Fees: Day £13,398.00–£18,279.00
WB £27,906.00–£27,957.00 FB
£30,780.00–£30,816.00

Cranleigh School
Horseshoe Lane, Cranleigh,
Surrey GU6 8QQ
Tel: +44 (0) 1483 273666
Headmaster: Mr Martin Reader
MA, MPhil, MBA
Age range: 7–18 (including
Prep School)
No. of pupils: 654 VIth240
Fees: Day £31,170.00 FB £37,905.00

Duke of Kent School
Peaslake Road, Ewhurst,
Surrey GU6 7NS
Tel: 01483 277313
Head: Mrs Sue Knox
Age range: 3–16
No. of pupils: 234
Fees: Day £6,960.00–£18,090.00

Epsom College
Epsom, Surrey KT17 4JQ
Tel: 01372 821000
Headmaster: Mr Jay A Piggot MA
Age range: 11–18
No. of pupils: 884
Fees: Day £18,765.00–£25,266.00
WB £33,849.00 FB £37,263.00

Frensham Heights
Rowledge, Farnham,
Surrey GU10 4EA
Tel: 01252 792561
Headmaster: Mr Andrew Fisher BA,
MEd, FRSA
Age range: 3–18
No. of pupils: 497 VIth105
Fees: Day £6,900.00–£20,430.00
FB £26,370.00–£30,810.00

ISL Surrey Primary School
Old Woking Road, Woking,
Surrey GU22 8HY
Tel: +44 (0)1483 750409
Principal: Richard Parker
Age range: 2–11 years
No. of pupils: 100
Fees: Day £10,450.00–£15,500.00

King Edward's Witley
Godalming, Surrey GU8 5SG
Tel: +44 (0)1428 686700
Headmaster: Mr John Attwater MA
Age range: 11–18
No. of pupils: 400
Fees: Day £20,460.00 FB £31,995.00

MARYMOUNT INTERNATIONAL SCHOOL LONDON
For further details see p. 94
George Road, Kingston upon
Thames, Surrey KT2 7PE
Tel: +44 (0)20 8949 0571
Email: admissions@
marymountlondon.com
Website:
www.marymountlondon.com
Headmistress: Mrs Margaret
Frazier
Age range: G11–18
No. of pupils: 250
Fees: Day £24,985.00 WB
£40,515.00 FB £42,305.00

Prior's Field
Priorsfield Road, Godalming,
Surrey GU7 2RH
Tel: 01483 810551
Head of School: Mrs T Kirnig
Age range: G11–18
No. of pupils: 450
Fees: Day £17,300.00 FB £29,925.00

Reed's School
Sandy Lane, Cobham,
Surrey KT11 2ES
Tel: 01932 869001
Headmaster: Mr Mark Hoskins BA
MA MSc
Age range: B11–18 G16–18
No. of pupils: 650 VIth230
Fees: Day £19,740.00–£24,675.00
FB £26,310.00–£31,800.00

Royal Russell School
Coombe Lane, Croydon,
Surrey CR9 5BX
Tel: 020 8657 3669
Headmaster: Christopher
Hutchinson
Age range: 11–18
No. of pupils: 590 VIth180
Fees: Day £18,480.00 FB £36,525.00

St Catherine's, Bramley
Bramley, Guildford, Surrey GU5 0DF
Tel: 01483 899609
Headmistress: Mrs A M Phillips
MA(Cantab)
Age range: G4–18
No. of pupils: 900
Fees: Day £8,985.00–
£18,375.00 FB £30,285.00

St James Senior Boys School
Church Road, Ashford,
Surrey TW15 3DZ
Tel: 01784 266930
Headmaster: Mr David Brazier
Age range: B11–18
No. of pupils: 403 VIth65
Fees: Day £18,930.00

St John's School
Epsom Road, Leatherhead,
Surrey KT22 8SP
Tel: 01372 373000
Head of School: Mrs Rowena Cole
Age range: 11–18
No. of pupils: 761
Fees: Day £19,200.00–£24,300.00
WB £24,330.00–£30,705.00

St Teresa's Effingham (Senior School)
Beech Avenue, Effingham,
Surrey RH5 6ST
Tel: 01372 452037
Head: Mr Mike Farmer
Age range: G11–18
No. of pupils: 640 VIth90
Fees: Day £16,980.00–£17,595.00
WB £27,489.00–£27,795.00 FB
£29,340.00–£29,955.00

TASIS The American School in England
Coldharbour Lane, Thorpe,
Surrey TW20 8TE
Tel: +44 (0)1932 582316
Head of School: Mr Bryan Nixon
Age range: 3–18
No. of pupils: 662
Fees: Day £11,230.00–
£23,890.00 FB £43,550.00

The Royal Junior School
Portsmouth Road, Hindhead,
Surrey GU26 6BW
Tel: 01428 607977
Head of School: Mrs Kerrie Daunter
B.Ed (Hons)
Age range: 6 weeks–11 years
Fees: Day £10,200.00–£11,955.00

The Royal School
Farnham Lane, Haslemere,
Surrey GU27 1HQ
Tel: 01428 605805
Principal: Mrs Anne Lynch BA
(Hons), PGCE, FRSA
Age range: 11–18 years
Fees: Day £17,925.00–£18,144.00
WB £26,895.00–£27,114.00 FB
£30,600.00–£30,819.00

Whitgift School
Haling Park, South Croydon,
Surrey CR2 6YT
Tel: +44 (0)20 8688 9222
Headmaster: Mr Christopher
Ramsey
Age range: B10–18
No. of pupils: 1464
Fees: Day £20,136.00 WB
£32,274.00 FB £37,866.00

Woldingham School
Marden Park, Woldingham,
Surrey CR3 7YA
Tel: 01883 349431
Headmistress: Mrs Alex Hutchinson
Age range: G11–18
No. of pupils: 530 VIth150
Fees: Day £20,580.00–£22,440.00
FB £33,570.00–£36,540.00

Yehudi Menuhin School
Stoke Road, Stoke d'Abernon,
Cobham, Surrey KT11 3QQ
Tel: 01932 864739
Head of School: Kate Clanchy
Age range: 7–19
No. of pupils: 80 VIth36
Fees: FB £34,299.00

West Berkshire

Downe House School
Hermitage Road, Cold Ash,
Thatcham, West Berkshire RG18 9JJ
Tel: 01635 200286
Headmistress: Mrs E McKendrick
BA(Liverpool)
Age range: G11–18
No. of pupils: VIth174
Fees: Day £27,495.00 FB £37,530.00

West Sussex

Ardingly College
College Road, Ardingly, Haywards
Heath, West Sussex RH17 6SQ
Tel: +44 (0)1444 893320
Headmaster: Mr Ben Figgis
Age range: 13–18
No. of pupils: 559
Fees: Day £22,995.00–£23,610.00
FB £33,405.00–£35,910.00

Burgess Hill Girls
Keymer Road, Burgess Hill,
West Sussex RH15 0EG
Tel: 01444 241050
Head of School: Liz Laybourn
Age range: B2.5–4 G2.5–18
No. of pupils: 505 VIth70
Fees: Day £7,800.00–£19,200.00
FB £28,050.00–£34,200.00

Christ's Hospital
Horsham, West Sussex RH13 0LJ
Tel: 01403 211293
Headmaster: Mr Simon Reid
Age range: 11–18
No. of pupils: 900
Fees: Day £16,950.00–
£21,330.00 FB £32,790.00

Farlington School
Strood Park, Horsham,
West Sussex RH12 3PN
Tel: 01403 282573
Headmistress: Ms Louise Higson
BSc, PGCE
Age range: B4–6 G3–18
No. of pupils: 300
Fees: Day £5,400.00–£17,670.00
WB £23,205.00–£28,515.00
FB £24,540.00–£29,850.00

Hurstpierpoint College
College Lane, Hurstpierpoint,
West Sussex BN6 9JS
Tel: 01273 833636
Headmaster: Mr. T J Manly BA, MSc
Age range: 4–18
No. of pupils: 1156
Fees: Day £8,790.00–
£22,860.00 WB £28,800.00

Lancing College
Lancing, West Sussex BN15 0RW
Tel: 01273 465805
Head Master: Mr Dominic T Oliver
MPhil
Age range: 13–18
No. of pupils: 550 VIth255
Fees: Day £8,190.00 FB £11,995.00

Rikkyo School in England
Guildford Road, Rudgwick,
Horsham, West Sussex RH12 3BE
Tel: 01403 822107
Headmaster: Mr Roger Munechika
Age range: 10–18
No. of pupils: 116
Fees: FB £15,000.00–£21,600.00

Seaford College
Lavington Park, Petworth,
West Sussex GU28 0NB
Tel: 01798 867392
Headmaster: J P Green MA BA
Age range: 7–18
No. of pupils: 732 VIth194
Fees: Day £10,320.00–£21,390.00
WB £21,510.00–£28,980.00
FB £33,090.00

Slindon College
Slindon House, Slindon, Arundel,
West Sussex BN18 0RH
Tel: 01243 814320
Head Teacher: Mr Mark Birkbeck
Age range: B8–18 years
No. of pupils: 80 VIth17
Fees: Day £21,795.00 FB £32,280.00

The Towers Convent School
Convent of the Blessed Sacrement,
Henfield Road, Upper Beeding,
Steyning, West Sussex BN44 3TF
Tel: 01903 812185
Headmistress: Mrs Clare Trelfa
Age range: B4–11 G4–16
No. of pupils: 320
Fees: Day £8,190.00–£11,550.00

Worth School
Paddockhurst Road, Turners Hill,
Crawley, West Sussex RH10 4SD
Tel: +44 (0)1342 710200
Head Master: Stuart McPherson
Age range: 11–18
No. of pupils: 580 VIth222
Fees: Day £15,960.00–£23,730.00
FB £21,210.00–£33,690.00

Specialist schools and sixth form colleges

London

Central London

CATS London
43-45 Bloomsbury Square,
London WC1A 2RA
Tel: 02078 411580
Principal: Mario Di Clemente
Age range: 15–24
🏫 Ⓐ 🏛 £ 16+

City of London School
Queen Victoria Street,
London EC4V 3AL
Tel: 020 3680 6300
Head: Mr A R Bird MSc
Age range: B10–18
No. of pupils: 930 VIth250
Fees: Day £17,901.00
🚹 Ⓐ £ 🖉 16+

City of London School for Girls
St Giles' Terrace, Barbican,
London EC2Y 8BB
Tel: 020 7847 5500
Headmistress: Mrs E Harrop
Age range: G7–18
No. of pupils: 725
🚺 Ⓐ £ 🖉 16+

Italia Conti Academy of Theatre Arts
Italia Conti House, 23 Goswell
Road, London EC1M 7AJ
Tel: 020 7608 0047
Director: Chris White
Age range: 10–21
16+ Ⓐ 16+

The College of Central London
Tower Bridge Business Centre, 46-48
East Smithfield, London E1W 1AW
Tel: +44 (0) 20 3667 7607
Principal: Nicolas Kailides
Fees: Day £3,850.00
16+ 16+

East London

Al-Mizan School
46 Whitechapel Road,
London E1 1JX
Tel: 020 7650 3070
Head: Mr Askor Ali
Age range: B7–11
No. of pupils: 200 VIth13
Fees: Day £3,400.00
🚹 Ⓐ 16+

Forest School
College Place, Snaresbrook,
London E17 3PY
Tel: 020 8520 1744
Warden: Mr Cliff Hodges
Age range: 4–18
No. of pupils: 1355 VIth260
Fees: Day £13,095.00–£18,681.00
Ⓐ £ 🖉 16+

North London

Channing School
The Bank, Highgate, London N6 5HF
Tel: 020 8340 2328
Head: Mrs B M Elliott
Age range: G4–18
No. of pupils: 746 VIth108
Fees: Day £17,610.00–£19,410.00
🚺 Ⓐ £ 🖉 16+

Dwight School London
6 Friern Barnet Lane,
London N11 3LX
Tel: +44 (0)20 8920 0637
Head: Mrs Alison Cobbin BA, Dip
Ed, MBA
Age range: 3–18
🏫 £ Ⓘ🅱 16+

Greek Secondary School of London
Avenue Lodge, Bounds Green
Road, London N22 7EU
Tel: 020 8881 9320
Headteacher: Georgia
Dimitrakopoulou
Age range: 13–18
No. of pupils: 200
Ⓐ 16+

Highgate
North Road, Highgate,
London N6 4AY
Tel: 020 8340 1524
Head Master: Mr A S Pettitt MA
Age range: 3–18
No. of pupils: 1541 VIth312
Fees: Day £18,165.00–£20,970.00
Ⓐ £ 🖉 16+

North-West London

Fine Arts College, Hampstead
Centre Studios, 41-43 England's
Lane, London NW3 4YD
Tel: 020 7586 0312
Head Teacher: Candida Cave MA
Age range: 13–19
No. of pupils: 210
Fees: Day £7,230.00
16+ Ⓐ 16+

Francis Holland School, Regent's Park, NW1
Clarence Gate, Ivor Place,
Regent's Park, London NW1 6XR
Tel: 020 7723 0176
Head: Mr C B Fillingham MA (King's
College London)
Age range: G11–18
No. of pupils: 495 VIth120
Fees: Day £19,260.00
🚺 Ⓐ £ 16+

International Community School
7B Wyndham Place,
London NW1 4PT
Tel: +44 (0) 20 7298 8817
Head of School: Ms Rose Threlfall
Age range: 3–18
No. of pupils: 190
Fees: Day £19,400.00–£26,000.00
🏫 Ⓘ🅱 🖉 16+

Lakefield Catering & Educational Centre
Maresfield Gardens,
Hampstead, London NW3 5RY
Tel: 020 7794 5669
Course Director: Mrs Maria Brown
Age range: G16–24
No. of pupils: 16
Fees: FB £1,160.00
🏫 16+ 🏛 £ 🖉 16+ 🏫

London Academy of Dressmaking and Design
18 Dobree Avenue, Willesden,
London NW10 2AE
Tel: 020 8451 7174
Principal: Mrs P A Parkinson MA
Age range: 13+
Fees: Day £2,650.00
16+ 🖉 16+ 🏫

Mill Hill School
The Ridgeway, Mill Hill
Village, London NW7 1QS
Tel: 020 8959 1176
Head: Mrs Jane Sanchez
Age range: 13–18
No. of pupils: 689 VIth259
Fees: Day £21,141.00 WB
£28,524.00 FB £33,717.00
🏫 Ⓐ 🏛 £ 🖉 16+

NW5 Theatre School
14 Fortess Road, London NW5 2EU
Tel: 020 7482 3236
Founder: George O'Gorman
Age range: 16–30
Fees: Day £3,600.00
16+ 16+

South Hampstead High School GDST
3 Maresfield Gardens,
London NW3 5SS
Tel: 020 7435 2899
Head of School: Mrs V Bingham
Age range: G4–18
No. of pupils: 900
Fees: Day £15,327.00–£18,654.00
🚺 Ⓐ £ 🖉 16+

The American School in London
One Waverley Place,
London NW8 0NP
Tel: 020 7449 1221
Head: Robin Appleby
Age range: 4–18
No. of pupils: 1350
Fees: Day £27,050.00–£31,200.00
🏫 16+

The King Alfred School
Manor Wood, North End
Road, London NW11 7HY
Tel: 020 8457 5200
Head: Robert Lobatto MA (Oxon)
Age range: 4–18
No. of pupils: 650 VIth100
Fees: Day £15,531.00–£18,723.00
Ⓐ £ 🖉 16+

University College School
Frognal, Hampstead,
London NW3 6XH
Tel: 020 7435 2215
Headmaster: Mr Mark J Beard MA,
MEd
Age range: B11–18 G16–18
No. of pupils: 875 VIth309
Fees: Day £20,328.00
🚹 Ⓐ £ 🖉 16+

Wentworth Tutorial College
6-10 Brentmead Place,
London NW11 9LH
Tel: 020 8458 8524/5
Principal: Manuel Guimaraes
Age range: 14–19
No. of pupils: 115
16+ Ⓐ 16+

South-East London

Alleyn's School
Townley Road, Dulwich,
London SE22 8SU
Tel: 020 8557 1500
Headmaster: Dr G Savage MA,
PhD, FRSA
Age range: 4–18
No. of pupils: 1252 VIth302
Fees: Day £17,361.00–£19,851.00
Ⓐ £ 🖉 16+

Blackheath High School GDST
Vanbrugh Park, Blackheath,
London SE3 7AG
Tel: 020 8853 2929
Head: Mrs Carol Chandler-
Thompson BA (Hons) Exeter, PGCE
Exeter
Age range: G3–18
No. of pupils: 780
🚺 Ⓐ £ 🖉 16+

Colfe's School
Horn Park Lane, Lee,
London SE12 8AW
Tel: 020 8852 2283
Head: Mr R F Russell MA(Cantab)
Age range: 3–18
No. of pupils: 1120
Ⓐ £ 🖉 16+

Dulwich College
London SE21 7LD
Tel: 020 8693 3601
Master: Dr J A F Spence
Age range: B0–18
No. of pupils: 1589 VIth470
Fees: Day £20,448.00 WB
£40,017.00 FB £42,681.00

(A) (£) (16+)

ELTHAM COLLEGE
For further details see p. 58
Grove Park Road, Mottingham,
London SE9 4QF
Tel: 0208 857 1455
Email: mail@eltham-
college.org.uk
Website:
www.elthamcollege.london
Headmaster: Guy Sanderson
Age range: 7–18
No. of pupils: 907 VIth194

(A) (£) (16+)

James Allen's Girls' School
144 East Dulwich Grove,
Dulwich, London SE22 8TE
Tel: 020 8693 1181
Head of School: Mrs Sally-Anne
Huang MA, MSc
Age range: G4–18
No. of pupils: 1075

(A) (£) (16+)

Riverston School
63-69 Eltham Road, Lee
Green, London SE12 8UF
Tel: 020 8318 4327
Headmistress: Mrs S E Salathiel
Age range: 9 months–19 years
No. of pupils: 215

(£) (16+)

St Dunstan's College
Stanstead Road, London SE6 4TY
Tel: 020 8516 7200
Headmaster: Mr Nicholas Hewlett
Age range: 3–18
No. of pupils: 870

(A) (£) (16+)

Sydenham High
School GDST
19 Westwood Hill, London SE26 6BL
Tel: 020 8557 7000
Headmistress: Mrs Katharine
Woodcock
Age range: G4–18
No. of pupils: 600 VIth70
Fees: Day £13,161.00–£16,737.00

(A) (£) (16+)

South-West London

Centre Academy London
92 St John's Hill, Battersea,
London SW11 1SH
Tel: 020 7738 2344
Headteacher: Rachel Maddison
Age range: 9–19
Fees: Day £27,600.00–£40,100.00

(£) (16+)

Emanuel School
Battersea Rise, London SW11 1HS
Tel: 020 8870 4171
Headmaster: Mr Robert Milne
Age range: 10–18
No. of pupils: 930
Fees: Day £18,372.00

(A) (£) (16+)

Francis Holland School,
Sloane Square, SW1
39 Graham Terrace,
London SW1W 8JF
Tel: 020 7730 2971
Head: Mrs Lucy Elphinstone
MA(Cantab)
Age range: G4–18
No. of pupils: 520 VIth70
Fees: Day £17,760.00–£20,085.00

(A) (£) (16+)

Ibstock Place School
Clarence Lane, London SW15 5PY
Tel: 020 8876 9991
Head: Mrs Anna Sylvester-Johnson
BA(Hons), PGCE
Age range: 4–18
No. of pupils: 970
Fees: Day £16,290.00–£20,880.00

(A) (£) (16+)

King's College School
Southside, Wimbledon
Common, London SW19 4TT
Tel: 020 8255 5300
Head Master: A D Halls MA
No. of pupils: 967
Fees: Day £19,530.00–£21,600.00

(A) (£) (IB) (16+)

Lycée Français
Charles de Gaulle
35 Cromwell Road,
London SW7 2DG
Tel: 020 7584 6322
Head of School: Mr Olivier Rauch
Age range: 5–19
No. of pupils: 4000

(A) (£) (16+)

MORE HOUSE SCHOOL
For further details see p. 70
22-24 Pont Street, Knightsbridge,
London SW1X 0AA
Tel: 020 7235 2855
Email: office@morehouse.org.uk
Website:
www.morehouse.org.uk
Co-Heads: Mrs. Amanda Leach
& Mr. Michael Keeley
Age range: G11–18
No. of pupils: 206
Fees: Day £6,650.00

(A) (£) (16+)

Putney High School GDST
35 Putney Hill, London SW15 6BH
Tel: 020 8788 4886
Headmistress: Mrs Suzie Longstaff
BA, MA, PGCE
Age range: G4–18
No. of pupils: 976 VIth150

(A) (£) (16+)

Queen's Gate School
131-133 Queen's Gate,
London SW7 5LE
Tel: 020 7589 3587
Principal: Mrs R M Kamaryc BA,
MSc, PGCE
Age range: G4–18
No. of pupils: VIth94

(A) (£) (16+)

St Paul's School
Lonsdale Road, Barnes,
London SW13 9JT
Tel: 020 8748 9162
High Master: Prof Mark Bailey
Age range: B13–18
No. of pupils: 897
Fees: Day £25,032.00 FB £37,611.00

(A) (£) (16+)

Streatham & Clapham
High School GDST
42 Abbotswood Road,
London SW16 1AW
Tel: 020 8677 8400
Headmaster: Dr Millan Sachania
Age range: G3–18
No. of pupils: 603 VIth70
Fees: Day £10,431.00–£19,743.00

(A) (£) (16+)

Swedish School
82 Lonsdale Road, London SW13 9JS
Tel: 020 8741 1751
Head of School: Ms. Annika
Simonsson Bergqvist
Age range: 3–18
No. of pupils: 300 VIth145
Fees: Day £8,600.00–£9,100.00

(16+)

The Harrodian School
Lonsdale Road, London SW13 9QN
Tel: 020 8748 6117
Headmaster: James R Hooke
Age range: 4–18
No. of pupils: 890 VIth95
Fees: Day £15,000.00–£23,040.00

(A) (16+)

Westminster School
Little Dean's Yard, Westminster,
London SW1P 3PF
Tel: 020 7963 1003
Headmaster: Mr Patrick Derham
Age range: B13–18 G16–18
No. of pupils: 744
Fees: Day £26,130.00–
£28,566.00 FB £37,740.00

(A) (£) (16+)

Wimbledon High
School GDST
Mansel Road, Wimbledon,
London SW19 4AB
Tel: 020 8971 0900
Headmistress: Mrs Jane Lunnon
Age range: G4–18
No. of pupils: 900 VIth155
Fees: Day £14,622.00–£18,810.00

(A) (£) (16+)

West London

Alan D Education
61-62 East Castle Street,
London W1W 8NQ
Tel: 020 7580 1030
Director of Education: Alan
Hemmings
Fees: Day £200.00 FB £12,400.00

(16+) (16+)

Ashbourne Middle School
17 Old Court Place,
Kensington, London W8 4PL
Tel: 020 7937 3858
Principal: M J Kirby MSc, BApSc
Age range: 13–16
No. of pupils: VIth150
Fees: Day £24,750.00–£26,250.00

(A) (£) (16+)

Blake College
162 New Cavendish Street,
London W1W 6YS
Tel: 020 7636 0658
Course Director: D A J Cluckie
BA, BSc
Fees: Day £4,720.00–£5,310.00

(16+) (16+)

David Game College
31 Jewry Street, London EC3N 2ET
Tel: 020 7221 6665
Principal: D T P Game MA, MPhil
Age range: 14–19
No. of pupils: 200 VIth150
Fees: Day £3,680.00–£30,630.00

(16+) (A) (£) (16+)

Ealing Independent
College
83 New Broadway, Ealing,
London W5 5AL
Tel: 020 8579 6668
Principal: Dr Ian Moores
Age range: 13–19
No. of pupils: 100 VIth70
Fees: Day £2,910.00–£18,120.00

(16+) (A) (16+)

International School
of London (ISL)
139 Gunnersbury Avenue,
London W3 8LG
Tel: +44 (0)20 8992 5823
Principal: Mr Richard Parker
Age range: 3–18 years
No. of pupils: 450
Fees: Day £19,000.00–£26,300.00

(IB) (16+)

King Fahad Academy
Bromyard Avenue, Acton,
London W3 7HD
Tel: 020 8743 0131
Director General: Dr Abdulghani
Alharbi
Age range: 3–19
No. of pupils: 500
Fees: Day £3,300.00–£4,300.00

(A) (£) (IB) (16+)

Latymer Upper School
King Street, Hammersmith,
London W6 9LR
Tel: 020862 92024
Head: Mr D Goodhew MA(Oxon)
Age range: 11–18
No. of pupils: 1200
Fees: Day £20,130.00
(A) (£) (🖊) (16·)

Notting Hill & Ealing High School GDST
2 Cleveland Road, West
Ealing, London W13 8AX
Tel: (020) 8799 8400
Headmaster: Mr Matthew Shoults
Age range: G4–18
No. of pupils: 903 VIth150
Fees: Day £14,313.00–£18,561.00
(🚹) (A) (£) (16·)

Portland Place School
56-58 Portland Place,
London W1B 1NJ
Tel: 0207 307 8700
Head: Mr David Bradbury
Age range: 9–18
No. of pupils: 300 VIth50
Fees: Day £21,030.00
(A) (£) (🖊) (16·)

Queen's College
43-49 Harley Street,
London W1G 8BT
Tel: 020 7291 7000
Principal: Mr Richard Tillet
Age range: G11–18
No. of pupils: 360 VIth90
(🚹) (A) (£) (16·)

Ray Cochrane Beauty School
118 Baker Street, London W1U 6TT
Tel: 02033224738
Principal: Miss Baljeet Suri
Age range: 16–50
No. of pupils: 30
Fees: Day £650.00–£8,495.00
(16·) (16·) (🌐)

Southbank International School - Westminster
63-65 Portland Place,
London W1B 1QR
Tel: 020 7243 3803
Principal: Dr Paul Wood
Age range: 11–19
(🌐) (IB) (🖊) (16·)

ST AUGUSTINE'S PRIORY
For further details see p. 80
Hillcrest Road, Ealing,
London W5 2JL
Tel: 020 8997 2022
Email: office@sapriory.com
Website: www.sapriory.com
Headteacher: Mrs Sarah Raffray M.A., N.P.Q.H
Age range: B3–4 G3–18
No. of pupils: 485
Fees: Day £11,031.00–£15,693.00
(🚹) (A) (🖊) (16·)

ST BENEDICT'S SCHOOL
For further details see p. 78
54 Eaton Rise, Ealing,
London W5 2ES
Tel: 020 8862 2000
Email: admissions@stbenedicts.org.uk
Website: www.stbenedicts.org.uk
Headmaster: Mr A Johnson BA
Age range: 3–18
No. of pupils: 1086 VIth213
Fees: Day £12,990.00–£16,845.00
(A) (£) (🖊) (16·)

St James Senior Girls' School
Earsby Street, London W14 8SH
Tel: 020 7348 1777
Headmistress: Mrs Sarah Labram BA
Age range: G11–18
No. of pupils: 295 VIth67
Fees: Day £20,100.00
(🚹) (A) (£) (🖊) (16·)

St Paul's Girls' School
Brook Green, London W6 7BS
Tel: 020 7603 2288
High Mistress: Mrs Sarah Fletcher
Age range: G11–18 years
No. of pupils: 750 VIth200
Fees: Day £24,891.00–£26,760.00
(🚹) (A) (£) (🖊) (16·)

The Godolphin and Latymer School
Iffley Road, Hammersmith,
London W6 0PG
Tel: +44 (0)20 8741 1936
Head Mistress: Dr Frances Ramsey
Age range: G11–18
No. of pupils: 800
Fees: Day £21,615.00
(🚹) (🌐) (A) (£) (IB) (🖊) (16·)

Berkshire

Bradfield College
Bradfield, Berkshire RG7 6AU
Tel: 0118 964 4516
Headmaster: Dr Christopher Stevens
Age range: 13–18
No. of pupils: 800
Fees: Day £29,925.00 FB £37,404.00
(🌐) (A) (🏫) (£) (IB) (🖊) (16·)

Claires Court Nursery, Girls and Sixth Form
1 College Avenue, Maidenhead,
Berkshire SL6 6AW
Tel: 01628 327700
Head of School: Mrs M Heywood
Age range: B16–18 G3–18
No. of pupils: 495 VIth111
Fees: Day £9,270.00–£16,740.00
(🚹) (A) (£) (🖊) (16·)

Claires Court Senior Boys
Ray Mill Road East, Maidenhead,
Berkshire SL6 8TE
Tel: 01628 327700
Headmaster: Mr J M Rayer BSc, PGCE
Age range: B11–16
No. of pupils: 335 VIth112
Fees: Day £15,930.00–£16,740.00
(🚹) (A) (£) (🖊) (16·)

Eton College
Windsor, Berkshire SL4 6DW
Tel: 01753 671249
Head Master: Simon Henderson MA
Age range: B13–18
No. of pupils: 1300 VIth520
Fees: FB £40,668.00
(🚹) (🌐) (A) (🏫) (£) (🖊) (16·)

Heathfield School
London Road, Ascot,
Berkshire SL5 8BQ
Tel: 01344 898342
Head of School: Mrs Marina Gardiner Legge
Age range: G11–18
No. of pupils: 200
(🚹) (🌐) (A) (🏫) (£) (🖊) (16·)

LEIGHTON PARK SCHOOL
For further details see p. 102
Shinfield Road, Reading,
Berkshire RG2 7ED
Tel: 0118 987 9600
Email: admissions@leightonpark.com
Website: www.leightonpark.com
Head: Mr Matthew L S Judd BA, PGCE
Age range: 11–18
No. of pupils: 460
(🌐) (A) (🏫) (£) (IB) (🖊) (16·)

Luckley House School
Luckley Road, Wokingham,
Berkshire RG40 3EU
Tel: 0118 978 4175
Head: Mrs Jane Tudor
Age range: G11–18
No. of pupils: 230
Fees: Day £16,620.00 WB £26,955.00 FB £29,082.00
(🌐) (A) (🏫) (£) (🖊) (16·)

LVS ASCOT
For further details see p. 104
London Road, Ascot,
Berkshire SL5 8DR
Tel: 01344 882770
Email: enquiries@lvs.ascot.sch.uk
Website: www.lvs.ascot.sch.uk
Headmistress: Mrs Christine Cunniffe BA (Hons), MMus, MBA
Age range: 4–18
No. of pupils: 830
Fees: Day £10,380.00–£19,896.00 FB £26,562.00–£34,953.00
(🌐) (A) (🏫) (£) (🖊) (16·)

Padworth College
Padworth, Reading,
Berkshire RG7 4NR
Tel: 0118 983 2644
Acting Principal: Mr Chris Randell
Age range: 13–19
No. of pupils: 116 VIth50
Fees: Day £14,400.00 FB £29,400.00
(🌐) (A) (🏫) (£) (16·)

PANGBOURNE COLLEGE
For further details see p. 105
Pangbourne, Reading,
Berkshire RG8 8LA
Tel: 0118 984 2101
Email: admissions@pangbourne.com
Website: www.pangbourne.com
Headmaster: Thomas J C Garnier
Age range: 11–18
No. of pupils: 429 VIth62
Fees: Day £17,655.00–£24,885.00 FB £24,870.00–£35,190.00
(🌐) (A) (🏫) (£) (🖊) (16·)

Queen Anne's School
6 Henley Road, Caversham,
Reading, Berkshire RG4 6DX
Tel: 0118 918 7300
Headmistress: Mrs Julia Harrington BA(Hons), PGCE, NPQH
Age range: G11–18
No. of pupils: 336 VIth100
Fees: Day £24,135.00 WB £32,070.00–£33,810.00 FB £35,580.00
(🚹) (🌐) (A) (🏫) (£) (🖊) (16·)

Queensmead School
King's Road, Windsor,
Berkshire SL4 2AX
Tel: 01753 863779
Head: Mr Simon Larter
Age range: 2–18
No. of pupils: 300
Fees: Day £7,128.00–£15,318.00
(🚹) (A) (£) (🖊) (16·)

Reading Blue Coat School
Holme Park, Sonning Lane, Sonning,
Reading, Berkshire RG4 6SU
Tel: 0118 944 1005
Headmaster: Mr Jesse Elzinga
Age range: B11–18 G16–18
No. of pupils: 710 VIth230
Fees: Day £16,695.00

Reddam House Berkshire
Bearwood Road, Sindlesham,
Wokingham, Berkshire RG41 5BG
Tel: 0118 974 8300
Principal: Mrs Tammy Howard
Age range: 3 months–18 years
No. of pupils: 570
Fees: Day £10,200.00–£17,280.00
WB £27,075.00–£31,215.00 FB
£28,665.00–£32,805.00

**Redroofs School for the
Performing Arts (Redroofs
Theatre School)**
26 Bath Road, Maidenhead,
Berkshire SL6 4JT
Tel: 01628 674092
Principal: June Rose
Age range: 8–18
No. of pupils: 100
Fees: Day £4,882.00–£5,527.00

St George's Ascot
Wells Lane, Ascot, Berkshire SL5 7DZ
Tel: 01344 629920
Headmistress: Mrs Liz Hewer MA
(Hons) (Cantab) PGCE
Age range: G11–18
No. of pupils: 270 VIth70
Fees: Day £22,800.00 WB
£34,050.00–£34,680.00
FB £35,460.00

St Joseph's College
Upper Redlands Road,
Reading, Berkshire RG1 5JT
Tel: 0118 966 1000
Headmaster: Mr Andrew Colpus
Age range: 3–18
No. of pupils: VIth65
Fees: Day £6,672.00–£11,406.00

St Mary's School Ascot
St Mary's Road, Ascot,
Berkshire SL5 9JF
Tel: 01344 296614
Headmistress: Mrs Mary Breen
BSc, MSc
Age range: G11–18
No. of pupils: 390 VIth120
Fees: Day £26,190.00 FB £36,780.00

Teikyo School UK
Framewood Road, Wexham,
Slough, Berkshire SL2 4QS
Tel: 01753 663711
Headmaster: Tadashi Nakayama
Age range: 16–18

The Abbey School
Kendrick Road, Reading,
Berkshire RG1 5DZ
Tel: 0118 987 2256
Head: Mrs Rachel S E Dent
Age range: G3–18
No. of pupils: 1100
Fees: Day £17,040.00

The Marist Schools
King's Road, Sunninghill,
Ascot, Berkshire SL5 7PS
Tel: 01344 624291
Head of Secondary School: Mr K
McCloskey
Age range: G2–18
No. of pupils: 550 VIth60
Fees: Day £9,780.00–£14,610.00

The Oratory School
Woodcote, Reading,
Berkshire RG8 0PJ
Tel: 01491 683500
Head Master: Mr J J Smith BA(Hons),
MEd, PGCE
Age range: B11–18
No. of pupils: 380 VIth120
Fees: Day £24,966.00 FB £34,299.00

Wellington College
Duke's Ride, Crowthorne,
Berkshire RG45 7PU
Tel: +44 (0)1344 444000
Master: Mr Julian Thomas
Age range: 13–18
No. of pupils: 1040 VIth455
Fees: Day £29,040.00–
£33,360.00 FB £39,750.00

Buckinghamshire

Pipers Corner School
Pipers Lane, Great
Kingshill, High Wycombe,
Buckinghamshire HP15 6LP
Tel: 01494 718 255
Headmistress: Mrs H J Ness-Gifford
BA(Hons), PGCE
Age range: G4–18
No. of pupils: VIth72
Fees: Day £8,880.00–£18,390.00

Stowe School
Buckingham, Buckinghamshire
MK18 5EH
Tel: 01280 818000
Headmaster: Dr Anthony
Wallersteiner
Age range: 13–18
No. of pupils: 769 VIth318
Fees: Day £26,355.00 FB £36,660.00

St Mary's School
94 Packhorse Road, Gerrards
Cross, Buckinghamshire SL9 8JQ
Tel: 01753 883370
Head of School: Mrs P Adams
Age range: G3–18
No. of pupils: 350 VIth50
Fees: Day £5,670.00–£16,980.00

**The Webber
Independent School**
Soskin Drive, Stantonbury
Fields, Milton Keynes,
Buckinghamshire MK14 6DP
Tel: 01908 574740
Principal: Mrs Hilary Marsden
Age range: 3–18
No. of pupils: 300 VIth15
Fees: Day £9,030.00–£12,705.00

Wycombe Abbey
High Wycombe,
Buckinghamshire HP11 1PE
Tel: +44 (0)1494 897008
Headmistress: Mrs Rhiannon J
Wilkinson MA (Oxon) MEd
Age range: G11–18
No. of pupils: 631
Fees: Day £29,205.00 FB £38,940.00

East Sussex

Battle Abbey School
Battle, East Sussex TN33 0AD
Tel: 01424 772385
Headmaster: Mr D Clark BA(Hons)
Age range: 2–18
No. of pupils: 286 VIth48
Fees: Day £6,939.00–£16,914.00
FB £26,649.00–£31,932.00

Bede's School
The Dicker, Upper Dicker,
Hailsham, East Sussex BN27 3QH
Tel: +44 (0)1323843252
Head: Mr Peter Goodyer
Age range: 3 months–18
No. of pupils: 800 VIth295
Fees: Day £10,230.00–£17,400.00
FB £22,290.00–£25,650.00

**Brighton & Hove
High School GDST**
Montpelier Road, Brighton,
East Sussex BN1 3AT
Tel: 01273 280280
Head: Jennifer Smith
Age range: G3–18
No. of pupils: 680 VIth70
Fees: Day £7,191.00–£14,421.00

Brighton College
Eastern Road, Brighton,
East Sussex BN2 0AL
Tel: 01273 704200
Head Master: Richard Cairns MA
Age range: 3–18
No. of pupils: 950
Fees: Day £10,050.00–£24,540.00
WB £33,390.00–£34,410.00
FB £37,470.00–£45,210.00

Buckswood School
Broomham Hall, Rye
Road, Guestling, Hastings,
East Sussex TN35 4LT
Tel: 01424 813 813
School Director: Mr Giles Sutton
Age range: 10–19
No. of pupils: 420

Buckswood St George's
Westwood House, 7-9
Holmesdale Gardens, Hastings,
East Sussex TN34 1LY
Tel: 01424 813696
College Director: Ian Godfrey
Age range: B16–19 G16–20
No. of pupils: VIth50

Eastbourne College
Old Wish Road, Eastbourne,
East Sussex BN21 4JX
Tel: 01323 452323 (Admissions)
Headmaster: Mr Tom Lawson
MA(Oxon)
Age range: 13–18
No. of pupils: 614 VIth284
Fees: Day £23,130.00–£23,505.00
FB £35,250.00–£35,655.00

Greenfields Independent Day & Boarding School
Priory Road, Forest Row,
East Sussex RH18 5JD
Tel: +44 (0)1342 822189
Executive Head: Mr. Jeff Smith
Age range: 2–19

Lewes Old Grammar School
High Street, Lewes, East
Sussex BN7 1XS
Tel: 01273 472634
Headmaster: Mr Robert Blewitt
Age range: 3–18
No. of pupils: 463 VIth50
Fees: Day £8,760.00–£14,625.00

Mayfield School
The Old Palace, Mayfield,
East Sussex TN20 6PH
Tel: +44 (0)1435 874600
Head: Ms Antonia Beary MA, Mphil
(Cantab), PGCE
Age range: G11–18
No. of pupils: 365 VIth100
Fees: Day £21,000.00 FB £33,900.00

Michael Hall School
Kidbrooke Park, Priory Road,
Forest Row, East Sussex RH18 5BG
Tel: 01342 822275
Age range: 0–18
Fees: Day £9,245.00–
£12,670.00 FB £8,065.00

Roedean Moira House
Upper Carlisle Road, Eastbourne,
East Sussex BN20 7TE
Tel: 01323 644144
Headmaster: Mr Andrew Wood
Age range: G0–18
No. of pupils: 289

ROEDEAN SCHOOL
For further details see p. 106
Roedean Way, Brighton,
East Sussex BN2 5RQ
Tel: 01273 667500
Email: info@roedean.co.uk
Website: www.roedean.co.uk
Headmaster: Mr. Oliver Bond
BA(Essex), PGCE, NPQH
Age range: G11–18
No. of pupils: 568 VIth171
Fees: Day £15,960.00–£20,865.00
WB £28,230.00–£31,470.00
FB £30,930.00–£37,440.00

Essex

BANCROFT'S SCHOOL
For further details see p. 88
High Road, Woodford
Green, Essex IG8 0RF
Tel: 020 8505 4821
Email: office@bancrofts.org
Website: www.bancrofts.org
Head: Mr Simon Marshall MA,
PGCE (Cantab), MA, MPhil
(Oxon)
Age range: 7–18
No. of pupils: 1130 VIth235

Brentwood School
Middleton Hall Lane,
Brentwood, Essex CM15 8EE
Tel: 01277 243243
Headmaster: Mr Ian Davies
Age range: 3–18
No. of pupils: 1600
Fees: Day £18,945.00 FB £37,128.00

Chigwell School
High Road, Chigwell, Essex IG7 6QF
Tel: 020 8501 5700
Headmaster: Mr M E Punt MA, MSc
Age range: 4–18
No. of pupils: 915 VIth185
Fees: Day £11,985.00–
£17,985.00 FB £30,885.00

Felsted School
Felsted, Great Dunmow,
Essex CM6 3LL
Tel: 01371 822605
Headmaster: Mr Chris Townsend
Age range: 13–18
No. of pupils: 550
Fees: Day £7,850.00 FB £11,995.00

Gosfield School
Cut Hedge Park, Halstead Road,
Gosfield, Halstead, Essex CO9 1PF
Tel: 01787 474040
Headteacher: Mr Guy Martyn
Age range: 4–18
No. of pupils: VIth21
Fees: Day £6,690.00–£15,525.00

New Hall School
The Avenue, Boreham,
Chelmsford, Essex CM3 3HS
Tel: 01245 467588
Principal: Mrs Katherine Jeffrey MA,
BA, PGCE, MA(Ed Mg), NPQH
Age range: Coed 3-11,
Single 11-16, Coed 16–18
No. of pupils: 1180 VIth217
Fees: Day £9,801.00–£19,878.00
WB £19,761.00–£28,569.00 FB
£21,531.00–£30,681.00

Park School for Girls
20-22 Park Avenue,
Ilford, Essex IG1 4RS
Tel: 020 8554 2466
Headmistress: Mrs Androulla
Nicholas
Age range: G4–16
No. of pupils: 230 VIth19
Fees: Day £6,795.00–£10,260.00

Hampshire

Alton School
Anstey Lane, Alton,
Hampshire GU34 2NG
Tel: 01420 82070
Head: Graham Maher
Age range: 0–18
No. of pupils: 502 VIth53

Bedales School
Church Road, Steep, Petersfield,
Hampshire GU32 2DG
Tel: 01730 711733
Head of School: Magnus Bashaarat
Age range: 13–18
No. of pupils: 463
Fees: Day £28,515.00 FB £36,285.00

Brockwood Park & Inwoods School
Brockwood Park, Bramdean,
Hampshire SO24 0LQ
Tel: +44 (0)1962 771744
Principal: Mr Antonio Autor
Age range: 14–19
No. of pupils: 112 VIth39
Fees: Day £5,630.00–
£6,400.00 FB £21,400.00

Churcher's College
Petersfield, Hampshire GU31 4AS
Tel: 01730 263033
Headmaster: Mr Simon Williams
MA, BSc
Age range: 3–18 years
Fees: Day £9,915.00–£15,420.00

Farnborough Hill
Farnborough Road, Farnborough,
Hampshire GU14 8AT
Tel: 01252 545197
Head: Mrs A Neil BA, MEd, PGCE
Age range: G11–18
No. of pupils: 550 VIth90
Fees: Day £14,796.00

Hampshire Collegiate School
Embley Park, Romsey,
Hampshire SO51 6ZE
Tel: 01794 512206
Headteacher: Mr Cliff Canning
Age range: 2–18
No. of pupils: 500
Fees: Day £8,499.00–£29,988.00

King Edward VI School
Wilton Road, Southampton,
Hampshire SO15 5UQ
Tel: 023 8070 4561
Head Master: Mr A J Thould
MA(Oxon)
Age range: 11–18
No. of pupils: 960
Fees: Day £16,050.00

Lord Wandsworth College
Long Sutton, Hook,
Hampshire RG29 1TB
Tel: 01256 862201
Head of School: Mr Adam Williams
Age range: 11–18 years
No. of pupils: 615
Fees: Day £20,430.00–£23,460.00
WB £28,290.00–£31,800.00
FB £29,250.00–£33,300.00

Portsmouth High School GDST
Kent Road, Southsea, Portsmouth,
Hampshire PO5 3EQ
Tel: 023 9282 6714
Headmistress: Mrs Jane Prescott
BSc NPQH
Age range: G3–18
No. of pupils: 500
Fees: Day £2,500.00–£4,663.00

Salesian College
Reading Road, Farnborough,
Hampshire GU14 6PA
Tel: 01252 893000
Headmaster: Mr Gerard Owens
Age range: B11–18 G16–18
No. of pupils: 650 VIth140
Fees: Day £11,961.00

Sherfield School
Sherfield-on-Loddon, Hook,
Hampshire RG27 0HU
Tel: +44 (0)1256 884 800
Acting Head Master: Mr
Christopher James-Roll BSc (Hons),
PGCE
Age range: 3 months–18 years
No. of pupils: 445 VIth16
Fees: Day £9,930.00–£16,594.00
WB £18,408.00–£25,375.00
FB £21,474.00–£29,601.00

St John's College
Grove Road South, Southsea,
Portsmouth, Hampshire PO5 3QW
Tel: 023 9281 5118
Headmaster: Mr Timothy Bayley BSc
(Hons), MA, PGCE
Age range: 2–18
No. of pupils: 560 VIth86
Fees: Day £9,225.00–£12,090.00
FB £25,200.00–£28,740.00

ST SWITHUN'S SCHOOL
For further details see p. 109
Alresford Road, Winchester,
Hampshire SO21 1HA
Tel: 01962 835700
Email: office@stswithuns.com
Website: www.stswithuns.com
Head of School: Jane Gandee
MA(Cantab)
Age range: G11–18
No. of pupils: 510

The Portsmouth Grammar School
High Street, Portsmouth,
Hampshire PO1 2LN
Tel: +44 (0)23 9236 0036
Headmistress: Dr Anne Cotton
Age range: 2–18
No. of pupils: 1556 VIth336
Fees: Day £10,233.00–£15,951.00

Winchester College
College Street, Winchester,
Hampshire SO23 9NA
Tel: 01962 621247
Headmaster: Dr. T R Hands
Age range: B13–18
No. of pupils: 690 VIth280
Fees: FB £39,912.00

Hertfordshire

Aldenham School
Elstree, Hertfordshire WD6 3AJ
Tel: 01923 858122
Headmaster: Mr James C Fowler
MA
Age range: 3–18
No. of pupils: 700
Fees: Day £16,491.00–£22,614.00
FB £22,791.00–£33,234.00

BERKHAMSTED SCHOOL
For further details see p. 99
Overton House, 131 High
Street, Berkhamsted,
Hertfordshire HP4 2DJ
Tel: 01442 358001
Email: admissions@
berkhamsted.com
Website:
www.berkhamsted.com
Principal: Mr Richard Backhouse
MA(Cantab)
Age range: 3–18
No. of pupils: 1792 VIth395
Fees: Day £10,365.00–£20,640.00
WB £27,635.00 FB £32,880.00

Bishop's Stortford College
10 Maze Green Road, Bishop's
Stortford, Hertfordshire CM23 2PJ
Tel: 01279 838575
Headmaster: Mr Jeremy Gladwin
Age range: 13–18
No. of pupils: VIth249
Fees: Day £19,662.00–£19,839.00
WB £30,228.00–£30,411.00
FB £30,528.00–£30,711.00

Champneys International College of Health & Beauty
Chesham Road, Wigginton,
Tring, Hertfordshire HP23 6HY
Tel: 01442 291333
College Principal: Ms Pam Clegg
Age range: 16+
No. of pupils: 61
Fees: Day £3,000.00–£9,050.00

Haberdashers' Aske's School
Butterfly Lane, Elstree,
Borehamwood,
Hertfordshire WD6 3AF
Tel: 020 8266 1700
Headmaster: Mr P B Hamilton MA
Age range: B5–18
No. of pupils: 1402 VIth310
Fees: Day £15,339.00–£20,346.00

Haberdashers' Aske's School for Girls
Aldenham Road,
Elstree, Borehamwood,
Hertfordshire WD6 3BT
Tel: 020 8266 2300
Headmistress: Miss Biddie A
O'Connor MA (Oxon)
Age range: G4–18
No. of pupils: 1190
Fees: Day £16,980.00–£18,393.00

Haileybury
Haileybury, Hertford,
Hertfordshire SG13 7NU
Tel: +44 (0)1992 706200
The Master: Mr Martin Collier MA
BA PGCE
Age range: 11–18
No. of pupils: 833 VIth317
Fees: Day £17,031.00–£25,620.00
FB £21,837.00–£34,422.00

Immanuel College
87/91 Elstree Road, Bushey,
Hertfordshire WD23 4EB
Tel: 020 8950 0604
Headmaster: Mr Gary Griffin
Age range: 4–18
No. of pupils: 520 VIth127
Fees: Day £10,995.00

MOUNT HOUSE SCHOOL
For further details see p. 95
Camlet Way, Hadley Wood,
Barnet, Hertfordshire EN4 0NJ
Tel: 020 8449 6889
Email: admissions@
mounthouse.org.uk
Website:
www.mounthouse.org.uk
Principal: Mr Toby Mullins
Age range: 11–18
No. of pupils: 190
Fees: Day £16,560.00

Princess Helena College
Preston, Hitchin,
Hertfordshire SG4 7RT
Tel: 01462 443888
Headmistress: Mrs Sue Wallace-
Woodroffe
Age range: G11–18
No. of pupils: 194 VIth35
Fees: Day £16,125.00–£19,635.00
FB £22,965.00–£28,545.00

North London Collegiate School
Canons, Canons Drive, Edgware, Middlesex HA8 7RJ
Tel: +44 (0)20 8952 0912
Headmistress: Mrs Sarah Clark
Age range: G4–18
No. of pupils: 1080
Fees: Day £5,641.00–£6,676.00

Northwood College for Girls GDST
Maxwell Road, Northwood, Middlesex HA6 2YE
Tel: 01923 825446
Head Mistress: Miss Jacqualyn Pain MA, MA, MBA
Age range: G3–18
No. of pupils: 840 VIth100

Regent College
Sai House, 167 Imperial Drive, Harrow, Middlesex HA2 7HD
Tel: 020 8966 9900
Principal: Mrs Tharshiny Pankaj
Age range: 11–19
No. of pupils: 167
Fees: Day £4,100.00–£15,525.00

St Catherine's School
Cross Deep, Twickenham, Middlesex TW1 4QJ
Tel: 020 8891 2898
Headmistress: Mrs Johneen McPherson MA
Age range: G3–18
No. of pupils: 430
Fees: Day £10,795.00–£14,910.00

St Helen's School
Eastbury Road, Northwood, Middlesex HA6 3AS
Tel: +44 (0)1923 843210
Headmistress: Dr Mary Short BA, PhD
Age range: G3–18
No. of pupils: VIth165

St John's Senior School
North Lodge, The Ridgeway, Enfield, Middlesex EN2 8BE
Tel: 020 8366 0035
Headmaster: Mr Andrew Tardios LLB(Hons), BA(Hons), CertEd
Age range: 11–18 years
No. of pupils: 309 VIth95
Fees: Day £13,170.00

The John Lyon School
Middle Road, Harrow on the Hill, Middlesex HA2 0HN
Tel: 020 8515 9400
Head: Miss Katherine Haynes BA, MEd, NPQH
Age range: B11–18
No. of pupils: 600

Surrey

ACS Cobham International School
Heywood, Portsmouth Road, Cobham, Surrey KT11 1BL
Tel: +44 (0) 1932 867251
Head of School: Mr Simon Leyshon
Age range: 2–18
No. of pupils: 1460
Fees: Day £11,250.00–£27,110.00 WB £38,810.00–£41,570.00 FB £44,170.00–£46,930.00

ACS Egham International School
Woodlee, London Road, Egham, Surrey TW20 0HS
Tel: +44 (0) 1784 430 800
Head of School: Jeremy Lewis
Age range: 4–18
Fees: Day £10,870.00–£25,360.00

Box Hill School
Old London Road, Mickleham, Dorking, Surrey RH5 6EA
Tel: 01372 373382
Headmaster: Mr Corydon Lowde
Age range: 11–18
No. of pupils: 425 VIth96
Fees: Day £17,850.00–£19,710.00 WB £27,510.00–£28,800.00 FB £33,690.00–£35,100.00

Cambridge Tutors College
Water Tower Hill, Croydon, Surrey CR0 5SX
Tel: 020 8688 5284/7363
Principal: Dr Chris Drew
Age range: 15–19
No. of pupils: 215 VIth200
Fees: Day £10,400.00–£22,995.00

Caterham School
Harestone Valley, Caterham, Surrey CR3 6YA
Tel: 01883 343028
Head: Mr C. W. Jones MA(Cantab)
Age range: 11–18
No. of pupils: VIth321
Fees: Day £18,045.00 WB £30,936.00 FB £34,710.00

Charterhouse
Godalming, Surrey GU7 2DX
Tel: +44 (0)1483 291501
Headmaster: Dr Alex Peterken
Age range: B13–18 G16–18
No. of pupils: 810

City of London Freemen's School
Ashtead Park, Ashtead, Surrey KT21 1ET
Tel: 01372 277933
Headmaster: Mr R Martin
Age range: 7–18
No. of pupils: 877 VIth213
Fees: Day £13,398.00–£18,279.00 WB £27,906.00–£27,957.00 FB £30,780.00–£30,816.00

Claremont Fan Court School
Claremont Drive, Esher, Surrey KT10 9LY
Tel: 01372 467841
Head: Mr William Brierly
Age range: 2–18
No. of pupils: 780
Fees: Day £10,680.00–£17,670.00

Cranleigh School
Horseshoe Lane, Cranleigh, Surrey GU6 8QQ
Tel: +44 (0) 1483 273666
Headmaster: Mr Martin Reader MA, MPhil, MBA
Age range: 7–18 (including Prep School)
No. of pupils: 654 VIth240
Fees: Day £31,170.00 FB £37,905.00

Croydon High School GDST
Old Farleigh Road, Selsdon, South Croydon, Surrey CR2 8YB
Tel: 020 8260 7500
Headmistress: Mrs Emma Pattison
Age range: G3–18
No. of pupils: 580 VIth75

Dunottar School
High Trees Road, Reigate, Surrey RH2 7EL
Tel: 01737 761945
Head of School: Mr Mark Tottman
Age range: 11–18
No. of pupils: 365
Fees: Day £16,035.00

Epsom College
Epsom, Surrey KT17 4JQ
Tel: 01372 821000
Headmaster: Mr Jay A Piggot MA
Age range: 11–18
No. of pupils: 884
Fees: Day £18,765.00–£25,266.00 WB £33,849.00 FB £37,263.00

Ewell Castle School
Church Street, Ewell, Epsom, Surrey KT17 2AW
Tel: 020 8393 1413
Principal: Mr Peter Harris
Age range: 3–18
No. of pupils: 557
Fees: Day £4,953.00–£16,692.00

Frensham Heights
Rowledge, Farnham, Surrey GU10 4EA
Tel: 01252 792561
Headmaster: Mr Andrew Fisher BA, MEd, FRSA
Age range: 3–18
No. of pupils: 497 VIth105
Fees: Day £6,900.00–£20,430.00 FB £26,370.00–£30,810.00

Guildford High School
London Road, Guildford, Surrey GU1 1SJ
Tel: 01483 561440
Headmistress: Mrs F J Boulton BSc, MA
Age range: G4–18
No. of pupils: 980 VIth160
Fees: Day £10,728.00–£17,214.00

King Edward's Witley
Godalming, Surrey GU8 5SG
Tel: +44 (0)1428 686700
Headmaster: Mr John Attwater MA
Age range: 11–18
No. of pupils: 400
Fees: Day £20,460.00 FB £31,995.00

Kingston Grammar School
70 London Rd, Kingston upon Thames, Surrey KT2 6PY
Tel: 020 8456 5875
Head: Mr Stephen Lehec
Age range: 11–18
No. of pupils: 829
Fees: Day £6,225.00

Lingfield College
Racecourse Road, Lingfield, Surrey RH7 6PH
Tel: 01342 833176
Headmaster: Mr R Bool
Age range: 2–18
No. of pupils: 935
Fees: Day £11,250.00–£19,473.00

MARYMOUNT INTERNATIONAL SCHOOL LONDON
For further details see p. 94
George Road, Kingston upon Thames, Surrey KT2 7PE
Tel: +44 (0)20 8949 0571
Email: admissions@marymountlondon.com
Website: www.marymountlondon.com
Headmistress: Mrs Margaret Frazier
Age range: G11–18
No. of pupils: 250
Fees: Day £24,985.00 WB £40,515.00 FB £42,305.00

Notre Dame School
Cobham, Surrey KT11 1HA
Tel: 01932 869990
Head of Seniors: Mrs Anna King MEd, MA (Cantab), PGCE
Age range: 2–18
No. of pupils: 600

Old Palace of John Whitgift School
Old Palace Road, Croydon, Surrey CR0 1AX
Tel: 020 8686 7347
Head: Mrs. C Jewell
Age range: B3 months–4 years G3 months–19 years
No. of pupils: 740 Vlth120
Fees: Day £11,316.00–£15,366.00

Prior's Field
Priorsfield Road, Godalming, Surrey GU7 2RH
Tel: 01483 810551
Head of School: Mrs T Kirnig
Age range: G11–18
No. of pupils: 450
Fees: Day £17,300.00 FB £29,925.00

Reed's School
Sandy Lane, Cobham, Surrey KT11 2ES
Tel: 01932 869001
Headmaster: Mr Mark Hoskins BA MA MSc
Age range: B11–18 G16–18
No. of pupils: 650 Vlth230
Fees: Day £19,740.00–£24,675.00 FB £26,310.00–£31,800.00

Reigate Grammar School
Reigate Road, Reigate, Surrey RH2 0QS
Tel: 01737 222231
Headmaster: Mr Shaun Fenton MA (Oxon) MEd (Oxon)
Age range: 11–18
No. of pupils: 969 Vlth262
Fees: Day £18,600.00–£18,720.00

Royal Grammar School, Guildford
High Street, Guildford, Surrey GU1 3BB
Tel: 01483 880600
Headmaster: Dr J M Cox BSc, PhD
Age range: B11–18
No. of pupils: 940
Fees: Day £18,285.00

Royal Russell School
Coombe Lane, Croydon, Surrey CR9 5BX
Tel: 020 8657 3669
Headmaster: Christopher Hutchinson
Age range: 11–18
No. of pupils: 590 Vlth180
Fees: Day £18,480.00 FB £36,525.00

Sir William Perkins's School
Guildford Road, Chertsey, Surrey KT16 9BN
Tel: 01932 574900
Head: Mr C Muller
Age range: G11–18 years
No. of pupils: 605 Vlth140
Fees: Day £15,915.00

St Catherine's, Bramley
Bramley, Guildford, Surrey GU5 0DF
Tel: 01483 899609
Headmistress: Mrs A M Phillips MA(Cantab)
Age range: G4–18
No. of pupils: 900
Fees: Day £8,985.00–£18,375.00 FB £30,285.00

St George's College
Weybridge Road, Addlestone, Weybridge, Surrey KT15 2QS
Tel: 01932 839300
Headmistress: Mrs Rachel Owens
Age range: 11–18
No. of pupils: 909 Vlth250
Fees: Day £16,845.00–£19,185.00

St James Senior Boys School
Church Road, Ashford, Surrey TW15 3DZ
Tel: 01784 266930
Headmaster: Mr David Brazier
Age range: B11–18
No. of pupils: 403 Vlth65
Fees: Day £18,930.00

St John's School
Epsom Road, Leatherhead, Surrey KT22 8SP
Tel: 01372 373000
Head of School: Mrs Rowena Cole
Age range: 11–18
No. of pupils: 761
Fees: Day £19,200.00–£24,300.00 WB £24,330.00–£30,705.00

St Teresa's Effingham (Senior School)
Beech Avenue, Effingham, Surrey RH5 6ST
Tel: 01372 452037
Head: Mr Mike Farmer
Age range: G11–18
No. of pupils: 640 Vlth90
Fees: Day £16,980.00–£17,595.00 WB £27,489.00–£27,795.00 FB £29,340.00–£29,955.00

Surbiton High School
13-15 Surbiton Crescent, Kingston upon Thames, Surrey KT1 2JT
Tel: 020 8546 5245
Principal: Mrs Rebecca Glover
Age range: B4–11 G4–18
No. of pupils: 1210 Vlth186
Fees: Day £10,857.00–£17,142.00

Sutton High School GDST
55 Cheam Road, Sutton, Surrey SM1 2AX
Tel: 020 8642 0594
Headmistress: Mrs Katharine Crouch
Age range: G3–18
No. of pupils: 600 Vlth60
Fees: Day £10,095.00–£17,043.00

Tante Marie Culinary Academy
Woodham House, Carlton Road, Woking, Surrey GU21 4HF
Tel: 01483 726957
Principal: Mr Andrew Maxwell
Age range: 16–60
No. of pupils: 72
Fees: Day £20,750.00

TASIS The American School in England
Coldharbour Lane, Thorpe, Surrey TW20 8TE
Tel: +44 (0)1932 582316
Head of School: Mr Bryan Nixon
Age range: 3–18
No. of pupils: 662
Fees: Day £11,230.00–£23,890.00 FB £43,550.00

The Royal Ballet School
White Lodge, Richmond, Surrey TW10 5HR
Tel: 020 7836 8899
Artistic Director: Christopher Powney
Age range: 11–19
No. of pupils: Vlth80
Fees: Day £18,939.00–£24,885.00 FB £29,328.00–£33,567.00

The Royal School
Farnham Lane, Haslemere, Surrey GU27 1HQ
Tel: 01428 605805
Principal: Mrs Anne Lynch BA (Hons), PGCE, FRSA
Age range: 11–18 years
Fees: Day £17,925.00–£18,144.00 WB £26,895.00–£27,114.00 FB £30,600.00–£30,819.00

Tormead School
27 Cranley Road, Guildford, Surrey GU1 2JD
Tel: 01483 575101
Headmistress: Mrs Christina Foord
Age range: G4–18
No. of pupils: 760 Vlth120
Fees: Day £8,100.00–£15,450.00

Trinity School
Shirley Park, Croydon, Surrey CR9 7AT
Tel: 020 8656 9541
Head: Alasdair Kennedy MA (Cantab)
Age range: B10–18 G16–18
No. of pupils: 1007
Fees: Day £16,656.00

Whitgift School
Haling Park, South Croydon, Surrey CR2 6YT
Tel: +44 (0)20 8688 9222
Headmaster: Mr Christopher Ramsey
Age range: B10–18
No. of pupils: 1464
Fees: Day £20,136.00 WB £32,274.00 FB £37,866.00

Woldingham School
Marden Park, Woldingham, Surrey CR3 7YA
Tel: 01883 349431
Headmistress: Mrs Alex Hutchinson
Age range: G11–18
No. of pupils: 530 Vlth150
Fees: Day £20,580.00–£22,440.00 FB £33,570.00–£36,540.00

Yehudi Menuhin School
Stoke Road, Stoke d'Abernon, Cobham, Surrey KT11 3QQ
Tel: 01932 864739
Head of School: Kate Clanchy
Age range: 7–19
No. of pupils: 80 Vlth36
Fees: FB £34,299.00

West Berkshire

Downe House School
Hermitage Road, Cold Ash,
Thatcham, West Berkshire RG18 9JJ
Tel: 01635 200286
Headmistress: Mrs E McKendrick
BA(Liverpool)
Age range: G11–18
No. of pupils: VIth174
Fees: Day £27,495.00 FB £37,530.00
(symbols)

St Gabriel's
Sandleford Priory, Newbury,
West Berkshire RG20 9BD
Tel: 01635 555680
Principal: Mr Richard Smith MA
(Hons), MEd, PGCE
Age range: B6 months–11
G6 months–18
No. of pupils: 469 VIth40
Fees: Day £10,668.00–£17,418.00
(symbols)

West Sussex

Ardingly College
College Road, Ardingly, Haywards
Heath, West Sussex RH17 6SQ
Tel: +44 (0)1444 893320
Headmaster: Mr Ben Figgis
Age range: 13–18
No. of pupils: 559
Fees: Day £22,995.00–£23,610.00
FB £33,405.00–£35,910.00
(symbols)

Burgess Hill Girls
Keymer Road, Burgess Hill,
West Sussex RH15 0EG
Tel: 01444 241050
Head of School: Liz Laybourn
Age range: B2.5–4 G2.5–18
No. of pupils: 505 VIth70
Fees: Day £7,800.00–£19,200.00
FB £28,050.00–£34,200.00
(symbols)

Christ's Hospital
Horsham, West Sussex RH13 0LJ
Tel: 01403 211293
Headmaster: Mr Simon Reid
Age range: 11–18
No. of pupils: 900
Fees: Day £16,950.00–
£21,330.00 FB £32,790.00
(symbols)

Farlington School
Strood Park, Horsham,
West Sussex RH12 3PN
Tel: 01403 282573
Headmistress: Ms Louise Higson
BSc, PGCE
Age range: B4–6 G3–18
No. of pupils: 300
Fees: Day £5,400.00–£17,670.00
WB £23,205.00–£28,515.00
FB £24,540.00–£29,850.00
(symbols)

Hurstpierpoint College
College Lane, Hurstpierpoint,
West Sussex BN6 9JS
Tel: 01273 833636
Headmaster: Mr. T J Manly BA, MSc
Age range: 4–18
No. of pupils: 1156
Fees: Day £8,790.00–
£22,860.00 WB £28,800.00
(symbols)

Lancing College
Lancing, West Sussex BN15 0RW
Tel: 01273 465805
Head Master: Mr Dominic T Oliver
MPhil
Age range: 13–18
No. of pupils: 550 VIth255
Fees: Day £8,190.00 FB £11,995.00
(symbols)

Our Lady of Sion School
Gratwicke Road, Worthing,
West Sussex BN11 4BL
Tel: 01903 204063
Headmaster: Dr Simon Orchard
Age range: 2–18
No. of pupils: 528 VIth55
Fees: Day £8,310.00–£13,050.00
(symbols)

Seaford College
Lavington Park, Petworth,
West Sussex GU28 0NB
Tel: 01798 867392
Headmaster: J P Green MA BA
Age range: 7–18
No. of pupils: 732 VIth194
Fees: Day £10,320.00–£21,390.00
WB £21,510.00–£28,980.00
FB £33,090.00
(symbols)

Worth School
Paddockhurst Road, Turners Hill,
Crawley, West Sussex RH10 4SD
Tel: +44 (0)1342 710200
Head Master: Stuart McPherson
Age range: 11–18
No. of pupils: 580 VIth222
Fees: Day £15,960.00–£23,730.00
FB £21,210.00–£33,690.00
(symbols)

Examinations and qualifications

Qualifications

Common Entrance

What is Common Entrance?

The Common Entrance examinations are used in UK independent schools (and some independent schools overseas) for transfer from junior to senior schools at the ages of 11+ and 13+. They were first introduced in 1904 and are internationally recognised as being a rigorous form of assessment following a thorough course of study. The examinations are produced by the Independent Schools Examinations Board and backed by HMC (Headmasters' and Headmistresses' Conference), GSA (Girls' Schools Association), and IAPS (Independent Association of Prep Schools) which together represent the leading independent schools in the UK, and many overseas.

Common Entrance is not a public examination as, for example, GCSE, and candidates may normally be entered only in one of the following circumstances:
a) they have been offered a place at a senior school subject to their passing the examination, or
b) they are entered as a 'trial run', in which case the papers are marked by the junior school concerned

Candidates normally take the examination in their own junior or preparatory schools, either in the UK or overseas.

How does Common Entrance fit into the progression to GCSEs?

Rapid changes in education nationally and internationally have resulted in regular reviews of the syllabuses for all the Common Entrance examinations. Reviews of the National Curriculum, in particular, have brought about a number of changes, with the Board wishing to ensure that it continues to set high standards. It is also a guiding principle that Common Entrance should be part of the natural progression from 11- 16, and not a diversion from it.

Common Entrance at 11+

At 11+, the examination consists of papers in English, mathematics and science. It is designed so that it can be taken by candidates either from independent preparatory schools or by candidates from schools in the maintained sector or overseas who have had no special preparation. The examination is normally taken in January for entrance to senior schools in the following September.

Common Entrance at 13+

At 13+, most candidates come from independent preparatory schools. The compulsory subjects are English, mathematics and science. Papers in French, geography, German, Classical Greek, history, Latin, religious studies and Spanish are also available and candidates usually offer as many subjects as they can. In most subjects, papers are available at more than one level to cater for candidates of different abilities. There are three examination sessions each year, with the majority of candidates sitting in the summer prior to entry to their senior schools in September.

Marking and grading

The papers are set centrally but the answers are marked by the senior school for which a candidate is entered. Mark schemes are provided by the Board but senior schools are free to set their own grade boundaries. Results are available within two weeks of the examinations taking place.

Pre-Testing and the ISEB Common Pre-Tests

A number of senior independent schools 'pre-test' pupils for entry, prior to them taking their main entrance examinations at a later date. Usually, these pre-tests take place when a pupil is in Year 6 or Year 7 of his or her junior school and will then be going on to sit Common Entrance in Year 8. The tests are designed to assess a pupil's academic potential and suitability for a particular senior school so that the child, the parents and the school know well in advance whether he/ she is going to be offered a place at the school, subject to a satisfactory performance in the entrance examinations. The tests enable senior schools which are heavily oversubscribed to manage their lists and help to ensure that pupils are not entered for examinations in which they are unlikely to be successful. In short, it reduces uncertainty for all concerned.

Pre-tests may be written specifically for the senior school for which the candidate is entered but a growing number of schools are choosing to use the Common Pre-Tests provided by the Independent Schools Examinations Board. These online tests are usually taken in the candidate's own junior school and one of their main advantages is that a pupil need sit the tests only once, with the results then made available to any senior school which wishes to use them. The multiple-choice tests cover verbal reasoning, non- verbal reasoning, English and mathematics, with the results standardised according to the pupil's age when they are taken. Further information is available on the ISEB website at www.iseb.co.uk.

Parents are advised to check the entrance requirements for senior schools to see if their child will be required to sit a pre-test.

Further information

Details of the Common Entrance examinations and how to register candidates are available on the ISEB website www.iseb.co.uk. Copies of past papers and a wide range of textbooks and other resources can be purchased from Galore Park Publishing Ltd at www.galorepark. co.uk. Support materials are also available from Hodder Education and other publishers; see the Resources section of the ISEB website for details.

Independent Schools Examinations Board Suite 3,
Endeavour House,
Crow Arch Lane,
Ringwood, Hampshire BH24 1HP

Telephone: 01425 470555
Email: enquiries@iseb.co.uk
Web: www.iseb.co.uk

7+ Entrance Exams

What is the 7+?

The 7+ is the descriptive name given to the entrance exams set by an increasing number of independent schools for pupils wishing to gain admission into their Year 3.

7+ entrance exams may be simply for admission into a selective preparatory school, which will then prepare the child for Common Entrance exams to gain a place at senior school. Alternatively, the 7+ can be a route into a school with both prep and senior departments, therefore often effectively bypassing the 11+ or 13+ Common Entrance exams.

The Independent Schools Examinations Board provides Common Entrance examinations and assessments for pupils seeking entry to independent senior schools at 11+ and 13+, but there is as yet no equivalent for the 7+. The testing is largely undertaken by the individual schools, although some schools might commission test from external agencies. Many schools in the incredibly competitive London area offer entrance exams at 7+ and some, such as Haberdasher's Aske's Boys' School,

share specimen papers on their website to clarify what 7+ children will face.

Who sits the 7+?

The 7+ is sat by Year 2 children, who may be moving from a state primary school or a stand-alone pre-prep school to an independent prep school (although many prep schools now have their own pre-prep department, with a cohort of children poised to pass into Year 3 there).

Registration for 7+ entrance exams usually closes in the November of Year 2, with the exams then sat in January or February, for entry that September.

How is the 7+ assessed?

Written exam content will be primarily English and maths based, whilst spelling, dictation, mental arithmetic and more creative skills may be assessed verbally on a one-to-one basis. Group exercises are also sometimes used to look at a child's initiative and their ability to work with others.

Schools will not only be looking for academic potential, but also good citizens and a mixture of personalities to produce a well-rounded year group. For this reason, children are often asked to attend an interview. Some schools interview all candidates, whilst others may call back a limited number with good test results. They will be looking for a child's ability to look an adult in the eye and think on their feet, but also simply to show some spark and personality.

After the assessments, children will be told if they have been successful in gaining a firm place, or a place on a waiting list.

Further Information

As the 7+ is not centrally regulated, it is best for parents to seek accurate admissions and testing information direct from the schools in which they are interested. In addition to a school's facilities and ethos, choosing a school for admission at 7+ will probably also involve whether the school has a senior department and if not, the prep school's record in gaining its students places at target senior schools.

Experienced educational consultants may be able to help parents decide which independent prep school is best suited for their child, based on their personality, senior school ambitions and academic potential. Many parents enlist the help of tutors to prepare children for the 7+, if only to reduce the fear of the unknown in these very young children. This is achieved by teaching them the required curriculum, what to expect on their test and interview days, and giving them the opportunity to practice tackling the type of assessments they will face.

Prep School Baccalaureate

The Prep School Baccalaureate (PSB) is a framework of study for children in junior and preparatory schools that was introduced in 2012, and focuses on the active development and assessment of 6 core skills: Communication, Collaboration, Leadership, Independence, Reviewing and improving and Thinking and Learning. Member schools promote the core skills across all areas of school life, and provide guidance for pupils in progressing these skills, which are seen as essential for developing capable and balanced adults, able to make the most of the opportunities of a fast-changing world. A strong but appropriate knowledge base compliments this, with the use of focused tutoring, pastoral care and Well Being programmes.

Schools do not work to a prescribed curriculum and the emphasis is upon promoting an independent approach which works for each individual school. There are subject INSET days for PSB school staff annually and these are supported by senior school colleagues, to ensure that work done in PSB schools compliments the demands of education at higher levels.

The PSB is a whole school initiative from Early Years to either Year 6 or Year 8, at which point the certificate is awarded at the time of matriculation to senior schools. An additional PSB Year 9 framework is being developed together with international membership.

The development of skills is now recognised as essential by the Independent Schools Inspectorate (ISI), and recent ISI reports on PSB schools highlight the excellent contribution the PSB has in schools achieving excellence.

Assessment

The PSB has a 10 point scale for all subjects studied with a compulsory spine covering: English, Maths, Science, Modern Languages, The Humanities, Art, Design Technology, Music, Sport and PE with each pupil additionally completing a cross curricular project. Optional subjects are agreed with schools but these must be supported by a scheme of work clearly identifying appropriate core skills which are assessed on a 5 point scale. There are distinction levels on both scales and the 10 point scale cross references both ISEB and National Curriculum assessment levels.

Pupils moving on to senior school do so via individual senior school pre-testing arrangements, the award of the PSB certificate, core ISEB papers or a combination of the above.

Membership categories

Partner membership is available to schools developing the PSB with support given from existing schools and the Communications director.

Full membership entitles schools to use the PSB matriculation certificate and join the PSB committee as voting members.

Affiliated membership is for schools that have developed their own skills based approach, in line with PSB principles; staff can participate in all training opportunities and the Heads of Affiliated Schools join committee meetings as non-voting guests.

Membership of the above categories is dependent upon strong ISI reports, the development of a skills based curriculum, with skills clearly identified in schemes of work and excellent teaching.

Associate membership is for senior schools that actively support the PSB in providing staff for subject meetings, hosting meetings, conferences and committee meetings and offer a valuable perspective on the demands of GCSE, A Level and the International Baccalaureate.

Further details

The PSB is an entirely independent charity overseen by a Board of Trustees who have expertise in both primary and secondary education. Details of the PSB can be found on the website – psbacc.org – together with contact details for the Communications Director who can provide further

details on request.

General Certificate of Secondary Education (GCSE)

What are the GCSE qualifications?
GCSE qualifications were first introduced in 1986 and are the principal means of assessment at Key Stage 4 across a range of academic subject areas. They command respect and have status not only in the UK but worldwide.

Main features of the GCSE
There are four unitary awarding organisations for GCSEs in England (see 'Awarding organisations and examination dates' section, p425). WJEC and CCEA also offer GCSE qualifications in Wales and Northern Ireland. Each examining group designs its own specifications but they are required to conform to set criteria. For some aspects of the qualification system, the exam boards adopt common ways of working. When the exam boards work together in this way they generally do so through the Joint Council of Qualifications (JCQ). The award of a grade is intended to indicate that a candidate has met the required level of skills, knowledge and understanding.

GCSEs are in the process of reform. New GCSEs in ancient languages (classical Greek, Latin), art and design, biology, chemistry, citizenship studies, combined science (double award), computer science, dance, drama, food preparation and nutrition, geography, history, modern foreign languages (French, German, Spanish), music, physics, physical education and religious studies were first taught in September 2016, with first results in summer 2018. Assessment in these reformed GCSEs consists primarily of formal examinations taken at the end of the student's two-year course. Other types of assessment, non-exam assessment (NEA), is used where there are skills and knowledge which cannot be assessed through exams. Ofqual have set the percentage of the total marks that will come from NEA.

The reformed GCSEs feature new and more demanding content, as required by the government and developed by the exam boards. Courses are designed for two years of study (linear assessment) and no longer divided into different modules.

Exams can only be split into 'foundation tier' and 'higher tier' if one exam paper does not give all students the opportunity to show their knowledge and their abilities. Such tiering is only available in maths, science and modern foreign languages; other subjects do not have tiers. Resit opportunities will only be available each

November in English language and maths, and then only for students who have turned 16 by the 31st of August in the year of the November assessment.

New GCSEs taught from September 2017: ancient history, astronomy, business, classical civilisation, design and technology, economics, electronics, engineering, film studies, geology, media studies, psychology, sociology, statistics, other (minority) foreign languages e.g. Italian, Polish.

New GCSEs taught from September 2018: ancient languages (biblical Hebrew) and modern foreign languages (Gujarati, Persian, Portuguese, Turkish).

Grading
The basic principle that exam boards follow when setting grade boundaries is that if the group of students (the cohort) taking a qualification in one year is of similar ability to the cohort in the previous year then the overall results (outcomes) should be comparable.

The reformed exams taken in summer 2017 were the first to show a new grading system, with the A* to G grades being phased out.

The new grading system is 9 to 1, with 9 being the top grade. Ofqual says this allows greater differentiation between students. It expects that broadly the same proportion of students will achieve a grade 4 and above as currently achieve a grade C and above, that broadly the same proportion of students will achieve a grade 7 and above as currently achieve a grade A and above. The bottom of grade 1 will be aligned with the bottom of grade G, grade 5 will be awarded to around the top third of students gaining the equivalent of a grade C and bottom third of a grade B. Grade 9 will be set using the tailored approach formula in the first award.

Grades 2, 3, 5 and 6 will be awarded arithmetically so that the grade boundaries are equally spaced in terms of marks from neighbouring grades.

The government's definition of a 'strong pass' will be set at grade 5 for reformed GCSEs. A grade 4 – or 'standard pass' – will continue to be a level 2 achievement. The DfE does not expect employers, colleges or universities to raise the bar to a grade 5 if a grade 4 would meet their requirements.

Can anyone take GCSE qualifications?
GCSEs are intended mainly for 16-year-old pupils, but are open to anyone of any age, whether studying full-time or part-time at a school, college or privately. There are no formal entry requirements.

Students normally study up to ten subjects over a two-year period. Short course GCSEs are available in some subjects (including PE and religious studies) – these include half the content of a full GCSE, so two short course GCSEs are equivalent to one full GCSE.

The English Baccalaureate

The English Baccalaureate (EBacc) is a school performance measure. It allows people to see how many pupils get a grade C or above (current grading) in the core academic subjects at Key Stage 4 in any government-funded school.

The DfE introduced the EBacc measure in 2010. In June 2015, it announced its intention that all pupils who start year 7 in September 2015 take the EBacc subjects when they reach their GCSEs in 2020.

Progress 8 and Attainment 8

Progress 8 aims to capture the progress a pupil makes from the end of primary school to the end of secondary school. It is a type of value added measure, which means that pupils' results are compared to the actual achievements of other pupils with the same prior attainment.

The new performance measures are designed to encourage schools to offer a broad and balanced curriculum with a focus on an academic core at Key Stage 4, and reward schools for the teaching of all their pupils, measuring performance across 8 qualifications. Every increase in every grade a pupil achieves will attract additional points in the performance tables.

Progress 8 will be calculated for individual pupils solely in order to calculate a school's Progress 8 score, and there will be no need for schools to share individual Progress 8 scores with their pupils. Schools should continue to focus on which qualifications are most suitable for individual pupils, as the grades pupils achieve will help them reach their goals for the next stage of their education or training.

Attainment 8 will measure the achievement of a pupil across 8 qualifications including mathematics (double weighted) and English (double weighted), 3 further qualifications that count in the English Baccalaureate (EBacc) measure and 3 further qualifications that can be GCSE qualifications (including EBacc subjects) or any other non-GCSE qualification on the DfE approved list.

General Certificate of Education (GCE) Advanced level (A level)

Typically, A level qualifications are studied over a two-year period. There are no lower or upper age limits. Schools and colleges usually expect students aged 16-18 to have obtained grades A*-C (grade 5 in the new criteria) in five subjects at GCSE level before taking an advanced level course. This requirement may vary between centres and according to which specific subjects are to be studied. Mature students may be assessed on different criteria as to their suitability to embark on the course.

GCE Qualifications

Over the past few years, AS level and A level qualifications have been in a process of reform. New subjects have been introduced gradually, with the first wave taught from September 2015. Subjects that have not been reformed are no longer be available for teaching from September 2018.

GCE qualifications are available at two levels: the Advanced Subsidiary (AS), which is generally delivered over one year and is seen as half an A level; and the A level (GCE). Nearly 70 titles are available, covering a wide range of subject areas, including humanities, sciences, language, business, arts, mathematics and technology.

One of the major reforms is that AS level results no longer count towards an A level (they previously counted for 50%). The two qualifications are linear, with AS assessments typically taking place after one year and A levels after two.

New-style AS and A levels were first taught from September 2015 for: art and design, biology, business studies, chemistry, computer studies, economics, English language, English language and literature, English literature, history, physics, psychology, and sociology.

Subjects first taught from September 2016 include: ancient languages such as Latin or Greek, dance, drama (theatre studies), geography, modern languages such as Spanish or French, music, physical education, religious studies.

Those introduced for first teaching from September 2017: accounting, design and technology, music technology, history of art, environmental science, philosophy, maths, further maths, archaeology, accounting, electronics, ancient history, law, classical civilisation, film studies, media studies, politics, geology, statistics, Chinese, Italian, Russian. In 2018 Biblical Hebrew, Modern Hebrew & languages such as Bengali, Polish and Urdu will be available for first teaching.

Some GCE AS and A levels, particularly the practical ones, contain a proportion of coursework. All GCE A levels that contain one or more types of assessment will have an element of synoptic assessment that tests students' understanding of the whole specification. GCE AS are graded A-E and A levels are graded A*-E.

Overall the amount of coursework at A level has been reduced in the reforms. In some subjects, such as the sciences, practical work will not contribute to the final A level but will be reported separately in a certificate of endorsement. In the sciences, students will do at least 12 practical activities, covering apparatus and techniques. Exam questions about practical work will make up at least 15% of the total marks for the qualification and students will be assessed on their knowledge, skills and understanding of practical work.

Cambridge International AS & A Level

Cambridge International AS & A Level is an internationally benchmarked qualification, taught in over 130 countries worldwide. It is typically for learners aged 16 to 19 years who need advanced study to prepare for university. It was created specifically for an international audience and the content has been devised to suit the wide variety of schools worldwide and avoid any cultural bias.

Cambridge International A Level is typically a two-year course, and Cambridge International AS Level is typically one year. Some subjects can be started as a Cambridge International AS Level and extended to a Cambridge International A Level. Students can either follow a broad course of study, or specialise in one particular subject area.

Learners use Cambridge International AS & A Levels to gain places at leading universities worldwide, including the UK, Ireland, USA, Canada, Australia, New Zealand, India, Singapore, Egypt, Jordan, South Africa, the Netherlands, Germany and Spain.

In places such as the US and Canada, good grades in carefully chosen Cambridge International A Level subjects can result in up to one year of university course credit.

Assessment options:
Cambridge International AS & A Levels have a linear structure with exams at the end of the course. Students can choose from a range of assessment options:

Option 1: take Cambridge International AS Levels only. The Cambridge International AS Level syllabus content is half a Cambridge International A Level.

Option 2: staged assessment, which means taking the Cambridge International AS Level in one exam session and the Cambridge International A Level at a later session. However, this route is not possible in all subjects.

Option 3: take all Cambridge International A Level papers in the same examination session, usually at the end of the course.

Grades and subjects
Cambridge International A Levels are graded from A* to E. Cambridge International AS Levels are graded from A to E.

Subjects: available in 55 subjects including accounting, Afrikaans, information technology, Arabic, art and design, biology, business, chemistry, Chinese, classical studies, computer science, design and technology, design and textiles, digital media and design, divinity, economics, English general paper, English language, English literature, environmental management, food studies, French, geography, German, Global Perspectives & Research™, Hindi, Hinduism, history, Islamic studies, Japanese, law, marine science, mathematics, further mathematics, media studies, music, physical education, physical science, physics, Portuguese, psychology, sociology, Spanish, Tamil, Telugu, thinking skills, travel and tourism, Urdu.
Website: www.cambridgeinternational.org/aleve

Cambridge International GCSE (IGCSE)

Cambridge IGCSE is the world's most popular international qualification for 14 to 16 year olds. It develops skills in creative thinking, enquiry and problem solving, in preparation for the next stage in a student's education. Cambridge IGCSE is taken in over 145 countries, and is widely recognised by employers and higher education institutions worldwide.

Cambridge IGCSE is graded A* to G around the world, however we are introducing the option of 9-1 grading in some countries. Schools in the UK can now choose between A*- G grading or 9-1 grading for our most popular syllabuses. For more information, go to www.cambridgeinternational.org/grading-choice.

In the UK, Cambridge IGCSE is accepted as equivalent to the GCSE. It can be used as preparation for Cambridge International A & AS Levels, UK A and AS levels, IB or AP and in some instances entry into university. Cambridge IGCSE First Language English and Cambridge IGCSE English Language qualifications are recognised by a significant number of UK universities as evidence of competence in the language for university entrance.

Subjects: available in over 70 subjects including accounting, Afrikaans agriculture, Arabic, art and design,

Bahasa Indonesia, biology, business studies, chemistry, Chinese, computer science, design and technology, development studies, drama, Dutch, economics, English – first language, English – literature, English – second language, enterprise, environmental management, food and nutrition, French, geography, German, Global Perspectives™, Greek, Hindi, history, Italian, information and communication technology, IsiZulu, Japanese, Korean, Latin, Malay, mathematics, mathematics – additional, international mathematics, music, Pakistan studies, physical education, physical science, physics, Portuguese – first language, Portuguese, religious studies, Russian, sanskrit, science – combined, sciences – co-ordinated (double), sociology, Spanish, Thai, travel and tourism, Turkish, Urdu, world literature.
Website: www.cambridgeinternational.org/igcse

Cambridge Pre-U

Cambridge Pre-U is a post-16 qualification that equips students with the skills they need to succeed at university. Developed with universities, it was first introduced in UK schools in September 2008. It is now taught in 170 schools, including some schools outside the UK.

Cambridge Pre-U is a linear course, with exams taken at the end of two years. It encourages the development of well-informed, open and independent-minded individuals; promotes deep understanding through subject specialisation, with a depth and rigour appropriate to progression to higher education; and develops skills in independent research valued by universities.

Assessment
Cambridge Pre-U Principal Subjects are examined at the end of two years. Cambridge Pre-U Short Courses are available in some subjects and are typically examined at the end of one year. Students can study a combination of A Levels and Principal Subjects.

In order to gain the Cambridge Pre-U Diploma, students must study at least three Cambridge Pre-U Principal Subjects (up to two A Levels can be substituted for Principal Subjects) and Cambridge Pre-U Global Perspectives & Research (GPR). Cambridge Pre-U GPR includes an extended project in the second year, developing skills in research and critical thinking.

Grades and subjects
Cambridge Pre-U reports achievement on a scale of nine grades, with Distinction 1 being the highest grade and Pass 3 the lowest grade.

Subjects: available in 24 subjects including art and design, art history, biology, business and management, chemistry, drama and theatre, economics, literature in English, French, further mathematics, geography, German, Global Perspectives & Research™, classical Greek, history, Italian, art history, Latin, Mandarin Chinese, mathematics, music, philosophy and theology, physics, psychology, Russian, Spanish.
Website: www.cambridgeinternational.org/preu

Edexcel International GCSEs

Pearson's Edexcel International GCSEs are academic qualifications aimed at learners aged 14 to 16. They're equivalent to a UK General Certificate of Secondary Education (GCSE), and are the main requirement for Level 3 studies, including progression to GCE AS or A levels, BTECs or employment. International GCSEs are linear qualifications, meaning that students take all of the exams at the end of the course. They are available at Level 1 (grades 3-1) and Level 2 (grades 9-4). There are currently more than 100,000 learners studying Edexcel International GCSEs, in countries throughout Asia, Africa, Europe, the Middle East and Latin America. Developed by subject specialists and reviewed regularly, many of Pearson's Edexcel International GCSEs include specific international content to make them relevant to students worldwide.

Pearson's Edexcel International GCSEs were initially developed for international schools. They have since become popular among independent schools in the UK, but are not approved for use in UK state schools. If you're a UK state school, you may be interested in offering Pearson's Edexcel GCSE qualifications. These qualifications are based on the Edexcel International GCSE specifications. They do not count towards national performance measures and are not eligible for funding in UK state schools.

International GCSEs are offered in over 35 subjects. Subject areas include: Business & Economics, Computer Science, English, Humanities, Information and Communication Technology, Languages, Mathematics, Sciences.

Free Standing Maths Qualifications (FSMQ)

Aimed at those students wishing to acquire further qualifications in maths, specifically additional mathematics and foundations of advanced mathematics (MEI).

Further UCAS points can be earned upon completion of the advanced FSMQ in additional mathematics.

For further details see the OCR website.

AQA Certificate in Mathematical Studies (Core Maths)

This new Level 3 qualification has been available from September 2015. It is designed for students who achieved a Grade 4 or above at GCSE and want to continue studying Maths. The qualification carries UCAS points equivalent to an AS level qualification

AQA Certificate in Further Maths

This level 2 qualification has been designed to provide stretch and challenge to the most able mathematicians. This will be best suited to students who either already have, or are expected to achieve the top grades in GCSE Mathematics and are likely to progress to A level Mathematics and Further Mathematics.

Additional and Alternative

AQA Baccalaureate

The AQA Baccalaureate is awarded to students who achieve at least three A levels (minimum grade E or 2/3), a broader study AS level subject and the EPQ, plus they must undertake a minimum of 100 hours of 'enrichment activities'.

This is a complete curriculum programme, which adds a broader range of study, and includes the Extended Project Qualification (EPQ).

This qualification is built on familiar subjects, so it can be tailored to fit in with existing curricula. It includes extracurricular activities and encourages a series of 'enrichment activities' covering personal qualities, perseverance, leadership, independence, time management, commitment and communication.

The AQA Bacc is accepted by universities; offers are based on the component parts of the baccalaureate, with students receiving their AQA Baccalaureate and enrichment certificates alongside their A level, AS level and EPQ certificates.

Cambridge Primary

Cambridge Primary is typically for learners aged 5 to 11 years. It develops learner skills and understanding through the primary years in English as a first or second language, mathematics, science, Global Perspectives™ and ICT. The flexible curriculum frameworks include optional assessment tools to help schools monitor learners' progress and give detailed feedback to parents. At the end of Cambridge Primary, schools can enter students for Cambridge Primary Checkpoint tests which are marked in Cambridge.
Website: www.cambridgeinternational.org/primary

Cambridge ICT Starters introduces learners, typically aged 5 to 14 years, to the key ICT applications they need to achieve computer literacy and to understand the impact of technology on our daily lives. It can be taught and assessed in English or Spanish.

Cambridge Lower Secondary

Cambridge Lower Secondary is typically for learners aged 11 to 14 years. It develops learner skills and understanding in English as a first or second language, mathematics, science, Global Perspectives™ and ICT for the first three years of secondary education, and includes assessment tools. At the end of Cambridge Lower Secondary, schools can enter students for Cambridge Lower Secondary Checkpoint tests which are marked in Cambridge and provide an external international benchmark for student performance.
Website: www.cambridgeinternational.org/lowersecondary

European Baccalaureate (EB)

Not to be confused with the International Baccalaureate (IB) or the French Baccalaureate, this certificate is available in European schools and recognised in all EU countries.

To obtain the baccalaureate, a student must obtain a minimum score of 60%, which is made up from: course-work, oral participation in class and tests (40%); five written examinations (36%) – mother-tongue, first foreign language and maths are compulsory for all candidates; four oral examinations (24%) – mother tongue and first foreign language are compulsory (history or geography may also be compulsory here, dependant on whether the candidate has taken a written examination in these subjects).

Throughout the EU the syllabus and examinations necessary to achieve the EB are identical. The only exception to this rule is the syllabus for the mother tongue language. The EB has been specifically designed to meet, at the very least, the minimum qualification requirements of each member state.

Study for the EB begins at nursery stage (age 4) and progresses through primary (age six) and on into secondary school (age 12).

Syllabus
Languages: Bulgarian, Czech, Danish, Dutch, English, Estonian, Finnish, Finnish as a second national language, French, German, Greek, Hungarian, Irish, Italian, Latvian,

Lithuanian, Maltese, Polish, Portuguese, Romanian, Slovak, Slovenian, Spanish, Swedish, Swedish for Finnish pupils.

Literary: art education, non-confessional ethics, geography, ancient Greek, history, human sciences, Latin, music, philosophy, physical education.

Sciences: biology, chemistry, economics, ICT, integrated science, mathematics, physics.

For more information, contact:

Office of the Secretary-General of the European Schools, c/o European Commission, Rue Joseph II, 30-2ème étage, B-1049 Brussels, Belgium

Tel: +32 2295 3745; Fax: +32 2298 6298

Website: www.eursc.eu

The International Baccalaureate (IB)

TThe International Baccalaureate (IB) offers four challenging and high quality educational programmes for a worldwide community of schools, aiming to develop internationally minded people who, recognizing their common humanity and shared guardianship of the planet, help to create a better, more peaceful world.

The IB works with schools around the world (both state and privately funded) that share the commitment to international education to deliver these programmes.

Schools that have achieved the high standards required for authorization to offer one or more of the IB programmes are known as IB World Schools. There are over half a million students attending more than 4500 IB World Schools in 153 countries and this number is growing annually.

The Primary Years, Middle Years and Diploma Programmes share a common philosophy and common characteristics. They develop the whole student, helping students to grow intellectually, socially, aesthetically and culturally. They provide a broad and balanced education that includes science and the humanities, languages and mathematics, technology and the arts. The programmes teach students to think critically, and encourage them to draw connections between areas of knowledge and to use problem-solving techniques and concepts from many disciplines. They instil in students a sense of responsibility towards others and towards the environment. Lastly, and perhaps most importantly, the programmes give students an awareness and understanding of their own culture and of other cultures, values and ways of life.

A fourth programme called the IB Career Related Certificate (IBCC) became available to IB World Schools from September 2012. All IB programmes include:

- a written curriculum or curriculum framework;
- student assessment appropriate to the age range;
- professional development and networking opportunities for teachers;
- support, authorization and programme evaluation for the school.

The IB Primary Years Programme

The IB Primary Years Programme (PYP), for students aged three to 12, focuses on the development of the whole child as an inquirer, both in the classroom and in the world outside. It is a framework consisting of five essential elements (concepts, knowledge, skills, attitude, action) and guided by six trans-disciplinary themes of global significance, explored using knowledge and skills derived from six subject areas (language, social studies, mathematics, science and technology, arts, and personal, social and physical education) with a powerful emphasis on inquiry-based learning.

The most significant and distinctive feature of the PYP is the six trans-disciplinary themes. These themes are about issues that have meaning for, and are important to, all of us. The programme offers a balance between learning about or through the subject areas, and learning beyond them. The six themes of global significance create a trans-disciplinary framework that allows students to 'step up' beyond the confines of learning within subject areas:

- Who we are.
- Where we are in place and time.
- How we express ourselves.
- How the world works.
- How we organize ourselves.
- Sharing the planet.

The PYP exhibition is the culminating activity of the programme. It requires students to analyse and propose solutions to real-world issues, drawing on what they have learned through the programme. Evidence of student development and records of PYP exhibitions are reviewed by the IB as part of the programme evaluation process.

Assessment is an important part of each unit of inquiry as it both enhances learning and provides opportunities for students to reflect on what they know, understand and can do. The teacher's feedback to the students provides the guidance, the tools and the incentive for them to become more competent, more skilful and better at understanding how to learn.

The IB Middle Years Programme (MYP)

The Middle Years Programme (MYP), for students aged 11 to 16, comprises eight subject groups:

- Language acquisition
- Language and literature
- Individuals and societies

- Sciences
- Mathematics
- Arts
- Physical and health education
- Design

The MYP requires at least 50 hours of teaching time for each subject group in each year of the programme. In years 4 and 5, students have the option to take courses from six of the eight subject groups within certain limits, to provide greater flexibility in meeting local requirements and individual student learning needs.

Each year, students in the MYP also engage in at least one collaboratively planned interdisciplinary unit that involves at least two subject groups.

MYP students also complete a long-term project, where they decide what they want to learn about, identify what they already know, discovering what they will need to know to complete the project, and create a proposal or criteria for completing it

The MYP aims to help students develop their personal understanding, their emerging sense of self and their responsibility in their community.

The MYP allows schools to continue to meet state, provincial or national legal requirements for students with access needs. Schools must develop an inclusion/special educational needs (SEN) policy that explains assessment access arrangements, classroom accommodations and curriculum modification that meet individual student learning needs.

The IB Diploma Programme (IBDP)

The IB Diploma Programme, for students aged 16 to 19, is an academically challenging and motivating curriculum of international education that prepares students for success at university and in life beyond studies.

DP students choose at least one course from six subject groups, thus ensuring depth and breadth of knowledge and experience in languages, social studies, the experimental sciences, mathematics, and the arts. With more than 35 courses to choose from, students have the flexibility to further explore and learn subjects that meet their interest. Out of the six courses required, at least three and not more than four must be taken at higher level (240 teaching hours), the others at standard level (150 teaching hours). Students can take examinations in English, French or Spanish.

In addition, three unique components of the programme – the DP core – aim to broaden students' educational experience and challenge them to apply their knowledge and skills. The DP core – the extended essay (EE), theory of knowledge (TOK) and creativity,

activity, service (CAS) – are compulsory and central to the philosophy of the programme.

The IB uses both external and internal assessment to measure student performance in the DP. Student results are determined by performance against set standards, not by each student's position in the overall rank order. DP assessment is unique in the way that it measures the extent to which students have mastered advanced academic skills not what they have memorized. DP assessment also encourages an international outlook and intercultural skills, wherever appropriate.

The IB diploma is awarded to students who gain at least 24 points out of a possible 45 points, subject to certain minimum levels of performance across the whole programme and to satisfactory participation in the creativity, activity, and service requirement.

Recognized and respected by leading universities globally, the DP encourages students to be knowledgeable, inquiring, caring and compassionate, and to develop intercultural understanding, open-mindedness and the attitudes necessary to respect and evaluate a range of viewpoints.

The IB Career Related Programme (IBCP)

The IB Career-related Programme, for students aged 16 to 19, offers an innovative educational framework that combines academic studies with career-related learning. Through the CP, students develop the competencies they need to succeed in the 21st century. More importantly, they have the opportunity to engage with a rigorous study programme that genuinely interests them while gaining transferable and lifelong skills that prepares them to pursue higher education, apprenticeships or direct employment.

CP students complete four core components – language development, personal and professional skills, service learning and a reflective project – in order to receive the International Baccalaureate Career-related Programme Certificate. Designed to enhance critical thinking and intercultural understanding, the CP core helps students develop the communication and personal skills, as well as intellectual habits required for lifelong learning.

Schools that choose to offer the CP can create their own distinctive version of the programme and select career pathways that suit their students and local community needs. The IB works with a variety of CRS providers around the world and schools seeking to develop career pathways with professional communities can benefit from our existing collaborations. All CRS providers undergo a rigorous curriculum evaluation to ensure that their courses align with the CP pedagogy and meet IB quality standards. The flexibility to meet the needs, backgrounds and contexts of learners allows CP schools to offer an education that is relevant and meaningful to their students.

Launched in 2012, there are more than 140 CP schools in over 23 countries to date. Many schools with the IB Diploma Programme (DP) and the Middle Years Programme (MYP) have chosen the CP as an alternative IB pathway to offer students. CP schools often report that the programme has helped them raise student aspiration, increase student engagement and retention and encouraged learners to take responsibility for their own actions, helping them foster high levels of self-esteem through meaningful achievements.

For more information on IB programmes, visit: www.ibo.org

Africa, Europe, Middle East Global Centre, Churchillplein 6, The Hague, 2517JW, The Netherlands
Tel: +31 (0)70 352 6233

Pearson Edexcel Mathematics Awards

Pearson's Edexcel Mathematics Awards are small, stand-alone qualifications designed to help students to develop and demonstrate proficiency in different areas of mathematics. These Awards enable students to focus on understanding key concepts and techniques, and are available across three subjects, including: Number and Measure (Levels 1 and 2), Algebra (Levels 2 and 3) and Statistical Methods (Levels 1, 2 and 3). The level 1 Award in Number and Measure is now also an approved stepping stone qualification for the 16-18 maths condition of funding

Designed to build students' confidence and fluency; the Awards can fit into the existing programme of delivery for mathematics in schools and colleges, prepare students for GCSE and/or GCE Mathematics, and to support further study in other subjects, training or the workplace. They offer a choice of levels to match students' abilities, with clear progression between the levels. These small, 60-70 guided learning hour qualifications are assessed through one written paper per level. Each qualification is funded and approved for pre-16 and 16-18 year old students in England and in schools and colleges in Wales.

Projects

Extended Project Qualification (EPQ)

AQA, OCR, Pearson and WJEC offer the Extended Project Qualification, which is a qualification aimed at developing a student's research and independent learning skills. The EPQ can be taken as a stand-alone qualification, and it is equivalent to half an A level in UCAS points (but only a third of performance points). It is also possible to take the EPQ as part of the AQA Baccalaureate.

Students complete a research based written report and may produce an artefact or a practical science experiment as part of their project

Cambridge International Project Qualification (IPQ)

Cambridge International is offering a new standalone project-based qualification from September 2018, which can be taken alongside Cambridge International AS & A levels. Students complete a 5000-word research project on a topic of their choice. The qualification is assessed by Cambridge International.

For more information, go to www.cambridgeinternational.org/advanced

Entry level and basic skills

Entry Level Qualifications

If you want to take GCSE or NVQ level 1 but have not yet reached the standard required, then entry level qualifications are for you as they are designed to get you started on the qualifications ladder.

Entry level qualifications are available in a wide range of areas. You can take an entry level certificate in most subjects where a similar GCSE exists. There are also vocational entry level qualifications – some in specific areas like retail or catering and others where you can take units in different work-related subjects to get a taster of a number of career areas. There are also entry level certificates in life skills and the basic skills of literacy and numeracy.

Anyone can take an entry level qualification – your school or college will help you decide which qualification is right for you.

Entry level qualifications are flexible programmes so the time it takes to complete will vary according to where you study and how long you need to take the qualification.

Subjects available: art and design, computer science, English, geography, history, Latin, mathematics, physical education and science.

Functional Skills

Functional Skills are qualifications in English, maths and ICT that equip learners with the basic practical skills required in everyday life, education and the workplace. They are available at Entry 1 through to Level 2. Functional Skills are identified as funded 'stepping stone' qualifications to English and maths GCSE for post-16 learners who haven't previously achieved a grade D in these subjects. There are part of apprenticeship completion requirements.

Vocational qualifications

Applied Generals/AQA Level 3 Certificates and Extended Certificates

Applied General qualifications are available in Business and Science and are a practical introduction to these subjects, they are a real alternative to A level support progression to further study or employment aimed at students aged 16 to 19.

Developed together with teachers, schools, colleges and higher education institutions, they help learners to develop knowledge and skills.

A mixture of assessment types means learners can apply their knowledge in a practical way. An integrated approach creates a realistic and relevant qualification for learners.

AQA Technical Awards and Level 1/2 Awards

AQA's new Technical Award and Level 1/2 Awards are practical, vocational level 1/2 qualifications for 14- to 16-year-olds to take alongside GCSEs.

Technical Awards and AQA Level 1/2 Awards provide an introduction to life and work within a range of vocational areas, equipping learners with the practical, transferable skills and core knowledge needed to progress to further general or vocational study, including level 3 qualifications, employment or apprenticeships.

There are nine individual qualifications, one Technical Award in Performing Arts, and nine AQA Level 1/2 awards in: Children's Learning and Development, Fashion and Textiles, Food and Catering, Health and Social Care, IT, Materials Technology, Sport STEM, and Visual Communication.

Learners are assessed on doing rather than knowing through the project-based internal assessments, where they can apply their knowledge to practical tasks.

Assignments will vary according to the subject, but activities range from designing and making a working product or prototype; making a short film; planning and putting on a performance, or presenting to others. There are two internally assessed units worth 30% each, and an externally assessed exam worth 40%. The AQA Level 1/2 Awards will not be available beyond 2019.

AQA Tech-levels

Level 3 technical qualifications have been designed in collaboration with employers and professional bodies. They're aimed at learners aged over 16 wanting to progress into a specific sector through apprenticeships, further study or employment. There are 16 individual qualifications within IT, Engineering, Business and Entertainment Technology. These vary in size of qualification.

Transferable skills have been contextualised explicitly within each qualification and are a mandatory part of the qualification outcome. Learners are assessed through a combination of examinations, internally and externally assessed assignments.

BTECs

BTEC Level 2 First qualifications
ie BTEC Level 2 Diplomas, BTEC Level 2 Extended Certificates, BTEC Level 2 Certificates and BTEC Level 2 Award.

BTEC Firsts are Level 2 introductory work-related programmes covering a wide range of vocational areas including business, engineering, information technology, health and social care, media, travel and tourism, and public services.

Programmes may be taken full or part-time. They are practical programmes that provide a foundation for the knowledge and skills you will need in work. Alternatively, you can progress onto a BTEC National qualification, Applied GCE A level or equivalent.

There are no formal entry requirements and they can be studied alongside GCSEs. Subjects available: agriculture; animal care; applied science; art and design; business; children's care, learning and development; construction; countryside and the environment; engineering; fish husbandry; floristry; health and social care; horse care; horticulture; hospitality; IT; land-based technology; business; creative media production; music; performing arts; public services; sport; travel and tourism; and vehicle technology.

BTEC Foundation Diploma in Art and Design (QCF)
For those students preparing to go on to higher education within the field of art and design. This diploma is recognised as one of the best courses of its type in the UK, and is used in preparation for degree programmes. Units offered include researching, recording and responding in art and design, media experimentation, personal experimental studies, and a final major project.

BTEC Nationals
ie BTEC Level 3 Extended Diplomas (QCF), BTEC Level 3 Diplomas (QCF), BTEC Level 3 Subsidiary Diplomas (QCF), BTEC Level 3 Certificates (QCF)

BTEC National programmes are long-established vocational programmes. They are practical programmes that are highly valued by employers. They enable you to gain the knowledge and skills that you will need in work, or give you the choice to progress on to a BTEC Higher National, a Foundation Degree or a degree programme.

BTEC Nationals, which hold UCAS points cover a range of vocationally specialist sectors including child care, children's play, learning and development, construction, art and design, aeronautical engineering, electrical/electronic engineering, IT, business, creative and media production, performing arts, public services, sport, sport and exercise sciences and applied science. The programmes may be taken full- or part-time, and can be taken in conjunction with NVQs and/or functional skills units at an appropriate level.

There are no formal entry requirements, but if you have any of the following you are likely to be at the right level to study a BTEC national qualification.

- a BTEC Level 2 First qualification

- GCSEs – at grades A* to C in several subjects

- Relevant work experience

There are also very specialist BTEC Nationals, such as pharmaceutical science and blacksmithing and metalworking.

BTEC Higher Nationals
Known as HNDs and HNCs – ie BTEC Level 5 HND Diplomas (QCF) and BTEC Level 4 HNC Diplomas (QCF)

BTEC HNDs and HNCs are further and higher education qualifications that offer a balance of education and vocational training. They are available in a wide range of work-related areas such as graphic design, business, health and social care, computing and systems development, manufacturing engineering, hospitality management, and public services.

Pearson is introducing a new suite of subjects between 2016 and 2018, to match growing demand. For full information on the subjects, visit: www.ocr.org.uk/qualifications/by-type/entry-level/entry-level-2016/

BTEC higher national courses combine study with hands-on work experience during your course. Once completed, you can use the skills you learn to begin your career, or continue on to a related degree course.

HNDs are often taken as a full-time course over two years but can also be followed part-time in some cases.

HNCs are often for people who are working and take two years to complete on a part-time study basis by day release, evenings, or a combination of the two. Some HNC courses are done on a full-time basis.

There are no formal entry requirements, but if you have any of the following you are likely to be at the right academic level:

- at least one A level
- a BTEC Level 3 National qualification
- level 3 NVQ

BTEC specialist and professional qualifications
These qualifications are designed to prepare students for specific and specialist work activities. These are split into two distinct groups:

- Specialist qualifications (entry to level 3)
- Professional qualifications (levels 4 to 7)

Cambridge Nationals

Cambridge Nationals, the updated version of OCR Nationals, are vocationally-related qualifications that take an engaging, practical and inspiring approach to learning and assessment.

They are industry-relevant, geared to key sector requirements and very popular with schools and colleges because they suit such a broad range of learning styles and abilities.

Cambridge Nationals are available in business, child development, engineering, health and social care, ICT, science, sport, and creative iMedia. Available as joint Level 1 and 2 qualifications, the updated Nationals are aimed at students aged 14 to 16 in full-time study.

Cambridge Technicals

OCR's Cambridge Technicals are practical and flexible vocationally-related qualifications, offering students in-depth study in a wide range of subjects, including business, health and social care, IT, sport, art and design, digital media, science, performing arts and engineering.

Cambridge Technicals are aimed at young people aged 16 to 19 who have completed Key Stage 4 of their education and want to study in a more practical, work-related way.

Cambridge Technicals are available at Level 2 and Level 3, and carry UCAS points at Level 3.

NVQs

NVQs reward those who demonstrate skills gained at work. They relate to particular jobs and are usefully taken while you are working. Within reason, NVQs do not have to be completed in a specified amount of time. They can be taken by full-time employees or by school and college students with a work placement or part-time job that enables them to develop the appropriate skills. There are no age limits and no special entry requirements.

NVQs are organised into levels, based on the competencies required. Levels 1-3 are the levels most applicable to learners within the 14-19 phase. Achievement of level 4 within this age group will be rare. See the OCR website for further information.

OCR Vocational Qualifications

These are available at different levels and different sizes. Levels 1-3 are the levels most applicable to learners within the 14-19 phase. The different sizes are indicated with the use of Award, Certificate and Diploma in the qualification title and indicate the number of hours it typically takes to complete the qualification.

Vocational Qualifications are assessed according to each individual specification, but may include practical assessments and/or marked assessments. They are designed to provide evidence of a student's relevant skills and knowledge in their chosen subject. These qualifications can be used for employment or as a path towards further education. See the OCR website for further details.

Awarding organisations and examination dates

Awarding organisations and examination dates

In England there are four awarding organisations, each offering GCSEs, AS and A levels (Eduqas offers only reformed qualifications in England, whereas WJEC offers in England, Wales, Northern Ireland and independent regions). There are separate awarding organisations in Wales (WJEC) and Northern Ireland (CCEA). The awarding organisation in Scotland (SQA) offers equivalent qualifications.

This information was supplied by the awarding bodies and was accurate at the time of going to press. It is intended as a general guide only for candidates in the United Kingdom. Dates are subject to variation and should be confirmed with the awarding organisation concerned.

AQA

Qualifications offered:
GCSE
AS and A level
Technical levels
Foundation Certificate of Secondary Education (FCSE)
Free Standing Maths Qualifications (FSMQ)
Entry Level Certificate (ELC)
Foundation and Higher Projects
Extended Project Qualification (EPQ)
AQA Baccalaureate
Applied Generals/AQA Level 3 Certificates and Extended Certificates
Functional Skills
AQA Certificate
Technical Award

Other assessment schemes:
Unit Award Scheme (UAS)
AQA Level 1/2 Tech Awards

Examination dates for summer 2019: 10 May – 25 June

Contact:
Email: eos@aqa.org.uk
Website: www.aqa.org.uk
Tel: 0800 197 7162 (8am–5pm Monday to Friday)
+44 161 696 5995 (Outside the UK)

Devas Street, Manchester M15 6EX
Stag Hill House, Guildford, Surrey GU2 7XJ
31-33 Windsor House, Cornwall Road, Harrogate, HG1 2PW
2nd Floor, Lynton House, 7–12 Tavistock Square, London, WC1H 9LT

CCEA – Council for the Curriculum, Examinations and Assessment

Qualifications offered:
GCSE
GCE AS/A level
Key Skills (Levels 1-4)
Entry Level Qualifications
Essential Skills (Levels 1,2 & Entry Level)
Occupational Studies (Levels 1 & 2)
QCF Qualifications
Applied GCSE, GCE and QCF Level 1 and 2 qualifications

Examination dates for summer 2019: 1 May – 21 June

Contact:
Email: info@ccea.org.uk
Website: www.ccea.org.uk

29 Clarendon Road, Clarendon Dock, Belfast, BT1 3BG
Tel: (028) 9026 1200

IB – International Baccalaureate

Qualification offered:
IB Diploma
IB Career-related Certificate

Contact:
www.ibo.org

Examination dates for summer 2019: 2 –24 May

IB Global Centre, The Hague, Churchillplein 6, 2517 JW, The Hague, The Netherlands

Tel: +31 70 352 60 00

OCR – Oxford Cambridge and RSA Examinations – and Cambridge International*

Qualifications offered by OCR or sister awarding organisation Cambridge Assessment International Education (Cambridge International) include:
GCSE
GCE AS/A level
IGCSE
International AS/A level
Extended Project
Cambridge International Project Qualification
Cambridge Pre-U
Cambridge Nationals
Cambridge Technicals
Functional Skills
FSMQ – Free Standing Maths Qualification
NVQ

Examination dates for summer 2019: 13 May to 25 June

Contact:
Website: www.ocr.org.uk
(or www.cambridgeinternational.org)

OCR Head Office, The Triangle Building, Shaftesbury Road, Cambridge, CB2 8EA
Tel: 01223 553998

Pearson

Qualifications offered:
Pearson's qualifications are offered in the UK but are also available through their international centres across the world. They include:
DiDA, CiDA
GCE A levels
GCSEs
Adult Literacy and Numeracy
Functional Skills
Foundation Learning
International GCSEs
Key Skills
ESOL (Skills for Life)
BTEC Customised Qualifications
BTEC Foundation Diploma in Art & Design
BTEC Nationals
BTEC Higher National Certificates and Higher National Diplomas (HNC/HND)
BTEC Firsts
BTEC Specialist qualifications
BTEC Professional qualifications
BTEC WorkSkills
NVQs
Project qualifications

Examination dates for summer 2019: 13 May – 26 June

Contact:
190 High Holborn, London WC1V 7BH

See website for specific contact details: www.edexcel.com

Educational organisations

Educational organisations

Artsmark

Arts Council England's Artsmark was set up in 2001, schools are awarded Silver, Gold or Platinum, based on their achievements.

All schools in England can apply for an Artsmark – primary, secondary, special and pupil referral units, maintained and independent.

Artsmark provides a clear framework for teachers to plan, develop and evaluate arts, culture and creativity across the curriculum.

Artsmark, Arts Council England, Brooklands, 24 Brooklands Avenue, Cambridge CB2 8BU
Tel: 0845 300 6200 / 0161 934 4317
Email: artsmark@artscouncil.org.uk
Website: www.artsmark.org.uk

Association for the Education and Guardianship of International Students (AEGIS)

AEGIS brings together schools and guardianship organisations to promote the welfare of international students. AEGIS provides accreditation for all reputable guardianship organisations.

AEGIS, The Wheelhouse,
Bond's Mill Estate, Bristol Road, Stonehouse,
Gloucestershire GL10 3RF
Tel/Fax: 01453 821293
Email: info@aegisuk.net
Website: www.aegisuk.net

The Association of American Study Abroad Programmes (AASAP)

Established in 1991 to represent American study programmes in the UK.

Contact: Kalyn Franke, c/o University of Maryland in London, Connaught Hall, 36-45 Tavistock Square, London WC1H 9EX
Email: info@aasapuk.org
Website: www.aasapuk.org

The Association of British Riding Schools (ABRS)

An independent body of proprietors and principals of riding establishments, aiming to look after their interests and those of the riding public and to raise standards of management, instruction and animal welfare.

Unit 8, Bramble Hill Farm, Five Oaks Road, Slinfold, Horsham, West Sussex RH13 0RL
Tel: 01403 790294
Email: office@abrs-info.org
Website: www.abrs-info.org

Association of Colleges (AOC)

Created in 1996 to promote the interests of further education colleges in England, Wales, Scotland and Northern Ireland.

2-5 Stedham Place, London WC1A 1HU
Tel: 020 7034 9900
Email: enquiries@aoc.co.uk
Website: www.aoc.co.uk

Association of Governing Bodies of Independent Schools (AGBIS)

AGBIS supports and advises governing bodies of schools in the independent sector on all aspects of governance. (Registered charity No. 1108756)
Enquiries should be addressed to: AGBIS General Secretary, Richard Harman, AGBIS, 3 Codicote Road, Welwyn, Hertfordshire AL6 9LY
Tel: 01438 840730
Fax: 0560 3432632
Email: gensec@agbis.org.uk
Website: www.agbis.org.uk

Association of Employment and Learning Providers (AELP)

AELP's purpose is to influence the education and training agenda. They are the voice of independent learning providers throughout England.
2nd Floor, 9 Apex Court, Bradley Stoke, Bristol BS32 4JT
Tel: 0117 986 5389
Email: enquiries@aelp.org.uk
Website: www.aelp.org.uk

The Association of School and Colleges Leaders (ASCL)

Formerly the Secondary Heads Association, the ASCL is a professional association for secondary school and college leaders.
130 Regent Road, Leicester LE1 7PG
Tel: 0116 299 1122
Fax: 0116 299 1123
Email: info@ascl.org.uk
Website: www.ascl.org.uk

Boarding Schools' Association (BSA)

For information on the BSA see editorial on page 36

The British Accreditation Council for Independent Further and Higher Education (BAC)

The British Accreditation Council (BAC) has now been the principal accrediting body for the independent further and higher education and training sector for over 30 years. There are now hundreds of BAC-accredited colleges in the UK, providing a wealth of academic programmes, including vocational and professional qualifications, foundation courses for university entry, and externally validated degree courses. Some students may also look to study outside UK at one of the institutions holding BAC international accreditation.
Ground Floor, 14 Devonshire Square, London EC2M 4YT
Tel: 0300 330 1400
Email: info@the-bac.org
Website: www.the-bac.org

The Choir Schools' Association (CSA)

Represents 46 schools attached to cathedrals, churches and college chapels, which educate cathedral and collegiate choristers.
CSA Information Officer, Village Farm, The Street, Market Weston, Diss, Norfolk IP22 2NZ
Tel: 01359 221333
Email: info@choirschools.org.uk
Website: www.choirschools.org.uk

The Council for Independent Education (CIFE)

CIFE is the professional association for independent sixth form and tutorial colleges accredited by the British Accreditation Council for Independent Further and Higher Education (BAC), the Independent Schools Council or the DfE (Ofsted). Member colleges specialise in preparing students for GCSE and A level (AS and A2) in particular and university entrance in general.
The aim of the association is to provide a forum for the exchange of information and ideas, and for the promotion of best practice, and to safeguard adherence to strict standards of professional conduct and ethical propriety. Further information can be obtained from CIFE:
Tel: 020 8767 8666
Email: enquiries@cife.org.uk
Website: www.cife.org.uk

Council of British International Schools (COBIS)

COBIS is a membership association of British schools of quality worldwide and is committed to a stringent process of quality assurance for all its member schools. COBIS is a member of the Independent Schools Council (ISC) of the United Kingdom.
55-56 Russell Square, Bloomsbury, London WC1B 4HP
Tel: 020 3826 7190
Email: pa@cobis.org.uk
Website: www.cobis.org.uk

Council of International Schools (CIS)

CIS is a not-for-profit organisation committed to supporting its member schools and colleges in achieving and delivering the highest standards of international education. CIS provides accreditation to schools, teacher and leader recruitment and best practice development. CIS Higher Education assists member colleges and universities in recruiting a diverse profile of qualified international students.
Schipholweg 113, 2316 XC Leiden, The Netherlands.
Tel: +31 71 524 3300
Email: info@cois.org
Website: www.cois.org

Dyslexia Action (DA)

A registered, educational charity (No. 268502), which has established teaching and assessment centres and conducts teacher-training throughout the UK. The aim of the institute is to help people with dyslexia of all ages to overcome their difficulties in learning to read, write and spell and to achieve their potential.
Centurion House, London Road,
Staines-upon-Thames TW18 4AX
Tel: 01784 222 304
Website: www.dyslexiaaction.org.uk

Early Education – The British Association for Early Childhood Education

Promotes quality provision for all children from birth to eight in whatever setting they are placed. Publishes booklets and organises conferences for those interested in early years education and care.
(Registered charity No. 313082; SC039472)
54 Clarendon Road, Watford WD17 1DU
Tel: 01923 438 995
Email: office@early-education.org.uk
Website: www.early-education.org.uk

European Association for International Education (EAIE)

A not-for-profit organisation aiming for internationalisation in higher education in Europe. Members share a common goal: to internationalise their institutions through collaboration, knowledge exchange and continuous professional development.
PO Box 11189, 1001 GD Amsterdam, The Netherlands
Tel: +31 20 344 5100
Fax: +31 20 344 5119
Email: info@eaie.org
Website: www.eaie.org

Educational Collaborative for International Schools (ECIS)

ECIS is a membership organisation which provides services to support professional development, good governance and leadership in international schools.
24 Greville Street, London, EC1N 8SS
Tel: 020 7824 7040
Email: ecis@ecis.org
Website: www.ecis.org

The Girls' Day School Trust (GDST)

The Girls' Day School Trust (GDST) is one of the largest, longest-established and most successful groups of independent schools in the UK, with 3,500 staff and 19,000 students between the ages of three and 18. As a charity that owns and runs a family of 23 schools and two academies in England and Wales, it reinvests all its income into its schools for the benefit of the pupils. With a long history of pioneering innovation in the education of girls, the GDST now also educates boys in some of its schools, and has two coeducational sixth form colleges.
(Registered charity No. 306983)
10 Bressenden Place, London, SW1E 5DH
Tel: 020 7393 6666
Fax: 020 7393 6789
Website: www.gdst.net

Girls' Schools Association (GSA)

For information on the GSA see editorial on page 37

The Headmasters' and Headmistresses' Conference (HMC)

For information on the HMC see editorial on page 38

Human Scale Education (HSE)

An educational reform movement aiming for small education communities based on democracy, fairness and respect.
(Registered charity No. 1000400)
Email: contact@hse.org.uk
Website: www.hse.org.uk

The Independent Association of Prep Schools (IAPS)

For further information about IAPS see editorial on page 39

The Independent Schools Association (ISA)

For further information about ISA see editorial on page 40

The Independent Schools' Bursars Association (ISBA)

Exists to support and advance financial and operational performance in independent schools. The ISBA is a charitable company limited by guarantee.
(Company No. 6410037; registered charity No. 1121757)
Bluett House, Unit 11-12 Manor Farm, Cliddesden, Basingstoke, Hampshire RG25 2JB
Tel: 01256 330369
Email: office@theisba.org.uk
Website: www.theisba.org.uk

The Independent Schools Council (ISC)

The Independent Schools Council exists to promote choice, diversity and excellence in education; the development of talent at all levels of ability; and the widening of opportunity for children from all backgrounds to achieve their potential. Over 1,300 member schools educate more than 500,000 children at all levels of ability and from all socio-economic classes. Nearly a third of children in ISC schools receive help with fees. Their work is directed by a Board where individuals are nominated for appointment by each of the seven member associations.
See also page 40.

Members:
Association of Governing Bodies of Independent Schools (AGBIS)
Girls' Schools Association (GSA)
Headmasters' and Headmistresses' Conference (HMC)
Independent Association of Prep Schools (IAPS)
Independent Schools Association (ISA)
Independent Schools Bursars' Association (ISBA)
The Society of Heads
The council also has close relations with the BSA, COBIS and the SCIS.
First Floor, 27 Queen Anne's Gate,
London SW1H 9BU
Tel: 020 7766 7070
Fax: 020 7766 7071
Email: research@isc.co.uk
Website: www.isc.co.uk

The Independent Schools Examinations Board (ISEB)

Details of the Common Entrance examinations are obtainable from:
Independent Schools Examinations Board,
Endeavour House, Crow Arch Lane, Ringwood BH24 1HP
Tel: 01425 470555
Email: enquiries@iseb.co.uk
Website: www.iseb.co.uk
Practice papers can be purchased from Galore Park Publishing Ltd: www.galorepark.co.uk

The Inspiring Futures Foundation (IFF)

The IFF provides careers education and guidance to schools and students. Professional support and training is available to school staff and our Futurewise programme provides individual, web-based, support for students and their parents. Career/subject insight courses, gap-year fairs and an information service are additional elements of the service.
The Fountain Building, Howbery Park, Benson Lane, Wallingford, Oxon OX10 8BA
Tel: 01491 820381
Email: helpline@inspiringfutures.org.uk
Website: www.inspiringfutures.org.uk

International Baccalaureate (IB)

For full information about the IB see full entry on page 194

International Schools Theatre Association (ISTA)

International body of teachers and students of theatre, run by teachers for teachers.
(Registered charity No. 1050103)
3 Omega Offices, 14 Coinagehall St,
Helston, Cornwall TR13 8EB
Email: office@ista.co.uk
Website: www.ista.co.uk

Maria Montessori Institute (MMI)

Authorised by the Association Montessori Internationale (AMI) to run their training course in the UK. Further information is available from:
26 Lyndhurst Gardens, Hampstead, London NW3 5NW
Tel: 020 7435 3646
Email: info@mariamontessori.org
Website: www.mariamontessori.org

The National Association of Independent Schools & Non-Maintained Schools (NASS)

A membership organisation working with and for special schools in the voluntary and private sectors within the UK. (Registered charity No. 1083632)
PO Box 705, York YO30 6WW
Tel/Fax: 01904 624446
Email: krippon@nasschools.org.uk
Website: www.nasschools.org.uk

National Day Nurseries Association (NDNA)

A national charity (No. 1078275) that aims to promote quality in early years.
NDNA, National Early Years Enterprise Centre, Longbow Close, Huddersfield, West Yorkshire HD2 1GQ
Tel: 01484 407070
Fax: 01484 407060
Website: www.ndna.org.uk

NDNA Cymru, Office 2, Crown House, 11 Well Street, Ruthin, Denbighshire LL15 1AE
Tel: 01824 707823
Fax: 01824 707824

NDNA Scotland, The Mansfield Traquair Centre, 15 Mansfield Place, Edinburgh EH3 6BB
Tel: 0131 516 6967

National Foundation for Educational Research (NFER)

NFER is the UK's largest independent provider of research, assessment and information services for education, training and children's services. Its clients include UK government departments and agencies at both national and local levels. NFER is a not-for-profit organisation and a registered charity No. 313392.
Head Office, The Mere, Upton Park, Slough, Berkshire SL1 2DQ
Tel: 01753 574123
Fax: 01753 691632
Email: enquiries@nfer.ac.uk
Website: www.nfer.ac.uk

Potential Plus UK

Potential Plus UK is an independent charity that supports the social, emotional and learning needs of children with high learning potential of all ages and backgrounds. (Registered charity No. 313182)
Challenge House, Sherwood Drive, Bletchley, Milton Keynes, Buckinghamshire MK3 6DP
Tel: 01908 646433
Email: amazingchildren@potentialplusuk.org
Website: www.potentialplusuk.org

The Round Square Schools (RSIS)

An international group of schools formed in 1966 following the principles of Dr Kurt Hahn, the founder of Salem School in Germany, and Gordonstoun in Scotland. The Round Square, named after Gordonstoun's 17th century circular building in the centre of the school, now has more than 180 Member Schools and Candidates. (Registered charity No. 327117)
Swan House, Madeira Walk, Windsor SL4 1EU
Website: www.roundsquare.org

Royal National Children's Foundation (RNCF)

The RNCF is a charity that helps children facing abuse, neglect or trauma, by enabling them to attend state and independent boarding schools.
Royal National Children's SpringBoard Foundation, 7 Grosvenor Gardens, London SW1W 0BD
Tel: 020 3405 3630
Email: admin@royalspringboard.org.uk
Website: www.rncf.org.uk

School Fees Independent Advice (SFIA)

See editorial on page 44

Schools Music Association of Great Britain (SMA)

The SMA is a national 'voice' for music in education. It is now part of the Incorporated Society of Musicians
(Registered charity No. 313646)
Website: www.ism.org/sma

Society of Education Consultants (SEC)

The Society is a professional membership organisation that supports management consultants who specialise in education and children's services. The society's membership includes consultants who work as individuals, in partnerships or in association with larger consultancies.
Bellamy House, 13 West Street, Cromer NR27 9HZ
Tel: 0330 323 0457
Email: administration@sec.org.uk
Website: www.sec.org.uk

The Society of Heads

For full information see editorial on page 41

State Boarding Forum

For full information see editorial on page 37

Steiner Waldorf Schools Fellowship (SWSF)

Representing Steiner education in the UK and Ireland, the SWSF has member schools and early years centres in addition to interest groups and other affiliated organisations. Member schools offer education for children within the normal range of ability, aged three to 18.
(Registered charity No. 295104)
Suite 1, 3rd Floor, Copthall House, 1 New Road, Stourbridge, West Midlands DY8 1PH
Tel: 01384 374116
Email: admin@steinerwaldorf.org
Website: www.steinerwaldorf.org

Support and Training in Prep Schools (SATIPS)

SATIPS provides support and training for teachers in the independent and maintained sectors of education.
(Registered charity No. 313688)
West Routengill, Walden, West Burton,
Leyburn, North Yorkshire DL8 4LF
Website: www.satips.org

The Tutors' Association

The Tutors' Association is the professional body for tutoring and wider supplementary education sector in the UK. Launched three years ago it now has over 500 members. Of these 150 are Corporate Members representing some 20,000 tutors throughout the UK.
Tel: 01628 306108
Email: info@thetutorsassociation.org.uk
Website: www.thetutorsassociation.org.uk

UCAS (Universities and Colleges Admissions Service)

UCAS is the organisation responsible for managing applications to higher education courses in England, Scotland, Wales and Northern Ireland.
(Registered charity Nos. 1024741 and SCO38598)
Rose Hill, New Barn Lane,
Cheltenham, Gloucestershire GL52 3LZ
Customer Service: 0371 468 0 468
Website: www.ucas.com

UKCISA – The Council for International Student Affairs

UKCISA is the UK's national advisory body serving the interests of international students and those who work with them.
(Registered charity No. 1095294)
9-17 St Albans Place, London N1 0NX
Tel: 020 7788 9214
Website: www.ukcisa.org.uk

United World Colleges (UWC)

UWC was founded in 1962 and their philosophy is based on the ideas of Dr Kurt Hahn (see Round Square Schools). (Registered charity No. 313690)
UWC International, Second Floor, 17-21 Emerald Street, London WC1N 3QN
Tel: 020 7269 7800
Fax: 020 7405 4374
Email: info@uwcio.uwc.org
Website: www.uwc.org

World-Wide Education Service of CfBT Education Trust (WES)

A leading independent service which provides home education courses worldwide.
Waverley House, Penton,
Carlisle, Cumbria CA6 5QU
Tel: 01228 577123
Email: office@weshome.com
Website: www.weshome.com

Glossary

Glossary

ACETS	Awards and Certificates in Education		COBIS	Council of British International)
AEA	Advanced Extension Award		CSA	The Choir Schools' Association
AEB	Associated Examining Board for the General Certificate of Education		CST	The Christian Schools' Trust
			DfE	Department for Education (formerly DfES and DCFS)
AEGIS	Association for the Education and Guardianship of International Students		DipEd	Diploma of Education
AGBIS	Association of Governing Bodies of Independent Schools		DipTchng	Diploma of Teaching
			EAIE	European Association for International Education
AHIS	Association of Heads of Independent Schools		ECIS	European Council of International Schools
AJIS	Association of Junior Independent Schools		EdD	Doctor of Education
ALP	Association of Learning Providers		Edexcel	GCSE Examining group, incorporating Business and Technology Education Council (BTEC) and University of London Examinations and Assessment Council (ULEAC)
ANTC	The Association of Nursery Training Colleges			
AOC	Association of Colleges			
AP	Advanced Placement			
ASCL	Association of School & College Leaders			
ASL	Additional and Specialist Learning		EFL	English as a Foreign Language
ATI	The Association of Tutors Incorporated		ELAS	Educational Law Association
AQA	Assessment and Qualification Alliance/ Northern Examinations and Assessment Board		EPQ	Extended Project qualification
			ESL	English as a Second Language
BA	Bachelor of Arts		FCoT	Fellow of the College of Teachers (TESOL)
BAC	British Accreditation Council for Independent Further and Higher Education		FEFC	Further Education Funding Council
			FRSA	Fellow of the Royal Society of Arts
BAECE	The British Association for Early Childhood Education		FSMQ	Free-Standing Mathematics Qualification
			GCE	General Certificate of Education
BD	Bachelor of Divinity		GCSE	General Certificate of Secondary Education
BEA	Boarding Educational Alliance		GDST	Girls' Day School Trust
BEd	Bachelor of Education		GNVQ	General National Vocational Qualifications
BLitt	Bachelor of Letters		GOML	Graded Objectives in Modern Languages
BPrimEd	Bachelor of Primary Education		GSA	Girls' Schools Association
BSA	Boarding Schools' Association		GSVQ	General Scottish Vocational Qualifications
BSc	Bachelor of Science		HMC	Headmasters' and Headmistresses' Conference
BTEC	Range of work-related, practical programmes leading to qualifications equivalent to GCSEs and A levels awarded by Edexcel			
			HMCJ	Headmasters' and Headmistresses' Conference Junior Schools
Cantab	Cambridge University			
CATSC	Catholic Association of Teachers in Schools and Colleges		HNC	Higher National Certificate
			HND	Higher National Diploma
CCEA	Council for the Curriculum, Examination and Assessment		IAPS	Independent Association of Prep Schools
			IB	International Baccalaureate
CDT	Craft, Design and Technology		ICT	Information and Communication Technology
CE	Common Entrance Examination		IFF	Inspiring Futures Foundation (formerly ISCO)
CEAS	Children's Education Advisory Service		IGCSE	International General Certificate of Secondary Education
CertEd	Certificate of Education			
CIE	Cambridge International Examinations		INSET	In service training
CIFE	Conference for Independent Education		ISA	Independent Schools Association
CIS	Council of International Schools		ISBA	Independent Schools' Bursars' Association
CISC	Catholic Independent Schools' Conference		ISCis	Independent Schools Council information service
CLAIT	Computer Literacy and Information Technology			
			ISC	Independent Schools Council
			ISEB	Independent Schools Examination Board
CNED	Centre National d'enseignement (National Centre of long distance learning)		ISST	International Schools Sports Tournament
			ISTA	International Schools Theatre Association

ITEC	International Examination Council
JET	Joint Educational Trust
LA	Local Authority
LISA	London International Schools Association
MA	Master of Arts
MCIL	Member of the Chartered Institute of Linguists
MEd	Master of Education
MIoD	Member of the Institute of Directors
MLitt	Master of Letters
MSc	Master of Science
MusD	Doctor of Music
MYP	Middle Years Programme
NABSS	National Association of British Schools in Spain
NAGC	National Association for Gifted Children
NAHT	National Association of Head Teachers
NAIS	National Association of Independent Schools
NASS	National Association of Independent Schools & Non-maintained Special Schools
NDNA	National Day Nurseries Association
NEASC	New England Association of Schools and Colleges
NFER	National Federation of Educational Research
NPA	National Progression Award
NQ	National Qualification
NQF	National Qualifications Framework
NQT	Newly Qualified Teacher
NVQ	National Vocational Qualifications
OCR	Oxford, Cambridge and RSA Examinations
OLA	Online Language Assessment for Modern Languages
Oxon	Oxford
PGCE	Post Graduate Certificate in Education
PhD	Doctor of Philosophy
PL	Principal Learning
PNEU	Parents' National Education Union
PYP	Primary Years Programme
QCA	Qualifications and Curriculum Authority
QCF	Qualifications and Credit Framework
RSIS	The Round Square Schools
SAT	Scholastic Aptitude Test
SATIPS	Support & Training in Prep Schools/Society of Assistant Teachers in Prep Schools
SBSA	State Boarding Schools Association
SCE	Service Children's Education
SCIS	Scottish Council of Independent Schools
SCQF	Scottish Credit and Qualifications Framework
SEC	The Society of Educational Consultants
SEN	Special Educational Needs
SFCF	Sixth Form Colleges' Forum
SFIA	School Fees Insurance Agency Limited
SFIAET	SFIA Educational Trust

SMA	Schools Music Association
SoH	The Society of Heads
SQA	Scottish Qualifications Authority
STEP	Second Term Entrance Paper (Cambridge)
SVQ	Scottish Vocational Qualifications
SWSF	Steiner Waldorf Schools Fellowship
TABS	The Association of Boarding Schools
TISCA	The Independent Schools Christian Alliance
TOEFL	Test of English as a Foreign Language
UCAS	Universities and Colleges Admissions Service for the UK
UCST	United Church Schools Trust
UKLA	UK Literacy Association
UKCISA	The UK Council for International Education
UWC	United World Colleges
WISC	World International Studies Committee
WJEC	Welsh Joint Education Committee
WSSA	Welsh Secondary Schools Association

Index

D

E

F

G